W9-CBW-062

MATHEMATICS
MAKING FINANCIAL DECISIONS 11

MATHEMATICS
MAKING FINANCIAL DECISIONS 11

AUTHORS

JEFF BROSSEAU, B.A., B.ED.
Greater Essex County District School Board

WAYNE ERDMAN, B.MATH., B.ED.
Toronto District School Board

GEORGE FAWCETT, B.A.
Hamilton, Ontario

JEFF IRVINE, B.MATH., B.ED., M.A., M.B.A., C.F.P.
Peel District School Board

BRIAN MCCUDDEN, M.A., M.ED., PH.D.
Etobicoke, Ontario

KRYSTA MEHLER, B.SC., H.B.COMM., B.ED.
Greater Essex County District School Board

TESS MILLER, B.SC., B.ED.
Durham District School Board

LILLIAN KOVACHIS PERIVOLARIS, B.A., B.ED., M.A.
Toronto District School Board

PETER SAARIMAKI, A.T.C.L., B.SC., M.ED.
Toronto District School Board

ASSESSMENT/PEDAGOGY CONSULTANTS
Brian McCudden
Etobicoke, Ontario

Peter Saarimaki
Toronto District School Board

COLLEGE EDUCATION CONSULTANT
Patricia Byers, B.Sc.N., B.A. (Math)
Georgian College

OCCUPATIONS/CAREERS CONSULTANT
Tess Miller
Durham District School Board

TECHNOLOGY CONSULTANT
Lillian Kovachis Perivolaris
Toronto District School Board

McGraw-Hill Ryerson

Toronto Montréal Boston Burr Ridge, IL Dubuque, IA Madison, WI New York
San Francisco St. Louis Bangkok Bogotá Caracas Kuala Lumpur Lisbon London
Madrid Mexico City Milan New Delhi Santiago Seoul Singapore Sydney Taipei

McGraw-Hill
Ryerson Limited
A Subsidiary of The McGraw-Hill Companies

Mathematics: MAKING FINANCIAL DECISIONS 11

ISBN 0-07-086488-8

http://www.mcgrawhill.ca

  5 6 7 8 9 0 TRI 0 9 8 7 6 5

Printed and bound in Canada

Care has been taken to trace ownership of copyright material contained in this text. The publishers will gladly take any information that will enable them to rectify any reference or credit in subsequent printings.

Corel® Quattro® Pro 8. Copyright © 1999–2000 Corel Corporation. All rights reserved. Company and product names are trademarks or registered trademarks of their respective companies.

Microsoft® Excel are either registered trademarks or trademarks of Microsoft Corporation in the United States and/or other countries.

National Library of Canada Cataloguing in Publication Data

Main entry under title:

Mathematics : making financial decisions 11

Includes index.

ISBN 0-07-086488-8

Finance, Personal – Mathematics. I. Brosseau, Jeff.

HG179.M3746 2001   332.024'001'513   C2001-930280-0

PUBLISHER: Diane Wyman
DEVELOPMENTAL EDITORS: Maggie Cheverie, Jacqueline Williams, Sheila Bassett, Julia Cochrane
COPY EDITOR: Julia Cochrane
SENIOR SUPERVISING EDITOR: Carol Altilia
PERMISSIONS EDITOR: Ann Ludbrook
EDITORIAL ASSISTANTS: Joanne Murray, Erin Parton
JUNIOR EDITORS: Christopher Cappadocia, Cheryl Stallabrass
ASSISTANT PROJECT COORDINATORS: Melissa Nippard, Janie Reeson
PRODUCTION SUPERVISOR: Yolanda Pigden
COVER DESIGN: Matthews Communications Design Inc.
INTERIOR DESIGN: Tom Dart/First Folio Resource Group, Inc.
ART DIRECTION: Tom Dart/First Folio Resource Group, Inc.
ELECTRONIC PAGE MAKE-UP: Alana Lai, Claire Milne, Greg Duhaney/First Folio Resource Group, Inc.
COVER IMAGE: John Still/Photonica

COPIES OF THIS BOOK MAY BE OBTAINED BY CONTACTING:

McGraw-Hill Ryerson Ltd.

WEB SITE:
http://www.mcgrawhill.ca

E-MAIL:
orders@mcgrawhill.ca

TOLL FREE FAX:
1-800-463-5885

TOLL FREE CALL:
1-800-565-5758

OR BY MAILING YOUR ORDER TO:
McGraw-Hill Ryerson
Order Department
300 Water Street
Whitby, ON L1N 9B6

Please quote the ISBN and title when placing your order.

Student Text ISBN:
0-07-086488-8

E-book ISBN:
0-07-089683-6

Acknowledgements

Reviewers of *Mathematics: MAKING FINANCIAL DECISIONS 11*

The authors and editors of Mathematics: MAKING FINANCIAL DECISIONS 11 wish to thank the reviewers listed below for their thoughtful comments and suggestions. Their input has been invaluable in ensuring that this text meets the needs of the students and teachers of Ontario.

Anthony Azzopardi
Toronto Catholic District School Board

Yolanda Baldasaro
Hamilton-Wentworth Catholic District School Board

Trevor Brown
Toronto District School Board

Mary Card
Toronto District School Board

Peter Clifford
Toronto District School Board

Chris Dearling
Burlington, Ontario

Steve Etienne
District School Board of Niagara

Eric Forshaw
Greater Essex County District School Board

Susan Harvey
Peel District School Board

Marilyn Hurrell
Thunder Bay, Ontario

David Kay
Peel District School Board

Louis Lim
Hastings and Prince Edward District School Board

Terry Paradellis
Toronto District School Board

Gizele M. Price
Dufferin-Peel District Catholic School Board

Susan Rozario
Peel District School Board

Silvana F. Simone
Toronto District School Board

Bob Smith
Rainbow District School Board

Susan Smith
Peel District School Board

Jacob Speijer
District School Board of Niagara

Le Sueur van der Riet
York Region District School Board

CONTENTS

Chapter 1
PERSONAL FINANCIAL PLANNING

Chapter 2
EXPONENTIAL EXPRESSIONS

Chapter 3
SEQUENCES AND SIMPLE AND COMPOUND INTEREST

Chapter 4
THE EFFECTS OF COMPOUNDING

Chapter 5
SERIES AND ANNUITIES

Chapter 6
EXPONENTIAL GROWTH

Chapter 7
VEHICLE COSTS

Chapter 8
CONSUMER SPENDING

Chapter *9*
ACCOMMODATION COSTS

Chapter *10*
PERSONAL FINANCIAL DECISIONS

A TOUR OF YOUR TEXTBOOK

This text will introduce you to important areas of personal finance. You will apply mathematical skills to make informed decisions about transportation, accommodation, careers, and other financial-based areas you might face now or after graduating from high school.

Interactive e-book

An exciting and interactive e-book in the back of the text will enrich your opportunities for understanding the mathematics you are studying. It contains:
• The entire student text in PDFs, including all technical art and most photos
• A glossary search capability to help you find and learn key terms and definitions
• An index search to link topics and expectations to content
• The ability to highlight key sections to copy to your own study notes
• All answers, including the graphical answers

CHAPTER OPENER

This two-page spread introduces you to what you will learn in the chapter.

Specific Expectations

This is a list of the skills and knowledge you will develop as you work through a chapter. The list includes references to the sections in which the specific expectations are covered.

Get Ready

Each chapter begins with a review of mathematical skills that you need in the chapter.

Case Study

Each chapter opens with a case study that poses a real-life problem that you will revisit as you develop your skills through the chapter.

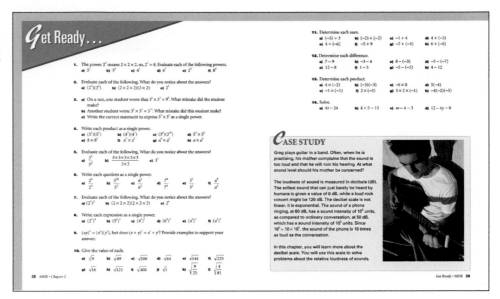

NUMBERED SECTIONS

Lesson Opener

Each lesson presents the mathematical concepts to be learned within a real-world setting.

Discover

These are step-by-step activities, leading you to build your own understanding of the math concepts of the lesson.

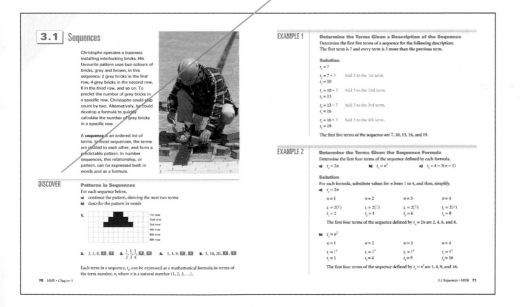

Examples

- Worked examples provide model solutions that show how the new concepts are used.
- You can refer to these examples as you solve problems.

Key Concepts

- This feature summarizes the concepts learned in the lesson.
- You can refer to this summary when you are studying or doing homework.

Discuss the Concepts

These questions allow you to reflect on and to demonstrate what you have just learned, through discussion or writing.

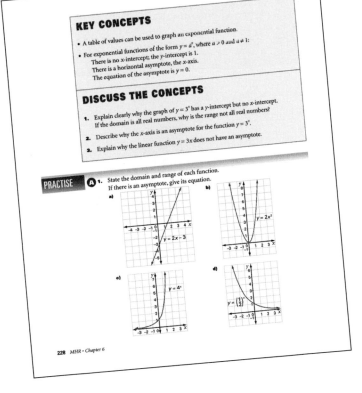

EXAMPLE 2

Calculate the Amount of an Investment

Cora invested $500 at 5%, compounded quarterly, for 2 years. What will the investment be worth at the end of the 2-year term?

Solution

Draw a time line diagram to organize the information:

$500 at 5%, compounded quarterly, for 2 years is $?

Use the formula $A = P(1 + i)^n$.
Determine the values of the variables:

$A = $?
$P = 500$
$n = 8$
$i = 0.0125$

The principal is $500.
quarterly, or 4 times a year, for 2 years is 8
5%, compounded 4 times a year is $0.05 \div 4$

Use the formula:
$A = P(1 + i)^n$
$A = 500(1 + 0.0125)^8$ Substitute for P, n, and i.
$A = 500(1.0125)^8$ Simplify.
$A \doteq 552.24$

The investment will be worth $552.24 at the end of the 2-year term.

Alternatively, a finance application of a graphing calculator could be used to find the final amount, or future value (FV). (See page 413 in the Technology Appendix.)

94   MHR • Chapter 3

KEY CONCEPTS

- A table of values can be used to graph an exponential function.
- For exponential functions of the form $y = a^x$, where $a > 0$ and $a \neq 1$:
  There is no x-intercept; the y-intercept is 1.
  There is a horizontal asymptote, the x-axis.
  The equation of the asymptote is $y = 0$.

DISCUSS THE CONCEPTS

1. Explain clearly why the graph of $y = 3^x$ has a y-intercept but no x-intercept.
   If the domain is all real numbers, why is the range not all real numbers?
2. Describe why the x-axis is an asymptote for the function $y = 3^x$.
3. Explain why the linear function $y = 3x$ does not have an asymptote.

PRACTISE **A 1.** State the domain and range of each function. If there is an asymptote, give its equation.

a) $y = 2x - 3$
b) $y = 2x^2$
c) $y = 4^x$
d) $y = \left(\frac{1}{2}\right)^x$

228   MHR • Chapter 6

Practise

Opportunities to show what you have just learned are provided. This section provides a check of how well you learned the new concepts.

Apply the Concepts

- These questions allow you to use what you learned to solve problems.
- Opportunities to use technology are provided throughout.
- Many questions begin with a label to suggest connections either to topics of interest or to the Achievement Chart categories: Thinking/Inquiry/Problem Solving, Communication, and Application.

Extend the Concepts

These questions extend your knowledge by making connections to other mathematical concepts, or between mathematics and other disciplines.

Levels

- **A** questions require straight-forward use of the concepts.
- The **B** questions can be completed using what you learned from the lesson and from previous lessons. Many opportunities to demonstrate and apply what you learned through short investigations are given.
- The **C** questions are more challenging and thought-provoking.

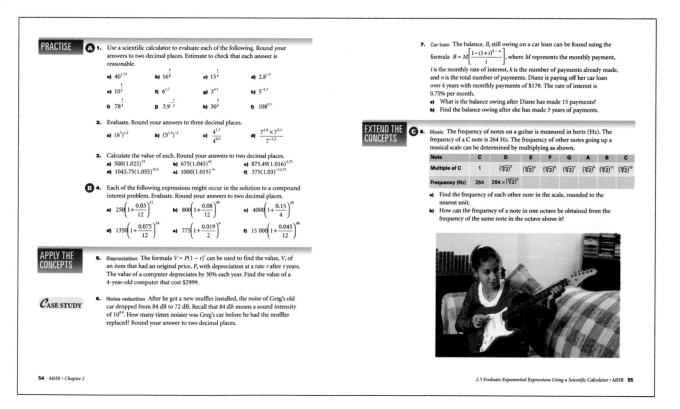

CAREER PROFILE

- One career or occupation is profiled in each chapter.
- Each career has been chosen to illustrate how the math you are learning in the chapter may be relevant in the work world. Each career profile has an Internet link where you can find out more about the career.
- Questions are presented to involve you in thinking and learning more about the career.

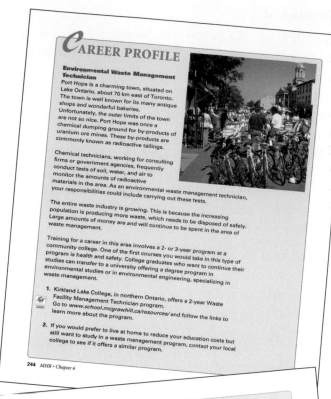

CAREER PROFILE

Environmental Waste Management Technician

Port Hope is a charming town, situated on Lake Ontario, about 70 km east of Toronto. The town is well known for its many antique shops and wonderful bakeries. Unfortunately, the outer limits of the town are not so nice. Port Hope was once a chemical dumping ground for by-products of uranium ore mines. These by-products are commonly known as radioactive tailings.

Chemical technicians, working for consulting firms or government agencies, frequently conduct tests of soil, water, and air to monitor the amounts of radioactive materials in the area. As an environmental waste management technician, your responsibilities could include carrying out these tests.

The entire waste industry is growing. This is because the increasing population is producing more waste, which needs to be disposed of safely. Large amounts of money are and will continue to be spent in the area of waste management.

Training for a career in this area involves a 2- or 3-year program at a community college. One of the first courses you would take in this type of program is health and safety. College graduates who want to continue their studies can transfer to a university offering a degree program in environmental studies or in environmental engineering, specializing in waste management.

1. Kirkland Lake College, in northern Ontario, offers a 2-year Waste Facility Management Technician program. Go to www.school.mcgrawhill.ca/resources/ and follow the links to learn more about the program.

2. If you would prefer to live at home to reduce your education costs but still want to study in a waste management program, contact your local college to see if it offers a similar program.

CASE STUDY WRAP-UP

- Case Study Wrap-Ups are presented before the Chapter Review in each chapter.
- These projects allow you to consolidate your skills and knowledge by organizing and presenting your solution to the case study problem.

CASE STUDY WRAP-UP

Theo is an 18-year old student. He has just obtained his G2 driver's licence. He has saved $5000 from his part-time job and would like to buy his own car. Theo is not sure what kind of car he can buy with that amount of money.

Theo's net monthly income is $570. He has decided a small, reliable car with high fuel efficiency would meet his needs the best.

Create a report to answer the following question. Provide support material for your response.

Should Theo buy or lease a new vehicle, or buy a used vehicle?
Give reasons to support your decision.
Points to consider:
- Can Theo afford a new car with $5000? Why or why not?
- Research what types of cars are available for $5000. Select five advertisements/listings that Theo could consider.
- If he decides to purchase a new vehicle and finance the balance after paying $5000, what monthly payments can he afford?
- From your research, what kind of used cars can Theo afford?
- If he decides to lease, what monthly payments can he afford?
- How much can he expect to spend on a monthly basis to operate the vehicle? List some of the unexpected costs he might have to pay.

Ideas for Your Presentation
1. Collect brochures from dealers and present them on poster board, listing costs for options.
2. Collect car sales advertisements from new and used car dealerships, classified listings of cars for sale, ads from car magazines, etc.
3. Create a multimedia presentation describing each of the steps you took in deciding which car would best meet Theo's needs.

TECHNOLOGY

- Scientific calculators and spreadsheets are technology tools that you will use. Graphing calculators may be used as an alternative.
- These tools will support you in problem solving and will save you time in computing, manipulating, and displaying data.
- Detailed instructions are provided for software use, and calculator keystrokes are provided in the worked examples and in the Technology Appendix.
- The Technology Appendix provides detailed help for some basic and specific functions of the graphing calculator and spreadsheet software.

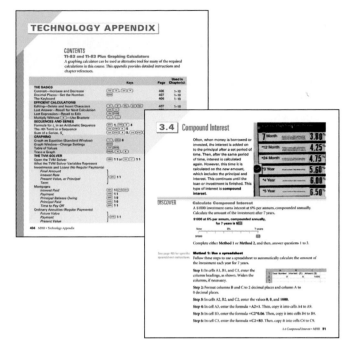

ASSESSMENT

Discuss the Concepts

- These questions provide you with the opportunity to communicate what you have learned before proceeding to practise your skills in the Practise, Apply the Concepts, and Extend the Concepts questions.
- These questions can be used to identify areas you need to review further.

Achievement Checks

- These questions assess your knowledge and understanding, your problem solving skills, your communication skills, and your ability to apply what you have learned.
- Achievement Checks appear throughout the chapter and in the Practice Test.
- Sample solutions and rubrics are included in the Teacher's Resource.

Case Study Wrap-Up

See page xiv for a description.

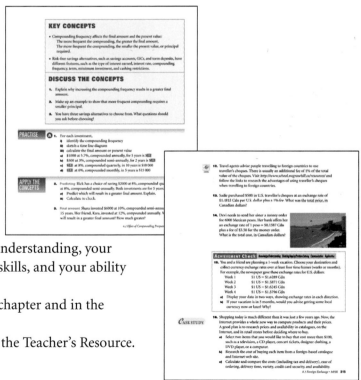

CHAPTER REVIEW

- This feature appears at the end of each chapter.
- By working through this feature, you will identify areas where you may need additional review before proceeding to the Practice Test.

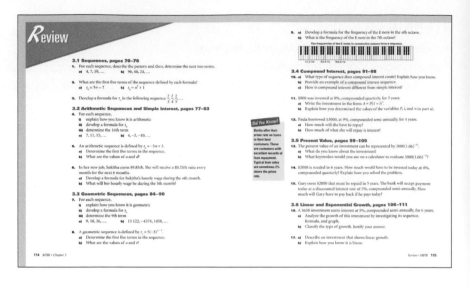

PRACTICE TEST

Each chapter ends with a test, designed to assess how well you understand the concepts and how well you can use the skills you learned in the chapter.

Achievement Chart Category Connections

This chart correlates each of the test questions to the categories of the Achievement Chart, so that you know which categories are being assessed in each question.

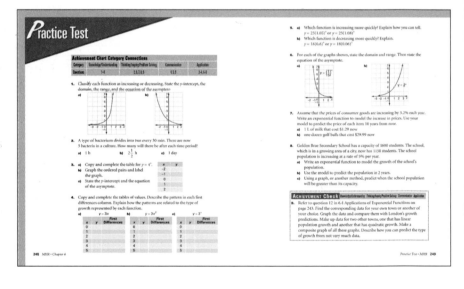

CUMULATIVE REVIEW

- A cumulative review appears at the end of Chapters 4 and 8, reviewing concepts you learned in the chapters since the last cumulative review.
- A third cumulative review appears after Chapter 10, reviewing concepts learned in the whole text.

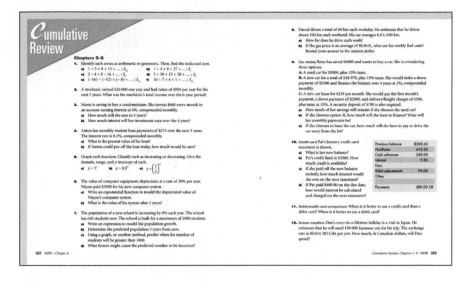

OTHER FEATURES

Internet Links

Throughout the book, you may explore the Internet to help you solve a problem or to research or collect information. Visit our website *www.school.mcgrawhill.ca/resources/* and link directly to other interesting web sites connected to content in the text.

Did You Know?

This feature appears in the margin of some pages. It provides interesting background information related to the topics.

E-STAT

Σ-STAT E-STAT is a resource designed by Statistics Canada and made available to schools. The database provides a large amount of Canadian census data. E-STAT also includes graphing and mapping tools. You can connect to E-STAT directly from our web site *www.school.mcgrawhill.ca/resources/*.

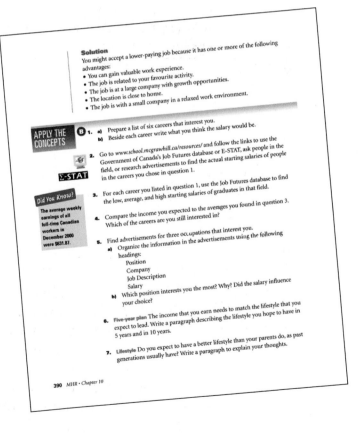

PERSONAL FINANCIAL PLANNING

Specific Expectations	Sections
• design an effective financial plan to facilitate the achievement of a long-term goal	1.1, 1.2, 1.3
• explain and justify budgets, using appropriate mathematical forms	1.2, 1.3
• summarize the advantages and disadvantages of the alternatives to a decision, using lists	1.2
• explain the process used in making a decision and justify the conclusions reached	1.3
• describe and estimate the living costs involved for different family groupings	1.2
• design a budget suitable for a family described in a given case study, reflecting the current costs of common items, using technology	1.2, 1.3
• determine the effect on an overall budget of changing one component, using a spreadsheet or budgeting software	1.2, 1.3
• solve problems involving the calculation of any variable in the simple interest formula ($I = Prt$), using scientific calculators	1.4
• determine, through investigation, the characteristics of various savings alternatives available from a financial institution	1.4

Get Ready...

1. Round to two decimal places.
   a) 45.6487
   b) 3.1234
   c) 156.0978
   d) 200.9954

2. Express as a percent. Round to two decimal places, if necessary.
   a) $50 of $300 is 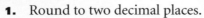%
   b) $100 of $150 is ?%
   c) $100 of $40 500 is ?%
   d) $175 of $320 is ?%

3. Calculate.
   a) 32% of 360 is ?
   b) 53% of 360 is ?
   c) 10% of 360 is ?
   d) 5% of 360 is ?

4. Express as a decimal.
   a) 6%
   b) 11%
   c) $4\frac{1}{2}$%
   d) 12.5%

   e) $8\frac{1}{2}$%
   f) $10\frac{1}{4}$%
   g) $12\frac{5}{8}$%
   h) 3.25%

5. Express as a percent. Round to two decimal places, if necessary.
   a) 0.06772
   b) 0.1238
   c) 0.0085
   d) 0.08376

   e) $\frac{1}{4}$
   f) $\frac{1}{3}$
   g) $\frac{3}{8}$
   h) $\frac{5}{6}$

Recall the order of operations: BEDMAS

6. Calculate without using a calculator.
   a) $15 - 3 \times 4 + 12$
   b) $(15 - 3) \times 4 + 12$
   c) $55 - 3(4 + 12)$
   d) $\dfrac{315}{4 \times 12 - 3}$
   e) $\dfrac{360}{4(12 - 3)}$
   f) $\dfrac{120}{4 + 2 \times 8}$

7. Use a calculator to recalculate each expression in question 6. Write the keystrokes for each.

8. i) Solve the formula for the volume of a rectangular prism, $V = lwh$, for the indicated variable.
   ii) Evaluate by substituting the given values.
   a) l; $V = 150$ cm^3, $w = 5$ cm, $h = 10$ cm, $l = $? cm
   b) w; $V = 384$ m^3, $l = 8$ m, $h = 12$ m, $w = $? m
   c) h; $V = 1000$ mm^3, $w = 10$ mm, $l = 10$ mm, $h = $? mm

9. Express as a fraction and as a decimal.

a) 9 months = $\dfrac{?}{?}$ years, or ? years   b) 18 months = $\dfrac{?}{?}$ years, or ? years

c) 26 weeks = $\dfrac{?}{?}$ years, or ? years   d) 13 weeks = $\dfrac{?}{?}$ years, or ? years

10. Express as a fraction.

a) 90 days = $\dfrac{?}{?}$ years   b) 120 days = $\dfrac{?}{?}$ years

c) 180 days = $\dfrac{?}{?}$ years

*C*ASE STUDY

In this chapter, you will be introduced to financial planning. In each section of the chapter, you will solve problems related to the Case Study described below. At the end of the chapter, in the Case Study Wrap-Up on page 31, you will be ready to design a financial plan that will help the couple in the Case Study achieve a long-term goal. Keep 5 or 6 pages of your notebook free for any work related to the Case Study, or keep your work in a Case Study Portfolio.

Jamal and Olivia recently completed college, and then, got married. Jamal works in customer service at a department store and Olivia works as an early childhood educator. They both have student loans and a car loan. They are currently renting an apartment that is close to work for both of them. They have many goals, including getting out of debt, taking a vacation, buying a house, and starting a day-care business. These goals seem impossible right now because of their living expenses and debt. They realize that they must manage their money better.

1.1 Understand Financial Planning

You probably have goals. They may be short-term goals, such as getting a driver's licence, or they might be more long-term, such as buying a car. You might have many goals, or you might be focused on a single goal. Because many goals involve money, financial planning can help you to reach them.

DISCOVER

Identify Personal Goals

1. **a)** Describe your goals for the next 3 years. Be ambitious but realistic and specific. For example, you may want to get a part-time job, go to college, and buy a car.
   b) Now, describe your goals for the next 10 years.
   c) Which was easier, setting 3-year or 10-year goals? Why?

2. **a)** Look at your goals. Put a dollar sign ($) beside those that involve money.
   b) If you had to choose one goal, which would you choose? Why?
   c) What steps have you taken to be sure that you will have enough money for your goal?

A **financial plan** is a step-by-step outline for achieving goals that involve money. **Financial planning** is the process followed to design and manage the plan.

EXAMPLE 1

Steps to Financial Planning

Put the following steps for designing a financial plan in order, and then, describe each step.
- Design a plan.
- Identify goals and state objectives.
- Collect information on the current situation.
- Monitor and adjust the plan.
- Put the plan into action.

Solution

Step 1: *Identify goals and state objectives* Goals drive the financial plan. Once you identify your goals, you can describe them more specifically.

Step 2: *Collect information on the current situation* You need answers to questions such as
- What is your net income?
- How much do you spend on day-to-day expenses?
- What do you owe?
- What do you own?
- Do you predict any significant changes in your life, for example, college in 2 years?

Step 3: *Design a plan* The plan will be a list of specific steps in the order you should follow them to achieve your goals with your current situation in mind.

Step 4: *Put the plan into action* Follow the plan. Note that this may require changes to things such as your spending habits, lifestyle, and accommodation.

Step 5: *Monitor and adjust the plan* Most financial plans must be adjusted from time to time because of changes to things such as income, health, and goals.

EXAMPLE 2
*C*ASE STUDY

Goals—What? When? How Much?

Recall Jamal and Olivia and their financial situation, as described on page 3. They need a financial plan to achieve their goals. Help them to identify their goals and state their objectives by getting answers to these questions:
- **a)** What are their goals?
- **b)** When do they want to achieve each goal?
- **c)** How much money will they need to achieve each goal?
- **d)** Which goals conflict? Which goals are related?
- **e)** If they were to choose one goal, which would it be?

Solution

a)

What?	**b)** When?	**c)** How Much?
get out of debt	3 years	$12 000
buy a house	3 to 5 years	$20 000 down payment
go on a vacation	1 year	$ 2 000
start own day-care business	7 years	$10 000

d) *Conflicting goals* Buying a house and taking a $2000 vacation would conflict if there was not enough money for both. They could adjust their goals, for example, buy a smaller house and take a less expensive vacation or, they could choose one goal over the other.

Related goals Getting out of debt, buying a house, and starting a day-care business are related because getting out of debt should happen before buying a house, and once they have bought a house, they may be able to set up the day care in their house.

e) Below are some methods for choosing goals:
  • by cost—the least expensive goals
  • by time—the goals that can be achieved the soonest
  • by feasibility—the goals that are most likely to be achieved
  • by importance—these are lifetime, dream goals

For both Jamal and Olivia, the most important goal is buying a house in 3 to 5 years because it will motivate them to get out of debt and because they cannot begin planning for a day-care business until they have a house. They will focus their financial plan on the goal of buying a house.

EXAMPLE 3

Design a Financial Plan

Jon got a job right out of high school in the auto industry in his home town. He sees more opportunity if he can get a diploma in Mechanical Engineering Technology. The local college offers the course but he cannot start right away because he has debts—he owes money on a credit card and a car loan. He currently shares an apartment with two friends. Develop a financial plan that will help him achieve his goal of going to college.

Solution

Step 1: *Identify goals and state objectives* Jon's goal is to attend college in 2 years.

Step 2: *Collect information* Jon needs to find out the following:
• the cost of tuition and related expenses
• his current income and expenses
• if he can move back home to reduce living expenses now and during college
• if he can find other sources of money: student loan, scholarship, summer job
• if he can get a low-interest loan to pay off high-interest debts
• what savings alternatives are available for his college savings fund

Step 3: *Design a plan* Jon can now design a plan based on the following:
• Tuition and related college expenses will be about $10 000.
• His current expenses are higher than his income so he must reduce them.
• He can move back home to reduce living expenses now and during college.
• Jon's employer offers scholarships and summer jobs to employees. Jon may be able to get a scholarship and a summer job to help pay for expenses during college.

- His parents will lend him money at a low interest rate to pay off his debts.
- He has found a savings account earning 5% interest for his college savings fund.

Step 4: *Put the plan into action* Jon can now do the following:
- He can borrow money from his parents to pay off his debts.
- He can move back home to reduce his living expenses.
- He can balance his budget, taking into account the lower debt payments and living expenses, and his monthly deposits into his college savings account.
- He can apply for a scholarship.

Step 5: *Monitor and adjust* Jon should evaluate his progress in 6 months.
- If he is having difficulty sticking to the plan, he can change the time from 2 to 3 years to allow him an increase in spending.
- If he is saving money faster than expected and he gets a scholarship, he can change the time to 1 year.

KEY CONCEPTS

- A financial plan is a logical sequence of steps and sub-steps that can be followed in order to achieve identified goals that involve money.

- Goals need to be stated in the What? When? How Much? format and can be sorted in different ways, for example, by cost, time, feasibility, and importance.

- To be effective, a financial plan should be specific and realistic, and monitored and adjusted regularly.

DISCUSS THE CONCEPTS

1. Jana and Will want to start a family but they have not considered it in their financial plan because they do not think it is money related.
   a) Explain why this goal should be considered in a financial plan.
   b) What other goals can you think of that may not seem money related but are?

2. a) What is wrong with goals such as "I want to be rich" and "I want to retire early"?
   b) What advice would you give someone with these goals?

3. a) George and Brenda, Olivia's parents, have different goals and a different financial plan than Olivia and Jamal. Why?
   b) What differences would you expect?

A *Work in small groups to discuss the following questions.*

1. Examine Jon's financial plan in the solution to Example 3 on pages 6 and 7.
   a) What changes might he make to the plan if he
      i) starts college in 3 years?   ii) does not move back home?
   b) What else might affect Jon's plan?

2. **Student plan** Farhad is in Grade 11 and plans to go to college in 2 years. He has chosen a course in hospitality and tourism in a community that is 100 km from home. His financial plan includes these steps:
   - pay first year's tuition
   - ask parents for loan
   - save money from summer job
   - research scholarships
   - open savings account
   - apply for student loan
   - get summer job
   - get part-time job
   - find out about tuition and other college expenses
   a) Order the steps. Explain why you ordered the steps the way you did.
   b) What other steps might be included?

3. **Communication** Below are some terms related to financial planning:

B
   - will
   - life insurance
   - power of attorney
   - tax planning
   - consumer debt
   - emergency fund
   - retirement fund
   - vacation fund
   - education fund
   a) Choose four terms and find out what each means.
   b) For each term you chose, describe a person that might consider it as part of his or her financial plan and explain why.

4. **Goals** Jana has listed goals and a possible time for each:
   - learn more about investing and tax planning: immediately
   - pay off car loan: 2 years
   - pay off house mortgage: 8 years
   - start own advertising business: 10 years
   - get a promotion at work: 1 year
   - buy a larger house: 10 years
   - have children: 5 years
   a) Identify conflicting goals. Explain how they conflict.
   b) Identify related goals. Explain how they relate.
   c) What assumptions have you made about Jana's situation?

5. **Wills** Joan is 18 years old and still living at home while going to college. She has heard on the radio and on television "Everyone should have a will!"
   a) Do you agree? Why or why not?
   b) Would your answer be different if Joan was 35 years old and had young children? Why or why not?

6. **Life insurance** Lyle is a single parent with two young children. As part of his financial plan, he has been advised to buy life insurance.
   a) Explain why life insurance should be part of Lyle's plan.
   b) Should it be part of everyone's plan? Explain.

7. **Savings** Paul is 30 years old. His financial plan specifies that he should start two funds: an emergency fund for a large unexpected expense, and a retirement fund. He plans to put $50 a month into a low-interest, risk-free savings account for emergencies and $50 a month into a high-interest, higher-risk retirement investment. Why has he chosen different ways to deal with these two funds?

8. **Debts** Erin's goal is to pay off debts:
   • a car loan of $12 000 with interest charged at 9%
   • a student loan of $8000 with interest charged at 7%
   • a credit card debt of $8000 with interest charged at 18.9%
   • a loan of $3500 for furniture, which will start charging interest in 1 year, at 15%
   a) Rank her debts in the order she should pay them. Explain your ranking.
   b) She is trying get a low-interest loan to consolidate her debts. What does this mean?

CASE STUDY

9. Recall Jamal and Olivia and their financial goals, as described on page 3 and in Example 2, on pages 5 and 6.
   a) What questions should a financial planner ask them in Steps 1 and 2 of the financial planning process (see Example 1)?
   b) Jamal and Olivia have decided to focus their financial plan on buying a house in 3 to 5 years. What does the planner need to know about Jamal and Olivia before designing a financial plan for them?
   c) A down payment on a house will be about $20 000. How much must they save per month if they want to buy a house in 3 years? 5 years?

10. **Communication** Does everyone need a professional financial planner?
    a) Describe a person for whom you feel a professional financial planner
       i) would not be needed   ii) would be needed
    b) Explain your answers in part a).

11. **Personal plan**
    a) What information do you need to plan your future education?
    b) How and where might you find out this information?
    c) What are some of the costs involved in attending college?
    d) What are possible sources of money for your education?

Did You Know?

Your credit rating is measured by a credit bureau. The rating is based on your ability to handle debt. This information is gathered from financial institutions and stores and remains in your file for 7 years.

12. Refer to your 10-year goals from the Discover on page 4.

a) State each goal in the What? When? How Much? format.

b) Identify conflicting and related goals.

c) Choose one goal that you would like to focus on. Explain your choice.

d) Consider the steps you would have to follow to achieve that goal, and then, list the steps in order.

e) List any information you need before finalizing your plan. For example, you might need to research interest rates on loans or the cost of tuition.

EXTEND THE CONCEPTS

 13. **Tax planning** Tax planning to increase net income is often part of financial planning. Find out how taxes can be reduced by investing in a registered retirement savings plan (RRSP) or by investing in investments that earn dividends.

14. **Planning fees** Professional financial planners are paid in different ways.
- Fee-for-service planners charge by the hour or by the plan and do not sell financial products.
- Commission-based planners prepare a financial plan for free but receive commission on financial products that they sell as part of the plan.

What are the advantages and disadvantages of each to the consumer? Explain.

 15. Go to *www.school.mcgrawhill.ca/resources/* to find out about any of the following topics. Write a brief report about what you found out.
- different types, or designations, of financial advisors
- buying a home
- education funds
- choosing a financial planner
- saving for a child
- vacation funds
- a topic of your choice

1.2 Budgeting: Part 1

Doreen is a college student who has been working with a financial planner to design a financial plan. She has identified two goals: get out of debt within 1 year and begin a savings fund for travelling when she graduates. The planner has told her that the next step in designing a financial plan is to collect information about her current financial situation.

DISCOVER

Income and Expenses

1. **a)** How much do you earn, or receive in allowance, in an average month?
   b) Make a list of what you spend in an average month, and then, find the total.
   c) How do the values from part a), your income, and part b), your expenses, compare?

2. Suppose you wanted to save for something very important. What changes could you make to your income and/or to your expenses in order to save money?

A **budget** compares expenses and income for the same time period, for example, monthly expenses would be compared to monthly income.

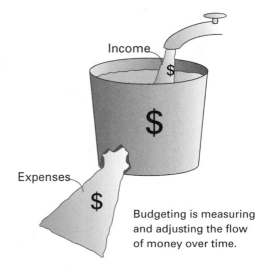

Budgeting is measuring and adjusting the flow of money over time.

EXAMPLE 1

Collect Information in a Current Budget

Doreen is a college student. To pay for her living expenses, she works 30 h a week at a restaurant, earning $8/h. Her weekly take-home pay is about $180. Doreen pays for the following living expenses while her parents pay for tuition and books:

Rent: $250/month   Food: $100/week

Transportation (transit pass): $75/month   Clothing: $50 bi-weekly

Entertainment: $50/week   Health/Personal: $25/month

Debt Repayment: $100/month

a) Construct a current monthly budget.

b) Analyze her current budget.

c) List possible changes to her current budget, keeping in mind her goals of getting out of debt and starting a savings fund for travelling.

Solution

a) Method 1: Construct a budget by hand

Doreen's Monthly Budget	
	Current
Monthly Income	$780
Monthly Living Expenses	
Rent	$250
Food	$433
Transportation	$75
Clothing	$108
Entertainment	$217
Health/Personal	$25
Debt Repayment	$100
Total Living Expenses	$1208
Left Over for Savings	−$428

Income: $(180 \times 52) \div 12$

Food: $(100 \times 52) \div 12$

Clothing: $(50 \times 26) \div 12$
Entertainment: $(50 \times 52) \div 12$

See page 405 in the Technology Appendix for specific spreadsheet instructions.

Method 2: Construct a budget using a spreadsheet

To prepare the spreadsheet:

Step 1: Open a blank spreadsheet.

Step 2: Format column B to currency with 0 decimal places.

Step 3: Widen column A.

Step 4: Enter the headings into column A as shown and the heading **Current** into cell B2.

To include current monthly income:

Step 5: In cell B3, enter =**180*52/12**.

	A	B
1	***Doreen's Monthly Budget***	
2		Current
3	MONTHLY INCOME	$ 780
4		
5		
6	MONTHLY LIVING EXPENSES:	
7	Rent	$ 250
8	Food	$ 433
9	Transportation	$ 75
10	Clothing	$ 108
11	Entertainment	$ 217
12	Health/Personal	$ 25
13	Debt Repayment	$ 100
14	TOTAL LIVING EXPENSES	$1 208
15	Left Over for Savings	-$ 428
16		

To include current monthly living expenses:
Step 6: In cells B7, B9, B12, and B13, enter the amounts for Rent (**250**), Transportation (**75**), Health/Personal (**25**), and Debt Repayment (**100**).

Step 7: In cell B8, enter the amount for Food as =**100*52/12**.

Step 8: In cell B10, enter the amount for Clothing as =**50*26/12**.

Step 9: In cell B11, enter the amount for Entertainment as =**50*52/12**.

Step 10: In cell B14, enter =**SUM(B7:B13)** or **@SUM(B7..B13)**.

To calculate the amount left over for savings:
Step 11: In cell B15, enter =**B3–B14**.

b) Doreen's monthly expenses are greater than her income. She must decrease her expenses or increase her income by *more than* $428/month in order to start a savings fund for travelling and balance her budget.

c) Possible changes to current budget:
Increase income:
Investigate other sources of income: parents, student loan, work more hours.
Decrease expenses:
Reduce food expenses by eating at home more often and taking lunches.
Eliminate clothing purchases for the rest of the school year.
Reduce entertainment expenses.
Eliminate debt repayment by paying off debts (see Example 2).

A **net worth statement** compares a person's **assets** (what is owned) and **liabilities** (what is owed) at a specific point in time. The difference between assets and liabilities is **net worth**. A person's net worth is how much cash he or she would have if all assets were sold and all debts paid.

EXAMPLE 2

Collect Information in a Net Worth Statement
Doreen may own something that she could sell for cash in order to pay off her debts.
Here is a list of what she owns and owes:
Jewellery: recently appraised at $1500
Furniture: bought 2 years ago for $2000
$5000 in Canada Savings Bonds: bought 3 years ago
Credit card balance: $1800
Debt to parents: $400

a) Prepare a net worth statement for Doreen.
b) Describe Doreen's net worth.
c) Analyze the statement to determine if she could sell assets to pay debts.

Solution

a) A personal net worth statement uses current market value for assets:
   - Her furniture, bought 2 years ago for $2000 has a current market value of $1000.
   - The $5000 in Canada Savings Bonds bought 3 years ago have a current market value of $5800.

Doreen's Current Net Worth Statement				
Assets	**$**		**Liabilities**	**$**
Furniture	1000		Credit card debt	1800
Jewellery	1500		Debt to parents	400
Savings bonds	5800			
Total Assets	8300		**Total Liabilities**	2200
Net Worth = $6100				

b) Doreen has a positive net worth—if she sold all her assets and paid off all her debts, she would have $6100 cash.

c) Analyze her statement to determine if she could sell assets to pay debts:
   - She will not sell the jewellery because it is a family heirloom.
   - She cannot sell her furniture until she finishes college.
   - She could cash in some of her savings bonds to pay off her debts—the interest rate that she is being charged on her credit card debt is much greater than the interest rate she is earning on the bonds.

KEY CONCEPTS

- A budget is a comparison of income to expenses for the same time period.

- The main reason for constructing a current budget is to determine if current income and expenses match financial goals.

- A net worth statement is a financial "snapshot" at a specific time that compares what a person owns (assets) and owes (liabilities):
  Net worth = total assets – total liabilities

- The main reason for constructing a net worth statement is to determine a person's financial "health." It can also be used to determine if assets can be sold to pay debts.

DISCUSS THE CONCEPTS

1. Explain how constructing a current budget might help someone whose
   a) expenses exceed income   b) income exceeds expenses

2. Why do personal net worth statements use current market value?

3. Financial planners use both budgets and net worth statements to make recommendations about money management.
   a) How are budgets and net worth statements related? different?
   b) How might changes to one affect the other?

APPLY THE CONCEPTS

A *Work in small groups to discuss the following questions. Note that questions 1, 2, 4, 5, 6, and 9 will be revisited in 1.3 Budgeting: Part 2 on pages 21 and 22.*

1. **Application**
   a) Examine Doreen's current monthly budget and net worth statement (see Examples 1 and 2).
   b) Summarize the advantages and disadvantages of each possible change she could make to balance her budget and start a savings fund for travelling.
   c) What changes would you recommend? Why?
   d) Create Doreen's current monthly budget using a spreadsheet. Make each change as described in part c) and determine its overall effect on the budget.

2. **Application** Donald's gross income is $38 000/year. His take-home pay just covers the following monthly expenses:

Telephone: $80	Clothing: $40	Loan payment: $320
Food: $430	Rent: $825	Vacation fund: $85
Transportation: $590	Savings: $75	Spending money: $100

   a) What is Donald's monthly net income?
   b) Construct a current monthly budget.
   c) Donald wants to double his spending money. What do you need to know before recommending changes to his current budget?

B 3. **Communication** Below are pairs of terms related to budgets and net worth.
   a) Choose two pairs of terms and find out what they mean.
   b) For each, describe how the terms relate to budgets or net worth statements.
   • fixed and variable expenses
   • discretionary and non-discretionary expenses
   • negative and positive net worth
   • liquid and non-liquid assets

Did You Know?

In budgeting, a negative amount can be shown in different ways: by using a negative sign, by enclosing it in brackets, or by using the colour red. For example, –$4000 can be written as ($4000) or as –$4000. The expression "in the red" means a negative balance.

4. **Application** Franco and Gayle have one child. They have a combined gross income of $90 000/year. Franco's net pay is $700/week and Gayle's is $1150 bi-weekly. Their living expenses are as follows:

Mortgage and taxes: $1320/month   Food: $150/week
Clothing: $2000/year   Utilities: $500/month
Charity: $100/month   Entertainment: $250/month
Loan payments: $200/month   Savings: $100/week
Vacation fund: $100/month   Transportation: $250 bi-weekly
Gifts: $1200/year   Spending money: $120/week
Day care: $150/week

a) Construct a current monthly budget.

b) The couple has a goal of paying an extra $1200 each year to pay down their mortgage. List possible changes they could make to their budget.

c) What changes would you recommend? Explain.

5. **Problem Solving**

a) Estimate monthly expenses for an individual or family in your community:
   • family of four
   • single working adult
   • single college student
   • single parent with one child
   • individual or family grouping of your choice

   Possible living expenses:
   Shelter (rent and utilities; or mortgage, taxes, insurance, utilities, and repairs)
   Transportation (transit costs or vehicle expenses)
   Food (groceries and eating out)
   Recreation (e.g., entertainment, books, hobbies)
   Education (e.g., tuition, books)
   Child care
   Regular savings (e.g., vacation fund, emergency fund, retirement fund)
   Loan and debt payments
   Clothing
   Miscellaneous (e.g., charity donations, club fees, gifts, spending money)

b) What monthly net income would your individual or family need to meet expenses?

c) Create a balanced budget for your individual or family .

d) Create a realistic financial goal for your individual or family that will require a change to their budget, for example, buy a car or start an education fund.

6. **Personal budget**
   a) Construct the following for yourself:
      i) a current monthly budget   ii) a current net worth statement
   b) Consider your long-term financial goal from question 12 on page 10. What changes could you make to your current budget and net worth statement to achieve your goal? List the advantages and disadvantages of each change.

7. **Net worth**
   a) Construct a net worth statement for Soni for the following assets and liabilities:

Car: $15 000	Car loan: $8500
Furniture: $8500	Furniture loan: $5800
Coin collection: $3200	Student loan: $9600
Debt to parents: $15 000	Bank account balance: $2800
Investments: $9100	

   b) How can Soni increase his net worth over time?

8. **Communication** Make up a list of questions you would ask someone in order to gather information to construct a current
   a) budget   b) net worth statement

CASE STUDY

9. Recall Jamal and Olivia and their goal of buying a house, as described on pages 3, 5, 6, and 9.
   Here are the details of their current income and living expenses:

Combined gross income: $55 000/year	Combined net income: $39 020/year
Rent: $750/month	Food: $200/week
Car loan payments: $375/month	Student loan payments: $400/month
Car expenses: $150 bi-weekly	Clothing: $1500/year
Entertainment: $175 bi-weekly	Health/Personal: $100/week
Credit card payments: $100	

   Here are the details of what they currently own and owe:

Car: $15 000	Car loan: $8000
Furniture: $2500	Student loan: $12 000
	Credit card balance: $2000

   a) Prepare a current monthly budget and net worth statement.
   b) They need to save between $333 and $555 a month to have $20 000 in 3 to 5 years for a down payment on a house. What changes to their current budget and net worth statement could they make? Summarize the advantages and disadvantages of each.
   c) What assumptions have you made?

10. Communication Paula kept all her receipts for food purchases over a 6-month period. She then divided the total by 6 to find her monthly food expenses. Explain why this method is a good one for estimating monthly expenses.

11. Interest rates Some people owe money on credit cards, which charge very high interest rates, while they save money in savings accounts, which earn very low interest rates. What advice would you give a person who is doing this? Explain.

 12. Mathematical budgeting One approach to budgeting is to consider savings as what is left over after expenses are paid:
Savings = income – expenses.
Another approach is to consider savings as an expense:
Income = savings + expenses.
a) Explain how the two approaches differ.
b) Why do you think financial planners think that the first approach is a "recipe for disaster" while the second approach is a "recipe for success"?

13. 10% solution Some planners recommend that 10% of gross income be dedicated to savings. Re-examine the current budgets you prepared in questions 1, 2, 4, 6, and 9.
a) What percent of gross income is dedicated to savings?
b) Would it be reasonable to make the change to 10% in each case? Why or why not?

14. Inquiry Statistics Canada collects information about how Canadians spend their money. Go to *www.school.mcgrawhill.ca/resources/* and follow the links to find out what household expenditures, or living expenses, Statistics Canada collects information on.
a) List the expenditures.
b) Did any surprise you?
c) Are there any that you feel were missed and should be included?
d) Why do you think this information is collected?

15. Liquidity ratio Doreen's net worth liquidity ratio is about 70% (see Example 2).
a) Find out what liquidity ratio is by checking the Glossary.
b) In order to calculate the liquidity ratio for the net worth statements from questions 6, 7, and 9, what information do you need?
c) Assume that only bank account balances and investments are liquid assets. Calculate the liquidity ratio for questions 6, 7, and 9.
d) Why do you think it is important to determine liquidity ratio?

1.3 Budgeting: Part 2

In order to achieve most financial goals, you must make changes to your current income or expenses, or to both. These changes must be realistic. There is no point in creating a balanced budget that you cannot stick to. For example, maintaining a car is very expensive—taking transit instead could reduce expenses considerably. But selling a car may not be a realistic sacrifice for some people.

EXAMPLE

Create a Balanced Budget and a Circle Graph

Doreen's current budget from Example 1 on pages 12 and 13 revealed that her expenses exceed her income. Yet, she wants to save money for travelling. To do this, she needs to increase her income and/or decrease her expenses by *more than* $428. She can do this by making changes such as the following:

Increase income:
- work more hours
- ask parents for money
- get a student loan

Decrease expenses:
- reduce food expenses
- eliminate or reduce clothing expenses
- eliminate or reduce entertainment expenses
- eliminate debt by cashing in Savings Bonds

Determine which changes are realistic. Then, create a balanced revised budget for Doreen and display it in a circle graph.

Solution
Method 1: By hand

Doreen's Monthly Budget		
	Current	Revised
Monthly Income	$780	$780
Monthly Living Expenses		
Rent	$250	$250
Food	$433	$217
Transportation	$75	$75
Clothing	$108	$0
Entertainment	$217	$109
Health/Personal	$25	$25
Debt Repayment	$100	$0
Total Living Expenses	$1208	$676
Left Over for Savings	–$428	$104

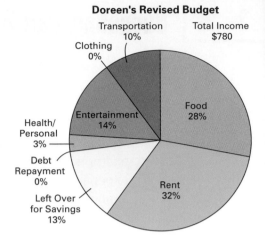

Doreen's Revised Budget

Information for Circle Graph	
% of Income	**Degrees**
$250 \div 780 \times 100 \doteq 32\%$	32% of $360° \doteq 115°$
$217 \div 780 \times 100 \doteq 28\%$	28% of $360° \doteq 101°$
$75 \div 780 \times 100 \doteq 10\%$	10% of $360° = 36°$
0%	$0°$
$109 \div 780 \times 100 \doteq 14\%$	14% of $360° \doteq 50°$
$25 \div 780 \times 100 \doteq 3\%$	3% of $360° \doteq 11°$
0%	$0°$
$104 \div 780 \times 100 \doteq 13\%$	13% of $360° \doteq 47°$

Rent
Food
Transportation
Clothing
Entertainment
Health/Personal
Debt Repayment
Left Over for Savings

See page 405 in the Technology Appendix for specific spreadsheet instructions.

Method 2: Use a spreadsheet
To revise the current budget:
Step 1: In cell C2, enter **Revised**.

Step 2: Copy the contents of cells B3 to B15 into cells C3 to C15.

Step 3: In cell C8, enter the new amount for Food as =**50*52/12**.

Step 4: In cell C10, enter the new amount for Clothing as **0**.

	A	B	C
1	***Doreen's Monthly Budget***		
2		Current	Revised
3	MONTHLY INCOME	$ 780	$ 780
4			
5			
6	MONTHLY LIVING EXPENSES:		
7	Rent	$ 250	$ 250
8	Food	$ 433	$ 217
9	Transportation	$ 75	$ 75
10	Clothing	$ 108	$ 0
11	Entertainment	$ 217	$ 108
12	Health/Personal	$ 25	$ 25
13	Debt Repayment	$ 100	$ 0
14	TOTAL LIVING EXPENSES	$1 208	$ 675
15	Left Over for Savings	-$ 428	$ 105

Step 5: In cell C11, enter the new amount for Entertainment as =**25*52/12**.

Step 6: In cell C13, enter the new amount for Debt Repayment as **0**.

To create a circle graph:
Step 1: Select cells A7 to A13 and A15 and cells C7 to C13 and C15.

Step 2: Follow the instructions for inserting a pie chart:
• For the chart title, enter **Doreen's Revised Budget**.
• Choose to label the chart with the percent values.

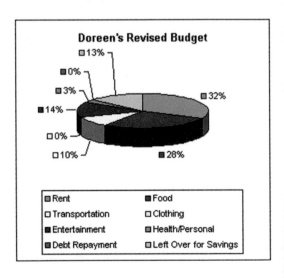

KEY CONCEPTS

- A balanced budget is one in which income matches expenses.

- A circle graph can be used to display a budget.

- A spreadsheet is a useful tool for creating and working with budgets.

DISCUSS THE CONCEPTS

1. Decisions must be made carefully about increasing income and/or decreasing expenses in order to balance a budget. Explain why.

2. **a)** Why is a circle graph a good way to display budget data?
   b) How would circle graphs help in comparing two budgets?

3. Explain how a spreadsheet makes it easier to work with budgets.

APPLY THE CONCEPTS

A *Work in small groups to discuss the following questions.*

1. **Thinking**
   a) What changes did Doreen make to her current budget in order to create her revised balanced budget? (See pages 19 and 20.)
   b) Why do you think she made each change?
   c) Why do you think she kept the subheadings Clothing and Debt Repayment, even though she eliminated those expenses?

2. **Net worth**
   a) To help balance her budget, Doreen liquidated $2200 in Canada Savings Bonds to pay off debts. Revise her net worth statement to include these changes (see Example 2, on pages 13 and 14).
   b) What do you notice about her net worth? Explain.

3. **Application** Choose one of these three situations from 1.2 Budgeting: Part 1:
   - Donald (question 2 on page 15)
   - Franco and Gayle (question 4 on page 16)
   - your chosen individual or family grouping (question 5 on page 16)
   a) Create a revised balanced budget that takes into account their financial goal.
   b) What changes did you make to the current budget? Explain each change and list any assumptions you made in making the change.
   c) Create a circle graph to display the revised balanced budget.

4. Personal budget

   a) Create a balanced budget for yourself that takes into account the long-term goal that you set in question 12 on page 10 and your current budget from question 6 on page 17.

   b) Create a circle graph.

   c) If necessary, revise your net worth statement from question 6 on page 17.

5. Communication Explain how budgets and net worth statements play a role in financial planning.

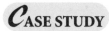

6. Recall Jamal and Olivia and their financial goal of buying a house, as described on pages 3, 5, 6, and 9. In question 9, on page 17, you created a current budget and net worth statement. You then listed changes that could be made to save between $333 and $556 a month.

   a) Jamal and Olivia are considering making some drastic short-term changes, including selling their car. Create a balanced monthly budget based on selling the car and any additional changes that they could make in order to maximize their savings.

   b) Create a circle graph.

   c) How long will it take them to save for a down payment of $20 000?

   d) Do you think that this budget is realistic? Explain.

   e) Revise their net worth statement. Has their net worth changed? Explain.

7. Gross income This graph shows how an average Canadian family spends their money. Note that it is based on gross income rather than net income. Recall each of these situations from 1.2 Budgeting: Part 1:

   • question 2 on page 15 (Donald)
   • question 4 on page 16 (Franco and Gayle)
   • question 9 on page 17 (Jamal and Olivia)

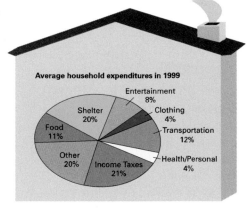

Average household expenditures in 1999

Entertainment 8%
Clothing 4%
Transportation 12%
Health/Personal 4%
Income Taxes 21%
Other 20%
Food 11%
Shelter 20%

   a) For each situation, what percent of gross income is spent on these expenses?

   i) shelter   **ii)** food   **iii)** transportation

   b) How does this compare to the average Canadian family?

8. **Circle graph** Seema's gross income is $25 500/year. She pays 30% in taxes and deductions. Her current monthly budget is shown here in a circle graph.

a) Determine how much she spends for each monthly expense.

b) Are there any expense categories missing? What are they?

c) Should Seema revise her budget? Explain.

d) If percent values had not been displayed, expense amounts could still be determined. Explain how. Use an example to illustrate.

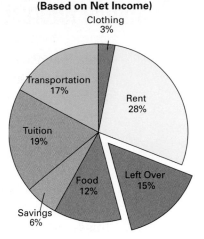

Seema's Current Monthly Budget (Based on Net Income)

- Clothing 3%
- Transportation 17%
- Rent 28%
- Tuition 19%
- Food 12%
- Left Over 15%
- Savings 6%

EXTEND THE CONCEPTS

9. **Lifetime patterns** The graph shows a typical household's pattern of income, expenses, and savings over a lifetime.

a) According to the graph, many people have negative savings up to age 32.

   i) Explain why.

   ii) Does this mean that younger people are careless with their money? Explain.

b) Explain the shape of each graph.

c) How are the three graphs related?

d) What else can you tell from reading the graphs?

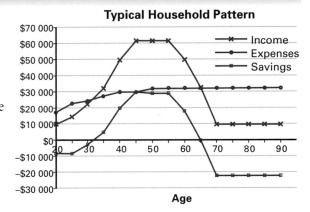

Typical Household Pattern

— Income
— Expenses
— Savings

10. **Lifetime patterns** The graph shows a typical pattern of net worth over a lifetime.

a) Explain the shape of the graph.

b) Make a list of the major events in a person's life that could account for the shape of the graph.

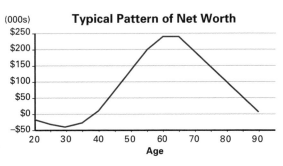

(000s) Typical Pattern of Net Worth

1.4 | Simple Interest

Many financial plans require paying off debts, particularly high-interest debts such as balances on credit cards. One way to do this is to take out a loan at a lower interest rate. If your credit rating is bad, often the only way to do this is to borrow money from family or friends.

EXAMPLE 1

Determine Interest and Amount

Jon owes $3000 on a credit card, which charges 16% interest, and $2000 on a car loan, at 7% interest. He wants to borrow $5000 at a lower interest rate to pay off the debts. His parents have offered to lend him the money at an annual simple interest rate of 6% for 3 years.

a) How much interest will he pay altogether?

b) How much will he have to pay back altogether?

c) Jon's parents want him to make regular monthly payments to pay off the interest in 3 years. What will the interest payments be?

Solution

a) Use the simple interest formula:

Interest = principal × rate × time

$$I = Prt$$

where

     I is the total interest to be paid

     P is the principal, or amount borrowed

     r is the interest rate, as a decimal

     t is the length of time

$I = Prt$

$I = 5000 \times 0.06 \times 3$ $6\% = 0.06$

$I = 900$

Jon will pay $900 in interest altogether.

b) Use the amount formula:

Amount = principal + interest

$$A = P + I$$
$$A = 5000 + 900$$
$$A = 5900$$

Jon will have to pay back $5900 altogether.

c) To determine the monthly interest payments, divide the total interest by the number of payments:

Monthly payments = 900 ÷ 36   3 years at 12 payments/year is 36.
= 25

Jon's interest payments will be $25 a month.

The simple interest formula, $I = Prt$, can be rearranged to solve for each variable.

For interest rate, r:	For principal, P:	For time, t:
$I = Prt$	$I = Prt$	$I = Prt$
$\dfrac{I}{Pt} = \dfrac{Prt}{Pt}$	$\dfrac{I}{rt} = \dfrac{Prt}{rt}$	$\dfrac{I}{Pr} = \dfrac{Prt}{Pr}$
$\dfrac{I}{Pt} = r$	$\dfrac{I}{rt} = P$	$\dfrac{I}{Pr} = t$

These variations of the simple interest formula can be used:

To determine interest: $I = Prt$ To determine interest rate: $r = \dfrac{I}{Pt}$

To determine principal: $P = \dfrac{I}{rt}$ To determine time: $t = \dfrac{I}{Pr}$

EXAMPLE 2

Determine Interest Rate

Tina invested $4000 for 55 months and earned $1200 in simple interest. What was the annual interest rate on her investment?

Solution

Determine the values of the variables of the simple interest formula:

$I = 1200$

$P = 4000$

$r = $ **?**

$t = 55 ÷ 12$ 55 months at 12 months/year

See pages 407 and 408 in the Technology Appendix for tips on calculating efficiently on a graphing calculator.

Use the simple interest formula for finding interest rate, $r = \dfrac{I}{Pt}$:

$$r = \frac{I}{Pt}$$

$$r = \frac{1200}{4000 \times 55 \div 12}$$

$$r \doteq 0.0655$$

Scientific Calculator

$\boxed{c}\ 1200\ \boxed{\div}\ \boxed{(}\ 4000\ \boxed{\times}\ 55$ $\boxed{\div}\ 12\ \boxed{)}\ \boxed{=}$

Change interest rate to a percent: $0.0655 = 6.55\%$

The annual interest rate on the investment was 6.55%.

EXAMPLE 3

Determine Principal

How much must Reena invest at an annual simple interest rate of 8% in order to earn $200 in interest over 260 days?

Solution

Determine the values of the variables:

$I = 200$

$P = \boxed{?}$

$r = 0.08 \qquad 8\% = 0.08$

$t = 260 \div 365 \qquad$ 260 days at 365 days/year

Use the formula for finding principal, $P = \dfrac{I}{rt}$:

$$P = \frac{I}{rt}$$

$$P = \frac{200}{0.08 \times 260 \div 365}$$

$$P \doteq 3509.62$$

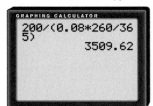

Scientific Calculator

$\boxed{c}\ 200\ \boxed{\div}\ \boxed{(}\ 0.08\ \boxed{\times}\ 260$ $\boxed{\div}\ 365\ \boxed{)}\ \boxed{=}$

Reena must invest a principal of $3509.62.

EXAMPLE 4

Determine Time

Fred lent $400 to Sheena at an annual simple interest rate of 12%. Sheena repaid a total of $664 to Fred. For how long did Sheena owe Fred the money?

Solution

Determine the values of the variables:

$I = 264 \qquad\qquad 664 - 400 = 264$

$P = 400$

$r = 0.12 \qquad\qquad 12\% = 0.12$

$t = \boxed{?}$

Use the formula for finding time, $t = \dfrac{I}{Pr}$:

$t = \dfrac{I}{Pr}$

$t = \dfrac{264}{400 \times 0.12}$

$t = 5.5$

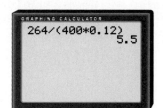

Scientific Calculator

Ⓒ 264 ÷ (400 × 0.12) =

Sheena owed Fred the money for 5.5 years, or 5 years and 6 months.

KEY CONCEPTS

- The simple interest formula is $I = Prt$, where
  I is the total interest to be paid or earned
  P is the principal, or what is borrowed or invested
  r is the interest rate, as a decimal
  t is the length of time

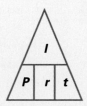

- Variations of the formula can be used to determine the value of each variable:

$$I = Prt \qquad r = \dfrac{I}{Pt} \qquad P = \dfrac{I}{rt} \qquad t = \dfrac{I}{Pr}$$

- The amount of an investment or loan is the principal plus the interest: $A = P + I$

- Unless otherwise stated, the simple interest rate is annual, or yearly, and the time is in years.

DISCUSS THE CONCEPTS

1. Consumers look for a low interest rate on a loan and a high interest rate on an investment. Explain why.

2. To find the principal of a loan, Joel used the formula $P = \dfrac{I}{rt}$. Helena approached it differently. She used the formula $I = Prt$ instead. She substituted the values for I, r, and t, and then, solved for P.
  a) Which method requires fewer steps?
  b) Which do you prefer? Explain why.

A 1. Copy and complete the table.

	Principal ($) P	Interest Rate (%) r	Time t	Interest Earned ($) I	Amount ($) A = P + I
a)	2 000	8.0	3 years		
b)	3 000	6.5	9 months		
c)	5 500		180 days	162.74	
d)	10 000		30 months	1375.00	
e)		5.0	2.5 years	750.00	
f)		1.5	5 weeks	10.10	
g)	1 650	3.5		86.63	
h)	1 675	6.75		84.80	

APPLY THE CONCEPTS

2. Interest earned $600 is invested for 8 years at 7% simple interest.
   a) How much interest is earned?
   b) What will the total value of the investment be when it matures?

3. Interest rate Susan's $2000 investment paid her $210 at the end of 1 year. What was the simple interest rate?

4. Principal Martha lent Aaron money 3 years ago at a simple interest rate of 14%. He repaid her in full plus interest of $399. How much did she lend him 3 years ago?

5. Time Thierry lent a friend $200 at 10% simple interest. He paid Thierry back a total of $215. After how long did Thierry's friend pay him back?

6. Term deposit Jenny invested in a 90-day term deposit at the bank earning 4.5% simple interest. She earned $5.73 in interest. How much money did she invest 90 days ago?

B

7. Term deposit Krista invested $6500 in a 181-day term deposit and received a total of $6637 when it matured. What was the interest rate?

8. Investing Kalpna's investment matured today. She invested $12 500, earned 5.5% simple interest, and received $12 671.88 at maturity. For how many months did she invest?

9. Application Iva borrowed $5000 at 6% simple interest for 2 years.
   a) How much will she have to pay back altogether?
   b) She plans to make regular monthly payments to pay off the interest in 2 years. How much will the interest payments be?

10. Inquiry Financial institutions such as banks and trust companies offer savings and investment alternatives that earn simple interest.

   a) Contact a financial institution or go to *www.school.mcgrawhill.ca/resources/* and follow the links to find the current interest rates on savings and investment alternatives that earn simple interest.

   b) What do you notice about the relationship between the interest rates and terms?

11. Recall Jamal and Olivia and their financial goal of buying a house, as described on pages 3, 5, 6, 9, 17, and 22. They want to borrow $14 000 at a low interest rate to pay off their student loan and credit card debt.

   a) They can get a 3-year $14 000 loan at 12% simple interest. They would like to make regular monthly interest payments over the 3 years. How much will the payments be?

   b) They are trying to keep their monthly expenses to a minimum. What simple interest rate on a 3-year loan will result in monthly interest payments of $100 or less?

   c) Their parents have offered them a loan at 6% simple interest. What will their monthly interest payments be for a 2-year loan? a 3-year loan? a 4-year loan? What do you notice?

ACHIEVEMENT Check Knowledge/Understanding Thinking/Inquiry/Problem Solving Communication Application

12. a) Create and solve a simple interest problem.

   b) What could you do to make your problem more challenging? easier?

EXTEND THE CONCEPTS

C 13. Two unknowns Four years ago, Hank lent Jim money. Jim repaid Hank a total of $1750, which included simple interest charged at 10%. How much did Hank originally lend Jim? (Hint: Use the formula, $A = P + I$, substituting Prt for I ($I = Prt$).)

14. Term deposit Riley invested in a 270-day term deposit that earned simple interest of $5\frac{3}{8}$%. When it matured, he received $5214.71. He then re-invested it in a 181-day term deposit at 3.95%.

   a) How much will he receive when the second term deposit matures?

   b) How much did he originally invest?

CAREER PROFILE

Introduction to Careers

Find a job you like and you will never have to work a day in your life. This is good advice, but finding a career that you like is not easy. And, staying in the same career throughout your working life is not likely.

You probably already have interests and skills that could lead to a career and are transferable from job to job, for instance, computer skills and organizational and communication skills. The following exercise will help you identify and relate interests, skills, and possible careers.

★★★★★ MAKE A CAREER CHANGE NOW!
Must have excellent communication skills and be able to build client relationships. Must be computer and Internet literate.

★★★★★ FULL-TIME POSITION AVAILABLE
Knowledge of PC hardware essential. Must be self-motivated and able to work independently with above-average communication skills.

★★★★★ EXCITING OPPORTUNITY
You should have excellent organizational and communication skills and experience working on a team. Advanced PC skills would be an asset.

1. Fold a piece of paper into four and record the following in the sections:

Your favourite subjects	*Your hobbies and interests that have possible career connections*
Your skills related to technology, for example, word processing and programming	*Your skills related to teamwork, communication, and organization. For example, you are a good listener and successfully manage a part-time job, school, and responsibilities at home.*

2. **a)** In each section, write careers that are directly or indirectly related. For example, if you are interested in travelling, a related career is a travel agent; if you are a good listener, you might write "counselling."
   b) Look for careers that you wrote in more than one section.

Each Career Profile page in this book will introduce you to a career by describing its related skills, required education, advantages, and disadvantages.

CASE STUDY WRAP-UP

Jamal and Olivia recently completed college, and then, got married. They are both working full-time and have student loans and a car loan to pay off. They are currently renting an apartment that is close to work for both of them. They have a goal of buying a house in 3 to 5 years, but this seems impossible because they feel overwhelmed with living expenses and debt. They realize they must manage their money better.

Throughout this chapter, you have solved problems related to Jamal and Olivia's financial goal. You are now ready to answer the following question:

Will Jamal and Olivia be able to save for a down payment on a house in 3 to 5 years?

Work in a small group. Each group member should pick a different time line for achieving the goal— 3 years, 4 years, or 5 years—and then, design a financial plan, budget, and net worth statement for Jamal and Olivia.

Consider the following:
- They need $20 000 for a down payment.
- Their income remains the same.
- They must make changes to their current budget and their net worth statement.
- A time line of 3 years will require more drastic changes than 5 years.
- Their parents have offered to lend them $14 000 at 6% simple interest for 4 years so that they can pay off their credit cards and student loans.
- They expect to make regular monthly interest payments to their parents.

When preparing your financial plan, budget, and net worth statement,
- refer to the Case Study questions on pages 5, 6, 9, 17, 22, and 29
- provide complete solutions, including all calculations
- justify, or explain, your answers
- include a list of any materials you used, all your original data, your sources of information, and any formulas, tables, and graphs that you used or created
- use technology, where appropriate

1.1 Understand Financial Planning, pages 4–10

1. Lois is in Grade 11 and wants to become a fashion designer.
   a) What are the five main steps she should follow in order to design a financial plan that will help her achieve her goal?
   b) Describe what might happen in each of the five steps, using Lois's situation as an example.

2. Elio is a single parent of two young children. He wants to take them on a vacation to visit his parents in Europe within the next 2 years. The following are steps in his financial plan:
   - investigate the cost of a vacation
   - begin a retirement fund
   - begin an emergency fund
   - begin a vacation fund
   - examine spending habits
   - take out a low-interest loan to consolidate debts
   - make a will
   - take out life insurance
   - pay off high-interest debts
   - create a current budget

   a) Arrange the steps in the order Elio should follow them.
   b) Explain why you ordered the steps the way you did.
   c) Explain why each step is important.
   d) Is there more than one way to order the steps? Explain.

1.2 and 1.3 Budgeting: Parts 1 and 2, pages 11–23

3. Justin and Hannah want to start a landscaping business within 18 months. They estimate they will need $10 000 to start the business. However, they cannot save money because they are paying off so many debts. Here is a summary of what they own and owe.
   What they own:
   - House: $150 000
   - Furniture: $6000
   - Two cars: $16 000
   - Savings bonds (6% interest): $5000
   - Retirement savings (15% interest): $10 000
   - Savings in bank (2% interest): $500

   What they owe:
   - Mortgage (5% interest): $125 000
   - Car loan (2% interest): $8000
   - Credit card balance (18% interest): $5500
   - Loan to parents (6% interest): $10 000

a) Create a net worth statement. What is their net worth?

b) What changes would you suggest to their net worth statement? Explain.

c) Would this mean a change to their net worth? Explain.

4. Hannah and Justin want to save $10 000 within 18 months to start a business.

a) How much must they save monthly to have $10 000 in 1 year? 18 months?

b) Use their current monthly budget, shown here, and the net worth statement from question 3 to create two revised budgets: one that will allow them to start their business in 1 year and another in 18 months.

c) Explain each revised budget in part b) by describing what changes you made and why.

	A	B
1	**Hannah and Justin's Budget**	
2		
3	MONTHLY INCOME	$3 500
4		
5		
6	MONTHLY LIVING EXPENSES:	
7	Mortgage and Utilities	$1 200
8	Food	$ 400
9	Transportation	$ 300
10	Clothing	$ 200
11	Entertainment	$ 400
12	Health/Personal	$ 100
13	Credit Card Payments	$ 500
14	Car Loan Payments	$ 400
15	Loan Payments to Parents	$ 200
16	TOTAL LIVING EXPENSES	$3 700
17	Left Over for Savings	-$ 200
18		

d) Which budget from part b) would you recommend? Explain.

e) What questions would you ask Justin and Hannah before finalizing changes to their budget and net worth statement?

5. Create a circle graph to display the budget you chose in question 4, part d).

6. Explain why budgeting is so important in financial planning.

1.4 Simple Interest, pages 24–29

7. Otto borrowed $5000 for 2 years at a simple interest rate of 9%.

a) How much interest will he pay altogether?

b) How much will he have to pay back altogether in 2 years?

c) Otto wants to make monthly interest payments over 2 years. How much will his payments be?

8. For how long must $4000 be invested at $6\frac{1}{4}$% simple interest to earn $875 in interest?

9. How much must Rico invest at $7\frac{1}{2}$% simple interest to earn $356.25 in interest after 5 years?

10. After 48 months, Janet's original investment of $2500 had grown to $3375. What rate of simple interest did her investment earn?

Practice Test

1. a) What questions should be asked before designing a financial plan?

b) Explain why each question should be asked.

2. Explain why each of the following might be a part of someone's financial plan.

a) emergency fund   **b)** savings fund   **c)** retirement fund

d) life insurance   **e)** will   **f)** vacation fund

3. Paul works part-time and wants to buy a car in 2 years for about $8000. His parents will lend him half the money if he can save the rest.
Here are his current income and expenses:

Net Income: $100/week   Transportation: $20/bi-weekly

Entertainment: $20/week   Clothing: $100/month

Health/Personal: $10/week   Food: $20/week

a) How much does he have to save each month to save $4000 in 2 years?

b) Create a current monthly budget for Paul.

c) What changes can he make to his current budget?

d) Design a budget that Paul can follow for 2 years in order to save for a car.

e) What assumptions have you made about Paul in order to design the budget?

4. This circle graph displays information about Beti's budget. How much does she spend monthly on each expense?

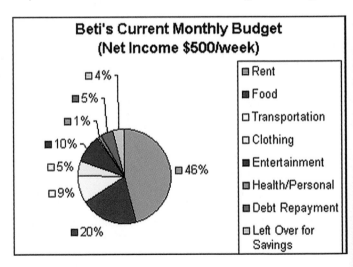

5. **a)** Create a net worth statement for an imaginary character that has
   i) a negative net worth   **ii)** a positive net worth
   b) Describe each character in part a).
   c) Does a negative net worth mean the person has poor spending habits? Explain.

6. Sujeet borrowed $1250 at 6.25% simple interest for 30 months. He paid the interest back in regular monthly payments. How much did he pay each month?

7. How long will it take $5000 to double at 6% simple interest?

8. Janice borrowed $10 000 for 5 years. She will make regular interest payments of $73.33 a month for 5 years. What is the annual simple interest rate?

9. John's 20-year investment earned $23 333.33 in interest. The average annual simple interest rate was 7%. How much did he invest 20 years ago?

10. The simple interest rate on an investment is doubled, and its term is divided in half. Does the interest earned change? Explain, using several examples.

ACHIEVEMENT Check   *Knowledge/Understanding Thinking/Inquiry/Problem Solving Communication Application*

11. In question 3 on page 34, you designed a budget for Paul to follow to save for a car. Assume he was successful. The budget now must be revised to include car-related expenses and monthly interest payments to his parents.
    a) The $4000 loan from his parents is at 6% simple interest for 2 years. How much will his interest payments be?
    b) Estimate monthly expenses for insurance, gas, and repairs. Justify your estimates.
    c) Design a budget that Paul can follow for the next 2 years. Keep in mind that he can increase his income by working an extra 5 h a week at $7/h.

DILBERT reprinted by permission of United Feature Syndicate, Inc.

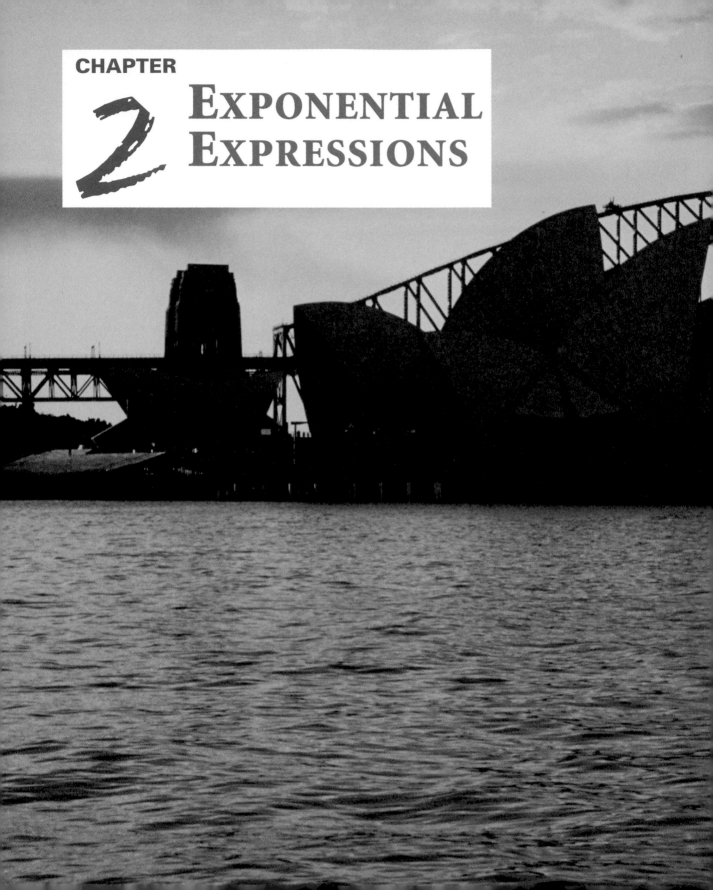

CHAPTER
2
EXPONENTIAL EXPRESSIONS

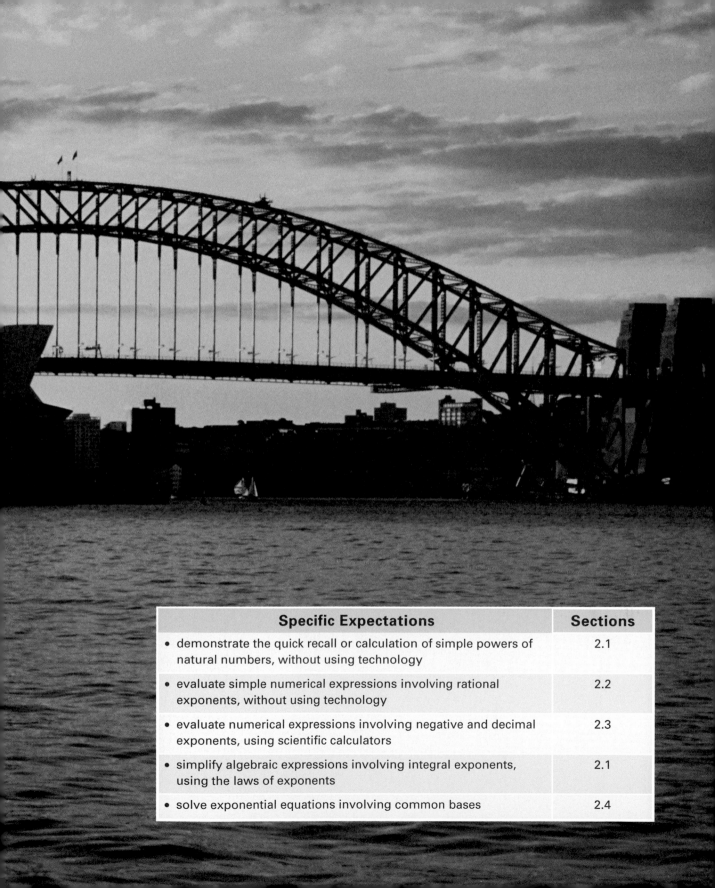

Specific Expectations	Sections
• demonstrate the quick recall or calculation of simple powers of natural numbers, without using technology	2.1
• evaluate simple numerical expressions involving rational exponents, without using technology	2.2
• evaluate numerical expressions involving negative and decimal exponents, using scientific calculators	2.3
• simplify algebraic expressions involving integral exponents, using the laws of exponents	2.1
• solve exponential equations involving common bases	2.4

Get Ready...

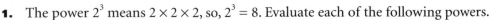

1. The power 2^3 means $2 \times 2 \times 2$, so, $2^3 = 8$. Evaluate each of the following powers.

   a) 5^2 b) 3^4 c) 4^3 d) 6^3 e) 2^5 f) 8^4

2. Evaluate each of the following. What do you notice about the answers?

   a) $(2^3)(2^2)$ b) $(2 \times 2 \times 2)(2 \times 2)$ c) 2^5

3. a) On a test, one student wrote that $3^5 \times 3^3 = 9^8$. What mistake did the student make?

   b) Another student wrote $3^5 \times 3^3 = 3^{15}$. What mistake did this student make?

   c) Write the correct statement to express $3^5 \times 3^3$ as a single power.

4. Write each product as a single power.

   a) $(5^2)(5^3)$ b) $(4^5)(4^7)$ c) $(3^6)(3^{10})$ d) $5^4 \times 5^6$

   e) 8×8^5 f) $x^3 \times x^5$ g) $a^4 \times a^5$ h) $a \times a^4$

5. Evaluate each of the following. What do you notice about the answers?

   a) $\dfrac{3^5}{3^2}$ b) $\dfrac{3 \times 3 \times 3 \times 3 \times 3}{3 \times 3}$ c) 3^3

6. Write each quotient as a single power.

   a) $\dfrac{2^6}{2^4}$ b) $\dfrac{5^{10}}{5^2}$ c) $\dfrac{6^3}{6^2}$ d) $\dfrac{7^8}{7^4}$ e) $\dfrac{3^5}{3^2}$ f) $\dfrac{a^9}{a^3}$

7. Evaluate each of the following. What do you notice about the answers?

   a) $(2^3)^2$ b) $(2 \times 2 \times 2)(2 \times 2 \times 2)$ c) 2^6

8. Write each expression as a single power.

   a) $(2^3)^4$ b) $(5^2)^3$ c) $(4^3)^6$ d) $(6^4)^5$ e) $(x^4)^2$ f) $(a^3)^3$

9. $(xy)^2 = (x^2)(y^2)$, but does $(x + y)^2 = x^2 + y^2$? Provide examples to support your answer.

10. Give the value of each.

    a) $\sqrt{9}$ b) $\sqrt{49}$ c) $\sqrt{100}$ d) $\sqrt{64}$ e) $\sqrt{144}$ f) $\sqrt{225}$

    g) $\sqrt{16}$ h) $\sqrt{121}$ i) $\sqrt{400}$ j) $\sqrt{1}$ k) $\sqrt{\dfrac{9}{25}}$ l) $\sqrt{\dfrac{4}{81}}$

11. Determine each sum.

   a) $(-5) + 3$ **b)** $(-2) + (-2)$ **c)** $-1 + 4$ **d)** $4 + (-3)$

   e) $4 + (-6)$ **f)** $-5 + 9$ **g)** $-7 + (-4)$ **h)** $6 + (-6)$

12. Determine each difference.

   a) $7 - 9$ **b)** $-3 - 4$ **c)** $8 - (-3)$ **d)** $-5 - (-7)$

   e) $12 - 8$ **f)** $1 - 5$ **g)** $-5 - (-5)$ **h)** $4 - 12$

13. Determine each product.

   a) $4 \times (-2)$ **b)** $(-3)(-3)$ **c)** -6×0 **d)** $5(-4)$

   e) $-1 \times (-1)$ **f)** $2 \times (-5)$ **g)** $3 \times 2 \times (-1)$ **h)** $-4(-2)(-5)$

14. Solve.

   a) $4t = 24$ **b)** $k + 5 = 13$ **c)** $m - 4 = 3$ **d)** $12 - 4y = 0$

CASE STUDY

Greg plays guitar in a band. Often, when he is practising, his mother complains that the sound is too loud and that he will ruin his hearing. At what sound level should his mother be concerned?

The loudness of sound is measured in decibels (dB). The softest sound that can just barely be heard by humans is given a value of 0 dB, while a loud rock concert might be 120 dB. The decibel scale is not linear, it is exponential. The sound of a phone ringing, at 60 dB, has a sound intensity of 10^6 units, as compared to ordinary conversation, at 50 dB, which has a sound intensity of 10^5 units. Since $10^6 = 10 \times 10^5$, the sound of the phone is 10 times as loud as the conversation.

In this chapter, you will learn more about the decibel scale. You will use this scale to solve problems about the relative loudness of sounds.

2.1 Evaluate Powers With Integral Exponents

You know that 4^3 means $4 \times 4 \times 4$ and has value 64. Exponents are used to write repeated multiplication in a shorter form.

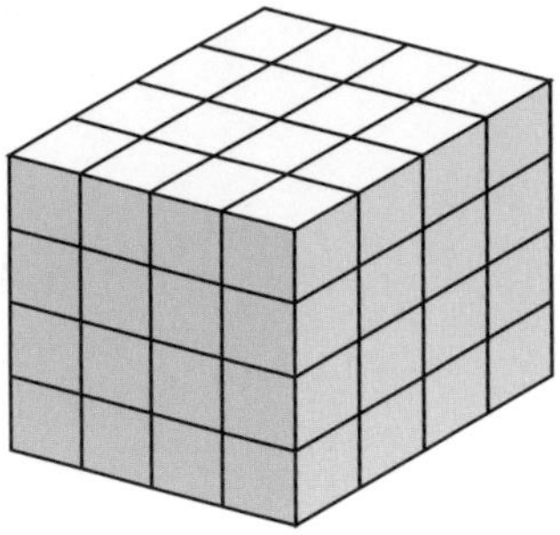

a^n means $\underbrace{a \times a \times a \times \ldots \times a}_{n \text{ factors of } a}$

You have worked with the basic laws of exponents, which can be used as shortcuts for multiplying and dividing powers of the same base and for raising powers to exponents.

Exponent Law for Multiplication

$a^m \times a^n = a^{m+n}$

For example, $4^3 \times 4^2 = 4^{3+2}$
$= 4^5$

Exponent Law for Division

$a^m \div a^n = a^{m-n}$

For example, $4^3 \div 4^2 = 4^{3-2}$
$= 4^1$
$= 4$

Power Law

$(a^m)^n = a^{mn}$

For example, $(4^2)^3 = 4^{2\times 3}$
$= 4^6$

You can use patterns and these basic laws of exponents to interpret the meaning of zero and negative exponents.

DISCOVER

Find a Meaning for Zero and Negative Exponents

Examine the pattern:

$2^5 = 32$
$2^4 = 16$
$2^3 = 8$
$2^2 = 4$
$2^1 = 2$
$2^0 = ?$
$2^{-1} = ?$

1. Describe the pattern on the left side. How does the power change as you move down the list?
2. Describe the pattern on the right side. How can the value be obtained from the line above, in every step?
3. Use the pattern to determine the value of 2^0.
4. Use the pattern to determine the value of 2^{-1}.
5. Write the next three equations in the pattern. Express the value on the right side in fraction form.
6. Create a similar pattern, using base 5.
7. What did you discover about the values of 2^0 and 5^0?
8. How does the value of 2^{-3} compare with the value of 2^3? Does the same rule seem to apply to other negative exponents in the two patterns?

Did You Know?

There are web sites that deal only with the special number 0 as an exponent.

The exponent laws verify the meanings for zero and negative exponents that the patterns show. Look carefully at the following.

$$4^3 \div 4^3 = 4^{3-3} \qquad \text{but also} \qquad 4^3 \div 4^3 = \frac{4^3}{4^3}$$
$$= 4^0 \qquad\qquad\qquad\qquad\qquad = \frac{64}{64}$$
$$= 1$$

Therefore, $4^0 = 1$.

$$4^3 \div 4^5 = 4^{3-5} \qquad \text{but also} \qquad 4^3 \div 4^5 = \frac{4 \times 4 \times 4}{4 \times 4 \times 4 \times 4 \times 4}$$
$$= 4^{-2} \qquad\qquad\qquad\qquad\qquad = \frac{1}{4 \times 4}$$
$$= \frac{1}{4^2}$$

Therefore, $4^{-2} = \frac{1}{4^2}$.

EXAMPLE 1

Evaluate Powers With Zero Exponents

Evaluate.

a) 7^0 **b)** 43^0 **c)** x^0 **d)** $56(1.03)^0$ **e)** $(-8)^0$

Solution

a) $7^0 = 1$ **b)** $43^0 = 1$ **c)** $x^0 = 1$ **d)** $56(1.03)^0 = 56(1)$ **e)** $(-8)^0 = 1$
                                                 $= 56$

EXAMPLE 2

Evaluate Powers With Negative Exponents

Evaluate.

a) 4^{-3} 　　　　　　　 **b)** 3^{-5} 　　　　　　　 **c)** $500(1.6)^{-2}$

Solution

a) $4^{-3} = \dfrac{1}{4^3}$

$\phantom{4^{-3}} = \dfrac{1}{64}$

b) $3^{-5} = \dfrac{1}{3^5}$

$\phantom{3^{-5}} = \dfrac{1}{243}$

c) $500(1.6)^{-2} = 500\left(\dfrac{1}{1.6^2}\right)$

$\phantom{500(1.6)^{-2}} = 500\left(\dfrac{1}{2.56}\right)$

$\phantom{500(1.6)^{-2}} = 195.3125$

It is often easier to use the laws of exponents to simplify first, and then, evaluate.

EXAMPLE 3

Simplify Exponential Expressions

Evaluate.

a) $2^{-3} \times 2^5$ 　　　　　 **b)** $(29^5)^0$ 　　　　　 **c)** $\dfrac{6^7 \times 6^{-2}}{(6^2)^2}$

Solution

a) $2^{-3} \times 2^5 = 2^{-3+5}$

$\phantom{2^{-3} \times 2^5} = 2^2$

$\phantom{2^{-3} \times 2^5} = 4$

b) $(29^5)^0 = 29^{5 \times 0}$

$ = 29^0$

$ = 1$

c) $\dfrac{6^7 \times 6^{-2}}{(6^2)^2} = \dfrac{6^{7+(-2)}}{6^{2 \times 2}}$

$\phantom{\dfrac{6^7 \times 6^{-2}}{(6^2)^2}} = \dfrac{6^5}{6^4}$

$\phantom{\dfrac{6^7 \times 6^{-2}}{(6^2)^2}} = 6^{5-4}$

$\phantom{\dfrac{6^7 \times 6^{-2}}{(6^2)^2}} = 6^1$

$\phantom{\dfrac{6^7 \times 6^{-2}}{(6^2)^2}} = 6$

EXAMPLE 4

Simplify Algebraic Expressions

Simplify.

a) $k^5 \times k^{-3}$ 　　　　 **b)** $\dfrac{n^3 \times n^2}{n^{-1}}$ 　　　　 **c)** $(3h^2)^3 \times 2(h^{-2})^2$

Solution

a) $k^5 \times k^{-3} = k^{5+(-3)}$

$\phantom{k^5 \times k^{-3}} = k^2$

b) $\dfrac{n^3 \times n^2}{n^{-1}} = \dfrac{n^{3+2}}{n^{-1}}$

$\phantom{\dfrac{n^3 \times n^2}{n^{-1}}} = \dfrac{n^5}{n^{-1}}$

$\phantom{\dfrac{n^3 \times n^2}{n^{-1}}} = n^{5-(-1)}$

$\phantom{\dfrac{n^3 \times n^2}{n^{-1}}} = n^6$

c) $ (3h^2)^3 \times 2(h^{-2})^2$

$= 3^3 h^{2 \times 3} \times 2h^{-2 \times 2}$

$= 27h^6 \times 2h^{-4}$

$= 27 \times 2 \times h^{6+(-4)}$

$= 54h^2$

KEY CONCEPTS

- The basic exponent laws apply to any values of the exponents.
  $$a^m \times a^n = a^{m+n} \qquad a^m \div a^n = a^{m-n} \qquad (a^m)^n = a^{mn}$$

- Any power with a zero exponent has value 1: $a^0 = 1$

- Any power with a negative exponent can be expressed in an equivalent fraction form with a positive exponent: $a^{-n} = \dfrac{1}{a^n}$

DISCUSS THE CONCEPTS

1. $3 \times 5 = 15$ but 3^5 does not equal 15. Explain why. Give the correct value for 3^5.

2. Is 3^4 the same as 4^3? Explain.

3. Sev claims that $(3h^2)^3 = 3h^6$. Explain why his answer is not correct.

4. Explain why $2^0 = 1$ using terms that a grade 9 student would understand.

PRACTISE

A 1. Give the value of each.

a) 7^2 b) 5^3 c) 10^4 d) 12^0 e) 25^0

f) $(-1)^{10}$ g) $(-14)^0$ h) $(-7)^0$ i) $(-1)^{15}$ j) $(-5)^3$

2. Evaluate.

a) 5^{-2} b) 4^{-3} c) 2^{-4} d) 11^{-2} e) 3^{-3}

f) 3^{-4} g) 2^{-5} h) 10^{-3} i) 5^{-3} j) 8^{-2}

3. Write as a single power. Then, evaluate.

a) $2^{-3} \times 2^5$ b) $7^4 \times 7^{-3}$ c) $3^2 \times 3^{-3}$ d) $5^3 \times 5^{-3}$ e) $8^{-2} \times 8^2$

f) $6^0 \times 6^{-1} \times 6^3$ g) $4^3 \times 4^{-4}$ h) $2^{-3} \times (2^2)^3$ i) $5^{-1} \times 5^{-1}$ j) $(3^0)^7 \times 3^{-2}$

4. Write as a single power. Then, evaluate.

a) $\dfrac{5^4}{5^2}$ b) $\dfrac{5^4}{5^2}$ c) $\dfrac{4^2}{4^5}$ d) $\dfrac{5^2}{5^5}$ e) $\dfrac{2^{-1}}{2^2}$

f) $\dfrac{4}{4^{-2}}$ g) $\dfrac{7^2}{7^{-2}}$ h) $\dfrac{5^{-2}}{5^{-3}}$ i) $\dfrac{10^{-3}}{10^{-5}}$ j) $\dfrac{6^{-3}}{6^{-3}}$

5. Simplify. Then, evaluate. Where appropriate, leave answers in fraction form.

a) $(2^3)^2$ **b)** $(5^2)^{-1}$ **c)** $(3^5)^0$ **d)** $(3^2)^{-2}$ **e)** $(4^{-1})^2$

f) $(7^{-1})^{-2}$ **g)** $(6^0)^{-7}$ **h)** $(11^{-1})^{-1}$ **i)** $(2^{-2})^3$ **j)** $(10^{-3})^3$

6. **Communication/Application** Write a sentence explaining when the value of $(-1)^n$ is $+1$ and when it is -1.

B **7.** Simplify.

a) $k^4 \times k^3$ **b)** $b^2 \times b^3 \times b^4$ **c)** $(3x^2)(x^3)$ **d)** $(5t)(2t^3)$

e) $n^{-2} \times n^3$ **f)** $(x^3)^2$ **g)** $(a^{-2})^5$ **h)** $(5p^2)^3$

i) $3(a^3)^2$ **j)** $(3a^3)^2$ **k)** $(x^3)^{-2}$ **l)** $\dfrac{a^4}{a^3}$

m) $\dfrac{16a^5}{4a^2}$ **n)** $\dfrac{18n^7}{3n^4}$ **o)** $\dfrac{(x^3)^{-2}}{x^{-5}}$ **p)** $\dfrac{m^4 \times m^{-5}}{m^{-2}}$

8. Simplify.

a) $\dfrac{(3a^2b^3)(7a^4b^3)}{21a^3b^3}$ **b)** $\dfrac{(6x^2y^2)(4x^2y)}{12xy^2}$ **c)** $\dfrac{(7m^2n^{-2})(3m^4n^4)}{7m^4n^4}$

d) $\dfrac{(3xy)(5xy^2)}{15x^{-2}y^{-1}}$ **e)** $\dfrac{(5a^{-4}b^{-3})(4ab^{-2})}{10a^{-1}b^{-1}}$ **f)** $\dfrac{24k^{-3}d^4}{(3k^{-2})(4d^{-2})}$

9. Express each as a single power of 2.

a) $2^a \times 2^b \times 2^c$ **b)** $2^{a+b} \times 2^{a-b}$ **c)** $\dfrac{2^a \times 2^b \times 2^c}{2^{a+b}}$

APPLY THE CONCEPTS

10. **Piano tuning** The frequency of notes on a piano is measured in vibrations per second, called hertz (Hz). When a piano is tuned, the first note to be tuned is the A above middle C. After it has been tuned to a frequency of 440 Hz, the rest of the A notes on the keyboard are tuned, so that each successive A has twice the frequency of the one below it. This means that the first A above "middle A" is tuned as 440×2^1 or 880 Hz.

Determine the frequencies of the next two A notes above middle A and the four A notes below middle A.

Middle C

11. Sound intensity When Greg plays his guitar plugged into the amplifier, the noise level is about 80 dB, which is a sound intensity of 10^8. By comparison, the noise of the family's vacuum cleaner is 70 dB. How many times as loud as the vacuum cleaner noise is Greg's playing?

12. Problem Solving The intensity, or brightness, of the light coming from an electric lamp can be calculated using the formula $I = kD^{-2}$, where I is the intensity, in lumens (lm), D is the distance from the light, in metres, and k is a constant that varies with the light source.

a) Use the formula with $k = 3200$ to copy and complete the table.

Distance from Light (m)	1	2	4	8	16	32
Intensity of Light (lm)						

b) What happens to the intensity of the light when the distance doubles?

c) What happens to the intensity of the light when the distance is halved?

d) What happens to the intensity of the light if the constant is doubled, for a different light source? Explain.

13. Binary numbers An Wang (1920–1990) was a pioneer of the computer industry. He grew up in Shanghai, China, but went to the United States to continue his studies in science. In 1948, he invented a magnetic pulse controlling device that greatly increased the storage capacity of computers. He later founded his own company, Wang Laboratories, and became a leader in the development of desktop calculators and word-processing systems. Historically, digital computers stored information as numbers. Electronic circuits can exist in only one of two states, open or closed. So, numbers were stored using only two digits, 0 and 1. Numbers written using only these two digits are called binary numbers. The decimal value of the binary number 1001101 can be determined using a base-2 place-value chart:

2^6	2^5	2^4	2^3	2^2	2^1	2^0
1	0	0	1	1	0	1

Then, $1001101 = 1 \times 2^6 + 1 \times 2^3 + 1 \times 2^2 + 1 \times 2^0$

$\qquad\qquad\quad = 64 + 8 + 4 + 1$

$\qquad\qquad\quad = 77$

a) Determine the decimal value of each binary number.

   i) 1111　　**ii)** 10000　　**iii)** 11000011　　**iv)** 10111001

b) Express each decimal number in binary form.

   i) 8　　**ii)** 11　　**iii)** 29　　**iv)** 117

14. Change each of the following to a power with base 2.

a) 4^3　　　　b) 8^2　　　　c) 16^{-2}

Powers With Rational Exponents

You know that 4^3 means $4 \times 4 \times 4$,
that $4^0 = 1$, and that $4^{-2} = \dfrac{1}{4^2}$.
What if the exponent is a fraction?

In this section you will learn how to
work with numbers such as $4^{\frac{1}{2}}$.

DISCOVER

Meaning of the Exponents $\frac{1}{2}$ and $\frac{1}{3}$

1. **a)** Use the fact that $\sqrt{9} = 3$ to copy and complete the following.

$$\sqrt{9} \times \sqrt{9} = \boxed{?} \times \boxed{?} = \boxed{?}$$

b) Use the law of exponents for multiplication to copy and complete the
following.

$$9^{\frac{1}{2}} \times 9^{\frac{1}{2}} = 9^{\boxed{?} + \boxed{?}} = \boxed{?}$$

c) Compare the statements in parts a) and b). What other mathematical
operation does the exponent $\dfrac{1}{2}$ seem to be equivalent to?

2. Because $2^3 = 8$ (two cubed equals eight), we say
that the cube root of 8 is 2, and we write $\sqrt[3]{8} = 2$.

a) Use the fact that $\sqrt[3]{8} = 2$ to copy and complete
the following.

$$\sqrt[3]{8} \times \sqrt[3]{8} \times \sqrt[3]{8} = \boxed{?} \times \boxed{?} \times \boxed{?} = \boxed{?}$$

b) Use the law of exponents for multiplication to copy
and complete the following.

$$8^{\frac{1}{3}} \times 8^{\frac{1}{3}} \times 8^{\frac{1}{3}} = 8^{\boxed{?} + \boxed{?} + \boxed{?}} = \boxed{?}$$

c) Compare the statements in parts a) and b). What other mathematical
operation does the exponent $\dfrac{1}{3}$ seem to be equivalent to?

Fractional exponents with a numerator of 1 are equivalent to roots. For example,
$32^{\frac{1}{5}}$ means the same as $\sqrt[5]{32}$ and has value 2 because $2^5 = 32$. These exponents are
called **unit rational exponents**.

EXAMPLE 1

Evaluate Powers With Unit Rational Exponents

Evaluate.

a) $16^{\frac{1}{4}}$ **b)** $27^{\frac{1}{3}}$ **c)** $64^{-\frac{1}{3}}$

Solution

a) $16^{\frac{1}{4}} = \sqrt[4]{16}$
$\qquad = 2 \qquad 2^4 = 16$

b) $27^{\frac{1}{3}} = \sqrt[3]{27}$
$\qquad = 3 \qquad 3^3 = 27$

c) $64^{-\frac{1}{3}} = \dfrac{1}{64^{\frac{1}{3}}}$ Rewrite with a positive exponent.

$\qquad = \dfrac{1}{\sqrt[3]{64}}$

$\qquad = \dfrac{1}{4} \qquad 4^3 = 64$

To evaluate some powers with rational exponents, you must first use the power law for exponents to rewrite the expression with a unit rational exponent. Study the following examples carefully to see how this is done.

EXAMPLE 2

Evaluate Powers With Rational Exponents

Evaluate.

a) $125^{\frac{2}{3}}$ **b)** $16^{\frac{3}{2}}$ **c)** $8^{-\frac{2}{3}}$

Solution

a) $125^{\frac{2}{3}} = \left(125^{\frac{1}{3}}\right)^2$
$\qquad = \left(\sqrt[3]{125}\right)^2$
$\qquad = (5)^2$
$\qquad = 25$

b) $16^{\frac{3}{2}} = \left(16^{\frac{1}{2}}\right)^3$
$\qquad = \left(\sqrt{16}\right)^3$
$\qquad = (4)^3$
$\qquad = 64$

c) $8^{-\frac{2}{3}} = \dfrac{1}{8^{\frac{2}{3}}}$

$\qquad = \dfrac{1}{\left(8^{\frac{1}{3}}\right)^2}$

$\qquad = \dfrac{1}{\left(\sqrt[3]{8}\right)^2}$

$\qquad = \dfrac{1}{(2)^2}$

$\qquad = \dfrac{1}{4}$

KEY CONCEPTS

- Exponents that are unit fractions represent roots:

$$a^{\frac{1}{2}} = \sqrt{a}, \quad a^{\frac{1}{3}} = \sqrt[3]{a}, \quad a^{\frac{1}{4}} = \sqrt[4]{a}, \quad \ldots, \quad a^{\frac{1}{n}} = \sqrt[n]{a}$$

- Fractional exponents where the numerator is not 1 can be rearranged:

$$b^{-\frac{1}{2}} = \frac{1}{b^{\frac{1}{2}}} \text{ or } \frac{1}{\sqrt{b}}, \quad b^{-\frac{1}{3}} = \frac{1}{b^{\frac{1}{3}}} \text{ or } \frac{1}{\sqrt[3]{b}}, \quad \ldots, \quad b^{-\frac{1}{n}} = \frac{1}{b^{\frac{1}{n}}} \text{ or } \frac{1}{\sqrt[n]{b}}$$

$$b^{\frac{3}{2}} = \left(b^{\frac{1}{2}}\right)^3 \text{ or } \left(\sqrt{b}\right)^3, \quad \ldots, \quad b^{\frac{x}{y}} = \left(b^{\frac{1}{y}}\right)^x \text{ or } \left(\sqrt[y]{b}\right)^x$$

DISCUSS THE CONCEPTS

1. Express each power in its root form and give its value.

   a) $25^{\frac{1}{2}}$ b) $27^{\frac{1}{3}}$ c) $81^{\frac{1}{4}}$

2. Describe the steps you would take to determine the value of $4^{-\frac{1}{2}}$. What is its value?

3. Describe the steps you would take to determine the value of $25^{\frac{3}{2}}$. What is its value?

PRACTISE

A 1. Evaluate.

   a) $\sqrt{49}$ b) $\sqrt{900}$ c) $\sqrt[3]{64}$ d) $\sqrt[5]{243}$ e) $\sqrt[5]{100\,000}$

2. Find the value of each expression.

   a) $64^{\frac{1}{2}}$ b) $100^{\frac{1}{2}}$ c) $400^{\frac{1}{2}}$ d) $16^{\frac{1}{4}}$ e) $125^{\frac{1}{3}}$

3. Find the value of each expression.

   a) $36^{\frac{1}{2}}$ b) $121^{\frac{1}{2}}$ c) $81^{\frac{1}{4}}$ d) $32^{\frac{1}{5}}$ e) $625^{\frac{1}{4}}$

4. Determine the value of each expression.

   a) $25^{-\frac{1}{2}}$ b) $36^{-\frac{1}{2}}$ c) $27^{-\frac{1}{3}}$ d) $16^{-\frac{1}{4}}$ e) $100^{-\frac{1}{2}}$

5. Determine the value of each expression.

a) $125^{-\frac{1}{3}}$ **b)** $64^{-\frac{1}{6}}$ **c)** $225^{-\frac{1}{2}}$ **d)** $216^{-\frac{1}{3}}$ **e)** $10\,000^{-\frac{1}{4}}$

B 6. Evaluate.

a) $25^{\frac{3}{2}}$ **b)** $36^{\frac{3}{2}}$ **c)** $16^{\frac{3}{4}}$ **d)** $32^{\frac{3}{5}}$ **e)** $27^{\frac{2}{3}}$

7. Evaluate.

a) $8^{-\frac{4}{3}}$ **b)** $81^{-\frac{3}{4}}$ **c)** $16^{-\frac{5}{4}}$ **d)** $1000^{-\frac{2}{3}}$ **e)** $9^{-\frac{3}{2}}$

8. Calculate the value of each expression.

a) $5^2 + 25^{\frac{1}{2}}$ **b)** $9^3 - 9^{\frac{1}{2}}$ **c)** $\left(8^{\frac{1}{3}} + 3\right)^2$ **d)** $64^{\frac{1}{2}} - 64^{\frac{1}{3}} + 64^{\frac{1}{6}}$

9. Write as a single power. Then, evaluate.

a) $2^{\frac{1}{5}} \times 2^{\frac{4}{5}}$ **b)** $\left(100^{\frac{1}{4}}\right)^2$ **c)** $5^{\frac{4}{3}} \div 5^{\frac{1}{3}}$ **d)** $16^{-\frac{1}{4}} \times 16^{\frac{3}{4}}$

10. Use $x = 64$ to verify that $\left(x^3\right)^{\frac{1}{2}} = \left(x^{\frac{1}{2}}\right)^3$.

APPLY THE CONCEPTS

11. Electricity In electrical circuits, voltage, power, and resistance are related by the formula $V = (PR)^{\frac{1}{2}}$, where V is the voltage, in volts (V), P is the power, in watts (W), and R is the resistance, in ohms (Ω).

a) What voltage is required to light a 24-W bulb that has a resistance of 6 Ω?

b) What voltage is required to light a 100-W bulb that has a resistance of 144 Ω?

12. Application Gift-wrapping services use a formula to determine the length of ribbon, L, in centimetres, required for a cube-shaped box. The formula is $L = 8V^{\frac{1}{3}} + 20$, where V is the volume of the box, in cubic centimetres. Calculate the length of ribbon required to tie cube-shaped boxes with each volume.

a) 216 cm^3 **b)** 27 000 cm^3

13. Skid marks When investigating car accidents, police use the skid marks to estimate the speed of the car. The formula $S = 1.6(FL)^{\frac{1}{2}}$ gives an approximation of the car's speed, S, in kilometres per hour, just before the brakes were applied. L is the length of the skid mark, in metres, and F is a factor for friction based on the road conditions. Use an F-value of 80 for dry pavement and 60 for wet pavement. Find the approximate speed of a car in each situation. Round your answers to the nearest kilometre per hour.

a) on dry pavement, length of skid mark is 20 m

b) on wet pavement, length of skid mark is 20 m

c) on wet pavement, length of skid mark is 40 m

ACHIEVEMENT Check | Knowledge/Understanding Thinking/Inquiry/Problem Solving Communication Application

14. Without evaluating the expressions, determine which is greater. Explain your reasoning.

a) 2^{100} or 16^{20} **b)** 8^{17} or 4^{26} **c)** 20^{100} or 400^{40} **d)** $125^{\frac{5}{3}}$ or $243^{\frac{2}{5}}$

EXTEND THE CONCEPTS

15. Radius of a sphere The radius, r, of a sphere is related to its volume, V, by the formula $r = \left(\dfrac{3V}{4\pi}\right)^{\frac{1}{3}}$. Calculate, to one decimal place, the radius of a sphere with each volume.

a) 8 m^3 **b)** 32.81 cm^3

16. Simplify.

a) $\left(16a^4\right)^{\frac{1}{4}}$ **b)** $\left(27a^3b^6\right)^{\frac{1}{3}}$ **c)** $\left(125a^3\right)^{\frac{2}{3}}$ **d)** $\left(-8a^3b^6\right)^{\frac{1}{3}}$

17. Simplify.

a) $\left(\dfrac{x^6}{x^{-3}}\right)^2$ **b)** $\dfrac{x^4 y^{\frac{3}{2}}}{xy}$ **c)** $\dfrac{25x^7 y^{\frac{10}{3}}}{x^4 y^{\frac{1}{3}}}$ **d)** $\left(5x^2 y^{\frac{1}{4}}\right)^3$

18. Evaluate.

a) $\dfrac{2^0 + 3}{1 - 2^{-1}}$ **b)** $\dfrac{9^{\frac{1}{2}} + 5^0}{4^{\frac{3}{2}} - 32^{\frac{1}{5}}}$

2.3 | Evaluate Exponential Expressions Using a Scientific Calculator

Many of the calculations in the previous two sections could be done using a scientific calculator. However, you should be able to decide whether it is quicker to use a calculator or mental math.

For example, you know that $36^{\frac{1}{2}}$ means $\sqrt{36}$ and has value 6. You do not need a calculator.

On the other hand, consider $30^{\frac{1}{2}}$. You know that this means the same as $\sqrt{30}$, but there is no exact number that gives 30 when squared. In this case, you need a calculator.

Since $\sqrt{25} = 5$ and $\sqrt{36} = 6$, you know that $\sqrt{30}$ is between 5 and 6.

A calculator gives $\sqrt{30} = 5.48$, to two decimal places.

You also need to understand the properties of exponents to be able to use a calculator power key correctly.

You know that $8^{\frac{2}{3}}$ means $\left(\sqrt[3]{8}\right)^2$ and has value 2^2 or 4.

You can use the exponent key to find the same result.

$\boxed{c} \; 8 \; \boxed{y^x} \; \boxed{(} \; 2 \; \boxed{\div} \; 3 \; \boxed{)} \; \boxed{=}$

Scientific calculators vary slightly. Refer to the manual provided with the calculator, or experiment to discover the correct key sequences for the exponent key, $\boxed{y^x}$, or $\boxed{x^y}$, or $\boxed{a^b}$.

Use the Power Key

1. a) Give the value of 2^3.

b) Use the power key on a calculator to evaluate 2^3. Record the key sequence you used.

2. a) What is the value of 3^2? Of 3^3?

b) Can $3^{2.6} \doteq 42$? Why or why not?

c) Use a calculator to find $3^{2.6}$ to one decimal place.

3. a) What is the value of $\sqrt[4]{16}$?

b) Write $\sqrt[4]{16}$ in exponential form.

c) Find two different ways to evaluate $\sqrt[4]{16}$ using a scientific calculator. Record the key sequence you used for each method.

4. a) What is the value of 2^{-1}? Express the answer as a decimal.

b) Confirm the value of 2^{-1} using a calculator. Record the key sequence you used.

EXAMPLE 1

Evaluate Exponential Expressions

Evaluate. Round your answers to two decimal places. Estimate to check that the answer is reasonable.

a) $10^{3.4}$ 　　　　　　　　　　　**b)** $16^{\frac{3}{8}}$

Solution

a) $10^{3.4} \doteq 2511.89$ 　　$\boxed{c}$ 10 $\boxed{y^x}$ 3.4 $\boxed{=}$ 2511.886432

Estimate:

$10^3 = 1000$ and $10^4 = 10\,000$.

The answer is between these two values, so, it is reasonable.

b) $16^{\frac{3}{8}} \doteq 2.83$ 　　$\boxed{c}$ 16 $\boxed{y^x}$ $\boxed{(}$ 3 $\boxed{\div}$ 8 $\boxed{)}$ $\boxed{=}$ 2.828427125

Estimate:

$16^{\frac{1}{2}}$ means $\sqrt{16}$ and has value 4. Since $\frac{3}{8}$ is less than $\frac{1}{2}$, or $\frac{4}{8}$, the value of $16^{\frac{3}{8}}$ should be less than 4. The answer is reasonable.

EXAMPLE 2	**Evaluate More Complex Exponential Expressions**

Evaluate. Round your answers to two decimal places.

a) $250(1.08)^{12}$

b) $3000\left(1+\dfrac{0.05}{12}\right)^{24}$

Solution

a) $250(1.08)^{12} \doteq 629.54$

$\boxed{c}\ 250\ \boxed{\times}\ 1.08\ \boxed{y^x}\ 12\ \boxed{=}\ \texttt{629.5425292}$

Scientific calculators are programmed to follow the order of operations. The calculator evaluates the power first, and then, multiplies by 250.

b) $3000\left(1+\dfrac{0.05}{12}\right)^{24} \doteq 3314.82$

$\boxed{c}\ 3000\ \boxed{\times}\ \boxed{(}\ 1\ \boxed{+}\ 0.05\ \boxed{\div}\ 12\ \boxed{)}\ \boxed{y^x}\ 24\ \boxed{=}\ \texttt{3314.824007}$

Key in the brackets to ensure that the expression $1+\dfrac{0.05}{12}$ is evaluated first.

KEY CONCEPTS

• You can use the power key on a scientific calculator to evaluate expressions involving exponents. Sometimes brackets must be keyed in to ensure the correct order of operations is used. If in doubt, key in extra brackets.

• If you can evaluate an exponential expression mentally, that method may be faster and less error prone than using a calculator.

DISCUSS THE CONCEPTS

For each of the following, either
• give an exact answer if you can find the value mentally, or
• give an estimate if you would need to use the power key on a calculator to find the value

1. 3^4
2. 5.2^0
3. $7^{\frac{1}{3}}$
4. $8^{0.5}$
5. $100^{\frac{3}{2}}$

A 1. Use a scientific calculator to evaluate each of the following. Round your answers to two decimal places. Estimate to check that each answer is reasonable.

a) $40^{1.75}$

b) $16^{\frac{5}{8}}$

c) $15^{\frac{1}{4}}$

d) $2.8^{1.9}$

e) $10^{\frac{1}{3}}$

f) $6^{1.7}$

g) $3^{4.5}$

h) $5^{-2.3}$

i) $78^{\frac{3}{4}}$

j) $3.9^{-\frac{1}{2}}$

k) $30^{\frac{3}{5}}$

l) $108^{0.5}$

2. Evaluate. Round your answers to three decimal places.

a) $(6^3)^{1.2}$

b) $(5^{1.4})^{-2}$

c) $\dfrac{4^{1.7}}{4^{0.5}}$

d) $\dfrac{7^{1.6} \times 7^{2.1}}{7^{-3.2}}$

3. Calculate the value of each. Round your answers to two decimal places.

a) $500(1.025)^{24}$

b) $675(1.045)^{42}$

c) $875.49(1.016)^{4.75}$

d) $1045.75(1.055)^{10.5}$

e) $1000(1.015)^{-6}$

f) $375(1.03)^{-12.75}$

B 4. Each of the following expressions might occur in the solution to a compound interest problem. Evaluate. Round your answers to two decimal places.

a) $250\left(1+\dfrac{0.03}{12}\right)^{12}$

b) $800\left(1+\dfrac{0.08}{12}\right)^{36}$

c) $4000\left(1+\dfrac{0.15}{4}\right)^{20}$

d) $1350\left(1+\dfrac{0.075}{12}\right)^{24}$

e) $775\left(1+\dfrac{0.019}{2}\right)^{6}$

f) $15\,000\left(1+\dfrac{0.045}{12}\right)^{48}$

5. **Depreciation** The formula $V = P(1 - r)^t$ can be used to find the value, V, of an item that had an original price, P, with depreciation at a rate r after t years. The value of a computer depreciates by 30% each year. Find the value of a 4-year-old computer that cost $2999.

*C*ASE STUDY

6. **Noise reduction** After he got a new muffler installed, the noise of Greg's old car dropped from 84 dB to 72 dB. Recall that 84 dB means a sound intensity of $10^{8.4}$. How many times noisier was Greg's car before he had the muffler replaced? Round your answer to two decimal places.

7. Car loan The balance, B, still owing on a car loan can be found using the

formula $B = M\left[\dfrac{1-(1+i)^{k-n}}{i}\right]$, where M represents the monthly payment,

i is the monthly rate of interest, k is the number of payments already made, and n is the total number of payments. Diane is paying off her car loan over 4 years with monthly payments of $178. The rate of interest is 0.75% per month.

a) What is the balance owing after Diane has made 15 payments?

b) Find the balance owing after she has made 3 years of payments.

EXTEND THE CONCEPTS

C 8. Music The frequency of notes on a guitar is measured in hertz (Hz). The frequency of a C note is 264 Hz. The frequency of other notes going up a musical scale can be determined by multiplying as shown.

Note	C	D	E	F	G	A	B	C
Multiple of C	1	$\left(\sqrt[12]{2}\right)^2$	$\left(\sqrt[12]{2}\right)^4$	$\left(\sqrt[12]{2}\right)^5$	$\left(\sqrt[12]{2}\right)^7$	$\left(\sqrt[12]{2}\right)^9$	$\left(\sqrt[12]{2}\right)^{11}$	$\left(\sqrt[12]{2}\right)^{12}$
Frequency (Hz)	264	$264 \times \left(\sqrt[12]{2}\right)^2$						

a) Find the frequency of each other note in the scale, rounded to the nearest unit.

b) How can the frequency of a note in one octave be obtained from the frequency of the same note in the octave above it?

Solve Exponential Equations Using Common Bases

You know how to solve linear equations, such as $5x + 4 = 19$, and quadratic equations, such as $x^2 + 4x + 3 = 0$. In applications, many other types of equations can occur. Here you will develop a method that can sometimes be used to solve an equation that has the variable as an exponent, such as $2^x = 2^3$.

DISCOVER

Equate Exponents and Bases

1. Consider the equation $2^x = 2^3$.
   a) Both sides of the equation are single powers of the same base, 2. What must be true about the exponents?
   b) What is the value of x?

2. Consider the equation $5^{n+1} = 5^3$.
   a) Since both sides are single powers of base 5, what must be true about the exponents?
   b) What is the value of n?

If an equation relates two powers of the same base, then, the exponents must be equal.

You can solve an equation with the variable in the exponent if you can write both sides of the equation as a power of the same base.

EXAMPLE 1

Change to a Common Base
Solve.
a) $2^x = 16$
b) $4^{x-3} = 1$

Solution

a) $2^x = 16$ 16 can be expressed as a power of 2.

$2^x = 2^4$ Both sides are powers of base 2, so, the exponents must be equal.

$x = 4$

b) $4^{x-3} = 1$ Any base with zero exponent has value 1. Replace 1 with 4^0.

$4^{x-3} = 4^0$ Equate exponents.

$x - 3 = 0$

$x = 3$

EXAMPLE 2

Solve by Using a Common Base

Solve and check.

a) $2^x - 4 = 28$ **b)** $8^x = 4^3$

Solution

a) $2^x - 4 = 28$

$2^x = 28 + 4$ Isolate the power with the variable on the left side.

$2^x = 32$ Simplify.

$2^x = 2^5$ Change to the common base, 2.

$x = 5$ Equate exponents.

To check, substitute the value $x = 5$ into the left side (**L.S.**) and the right side (**R.S.**). The results should be the same.

L.S. $= 2^x - 4$ **R.S.** $= 28$

$= 2^5 - 4$

$= 32 - 4$

$= 28$

Since **L.S.** = **R.S.**, the answer $x = 5$ is correct.

b) $8^x = 4^3$ Find a common base.

$(2^3)^x = (2^2)^3$ Both 8 and 4 can be written as powers of 2.

$2^{3x} = 2^6$ Simplify using the laws of powers.

$3x = 6$ Equate exponents.

$x = 2$

Check:

L.S. $= 8^x$ **R.S.** $= 4^3$

$= 8^2$ $= 64$

$= 64$ ✔

The solution is $x = 2$.

KEY CONCEPTS

- If two powers with the same base are equal, then, the exponents are equal.

- You can solve for a variable that occurs as part of an exponent if you can write powers with the same base on each side of the equation, and then, equate the exponents.

DISCUSS THE CONCEPTS

1. If $2^x = 8$, describe how to find the value of x. What is the value of x?

2. To solve the equation $8^2 = 16^x$, one student said $x = 1$. This student reasoned that the base 16 is double the base 8, so, the exponent on the right should be half the exponent on the left. Is this correct? If not, describe how to solve the equation correctly.

PRACTISE

(A) 1. Solve for x.

    a) $2^x = 2^5$ **b)** $3^x = 3^{-4}$ **c)** $5^x = 5^{-7}$

    d) $10^4 = 10^x$ **e)** $6^{0.5} = 6^x$ **f)** $4.9^x = 4.9^{-3}$

2. Determine the value of x in each.

    a) $5^x = 25$ **b)** $6^x = 36$ **c)** $4^x = 64$

    d) $3^x = 81$ **e)** $5^x = 1$ **f)** $2^x = 32$

    g) $7^x = 1$ **h)** $2^x = \dfrac{1}{2}$ **i)** $3^x = 243$

    j) $5^x = 625$ **k)** $3^x = \dfrac{1}{9}$ **l)** $10^x = 1\ 000\ 000$

(B) 3. Solve.

    a) $6^{x-3} = 6^4$ **b)** $4^{3x} = 4^{-15}$ **c)** $7^{-8} = 7^{2x}$

    d) $2^x = 2^{2x-6}$ **e)** $4^{5x-1} = 4^{x+11}$ **f)** $3^{x-4} = 3^{3x-7}$

4. Solve and check.

    a) $3^x - 4 = 77$ **b)** $5^{2x-4} = 1$ **c)** $4^{x-1} = 8^x$

5. Solve.

a) $3^x = 9^2$

b) $5^a = 25^3$

c) $4^{2x} = 16^2$

d) $5(2^n) = 80$

e) $10(5^{2x}) = 1250$

f) $3^{x+8} = 27^x$

g) $5^{3x} = 5^{-3}$

h) $2^{x+4} = 2^{-4}$

i) $5^{3y+4} = 5^y$

j) $3^x = 9^{x+1}$

k) $5^x = 5^{3x+1}$

l) $10^x = 0.001$

6. Solve.

a) $2^{2x} = \dfrac{1}{8}$

b) $16^{x-1} = 64^x$

c) $4^{-2x} = 8^{x+1}$

d) $4^x = 32$

e) $5^{2x} = \dfrac{1}{125}$

f) $7^{2x} = 49^{-2}$

7. **Communication/Problem Solving** Consider the equation $2^x = 10$. Discuss with a partner how you might solve this equation. Can you use the same strategy as you used for other equations in this section? Explain. Find the value of x, to one decimal place.

8. Solve.

a) $\left(\dfrac{1}{2}\right)^3 = 16^x$

b) $\left(\dfrac{1}{6}\right)^q = 6^{q-6}$

c) $\left(\dfrac{1}{5}\right)^{x+1} = 25^{2x-3}$

C 9. Solve.

a) $6^{x^2-3} = 36^x$

b) $25^x = 5^{x^2-15}$

c) $2^{5x} = 16^{1-x}$

Frank and Ernest

I THOUGHT I HAD THE ANSWER TO THE MEANING OF LIFE, BUT EVERYTHING CANCELLED OUT.

THAVES

© 1994 Thaves / Reprinted with permission. Newspaper dist. by NEA, Inc.

CAREER PROFILE

Audio Recording Technician

When a guitar string is plucked, it produces a sound wave. When the string is plucked harder, the sound wave is more intense, and produces a louder sound. The difference in intensities between a soft pluck and hard pluck can be very large. The sounds that humans hear fall into a large range. The quietest sound humans can hear is called the threshold of hearing, and is recorded as 0 dB. At the other end of the scale is the loudest sound. This sound will instantly break your eardrum and registers 160 dB.

Audio recording technicians use the decibel scale to measure sound. These technicians need a strong understanding of mathematics to understand not only the decibel scale but also many other areas of music, which are very mathematical.

Becoming an audio recording technician requires 1 year of study at a community college or specialized post-secondary institution. A diploma program in audio recording is offered at
• Fanshawe College
• Ontario Institute of Audio Recording Technicians
• Harris Institute for the Arts   • Trebas Institute of Ontario

1. Some people cannot hear sound as clearly or intensely as others can. What kinds of skills or talents should someone who is interested in pursuing a career as an audio recording technician have?

2. The ability to distinguish between the different types of sound is important to an audio recording technician. Musical instruments produce sounds that vibrate at particular intervals. For example, a flute vibrates at a single frequency and produces a very pure sound. A trombone produces a combination of frequencies that results in a very rich sound. Instruments with multiple frequencies have very mathematical relationships between the frequencies. Noise, on the other hand, has multiple frequencies with no mathematical relationship between the frequencies. Other than in the music industry, where could an audio recording technician use his or her skills?

CASE STUDY WRAP-UP

The table shows the decibel levels and relative intensities of some sounds.

Sound	Decibel Level	Intensity
barely audible	0 dB	10^0
rustle of leaves	10 dB	10^1
soft music	40 dB	10^4
ordinary traffic	70 dB	10^7

Any sound over 140 dB causes pain to the human ear. Prolonged exposure to noises of more than 90 dB is dangerous to your hearing. The guidelines for safe exposure are as follows:

Decibel Level	Time Limit
95 dB	4 h
100 dB	3 h
110 dB	30 min
120 dB	7.5 min

1. When Greg plays his stereo loudly, the noise level is 80 dB. How many times as intense as soft music is this?

2. A power lawn mower makes a noise that is 100 times as intense as Greg's loud stereo.
   a) What is the decibel level of the lawn mower?
   b) If you get a summer job with a lawn-cutting service, should you be concerned about harm to your hearing? Explain.

3. The special earmuffs that are worn by airport workers can reduce sound levels by up to 45 dB. When a jet is taking off, the noise can be as high as 140 dB. Should an airport employee who drives the baggage cart to planes and wears the earmuffs be concerned about damage to her hearing?

4. When Greg plays his acoustic guitar without amplification, its sound level is about 50 dB. If a friend practises with Greg, and the second guitarist also plays at 50 dB, will their combined noise level be 100 dB? Explain your answer.

5. Research to find at least two other fields in which exponential scales of measurement are used. In what kinds of situations is an exponential scale more useful than a linear one?

Review

1. Evaluate.

a) 5^3
b) 7^0
c) 4^{-2}
d) $(-2)^3$
e) $(-1)^{13}$
f) $(-12)^0$

2. Write as a single power.

a) $3^4 \times 3^5$
b) $(-2)^5 \times (-2)^3$
c) $5^3 \div 5^2$
d) $(3^2)^3$
e) $(6^3)^{-2}$
f) $(4^2)^4 \times (4^3)^{-1}$

3. Write as a single power. Then, evaluate. Leave your answers in fraction form, where appropriate.

a) $5^4 \times 5^{-2}$
b) $4^{-2} \times 4^2$
c) $6^2 \times 6^{-3}$
d) $\dfrac{7^2}{7^4}$
e) $\dfrac{3^2}{3^{-2}}$
f) $(6^8)^0$

4. Simplify.

a) $b^3 \times b^{-5}$
b) $(x^2)^3$
c) $m^3 \times m^{-2} \times m^5$
d) $\dfrac{30x^4}{15x^{-2}}$
e) $\dfrac{4x^3 y^{-2}}{2x^{-1} y^4}$
f) $(5a^3b^2)(4a^{-3}b)$

2.2 Powers With Rational Exponents, pages 46–50

5. Evaluate.

a) $49^{\frac{1}{2}}$
b) $64^{\frac{1}{3}}$
c) $16^{-\frac{1}{4}}$
d) $36^{\frac{3}{2}}$
e) $8^{\frac{5}{3}}$

6. Calculate the value of each expression.

a) $5^0 + 25^{\frac{1}{2}}$
b) $9^{\frac{1}{2}} - 9^{-1}$
c) $\left(16^{\frac{1}{4}} + 9^{\frac{1}{2}}\right)^3$
d) $\left(125^{\frac{1}{3}} - 7^0\right)^{\frac{1}{2}}$

7. The side length, s, of a cube is related to its volume, V, by the formula $s = V^{\frac{1}{3}}$. At the end of the day, a potter likes to shape her extra clay into a cube. What is the side length of a cube formed from each volume of clay?

a) 1000 cm³
b) 8000 cm³
c) 216 cm³

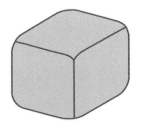

2.3 Evaluate Exponential Expressions Using a Scientific Calculator, pages 51–55

8. Evaluate. Round your answers to two decimal places.

a) $50^{3.5}$ **b)** $12^{1.6}$ **c)** $7^{-2.1}$ **d)** $18^{\frac{2}{5}}$ **e)** $81^{-\frac{1}{3}}$

9. Simplify. Then, evaluate. Round your answers to two decimal places.

a) $7^{45} \times 7^{-53}$ **b)** $(10^{15})^{2.3}$ **c)** $\dfrac{8^{-3.2}}{8^{-5.8}}$

10. Each expression could occur in a situation involving compound interest. Find the value of each, to two decimal places.

a) $742.63(1.08)^{7.5}$ **b)** $4600(1 + 0.045)^{-8}$ **c)** $750\left(1 + \dfrac{0.06}{12}\right)^{24}$

11. The radius, r, of a sphere is related to its volume, V, by the formula $r = \left(\dfrac{3V}{4\pi}\right)^{\frac{1}{3}}$.

Determine the radius of a sphere that has a volume of 80.46 cm^3. Round your answer to two decimal places.

2.4 Solve Exponential Equations Using Common Bases, pages 56–59

12. Solve.

a) $8^x = 8^3$ **b)** $5^k = 25^2$ **c)** $5^{4n} = 5^8$

d) $5^a = \dfrac{1}{125}$ **e)** $4^{x+3} = 4^{7-x}$ **f)** $2(7^{3y}) = 98$

g) $9^{3y} = 27^{y+2}$ **h)** $8^{k-1} = 16^{3k}$ **i)** $36^t = 216^{2t-1}$

$\mathcal{P}$ractice Test

Achievement Chart Category Connections

Category	Knowledge/Understanding	Thinking/Inquiry/Problem Solving	Communication	Application
Questions	1–10			8, 10

1. Evaluate.

   a) 10^3 **b)** 8^0

   c) $(-5)^3$ **d)** $(-1)^{16}$

2. Evaluate. Leave your answers in fraction form.

   a) 4^{-2} **b)** $(-2)^{-4}$

   c) 5^{-3} **d)** 7^{-1}

3. Write as a single power. Then, evaluate.

   a) $5^0 \times 5^2 \times 5$ **b)** $3^6 \div 3^4$

   c) $(2^5)^0$ **d)** $(4^2)^{-1}$

4. Evaluate.

   a) $49^{\frac{1}{2}}$ **b)** $81^{\frac{3}{4}}$ **c)** $36^{-\frac{1}{2}}$

   d) $125^{-\frac{2}{3}}$ **e)** $16^{\frac{5}{4}}$

5. Simplify.

   a) $a^5 \times a^{-2}$ **b)** $\dfrac{24x^5}{6x^3}$

   c) $(x^2 y^3)^3$ **d)** $(3a^{-2})^3$

6. Evaluate. Round your answers to two decimal places.

   a) $10^{2.3}$ **b)** $9^{-\frac{5}{4}}$ **c)** $12^{-0.5}$ **d)** $75^{\frac{3}{5}}$

7. Calculate the value of each exponential expression. Round your answers to two decimal places.

   a) $1863.50(1.055)^{16}$ **b)** $4000(1.02)^{-12}$ **c)** $875\left(1 + \dfrac{0.05}{2}\right)^6$

8. Greta bought an oil painting in 2000 for $6000. The value of the work is increasing and can be approximately determined by the expression $6000(1.15)^t$, where t is the number of years since 2000. Find the approximate value of the painting in 2010.

9. Solve for x.

a) $6^x = 6^4$

b) $3^x = 9^2$

c) $4(5^x) = 100$

d) $\left(\dfrac{1}{3}\right)^x = 27$

e) $3^{x+3} = \dfrac{1}{81}$

f) $4^{2x} = \dfrac{1}{32}$

ACHIEVEMENT Check | *Knowledge/Understanding* Thinking/Inquiry/Problem Solving Communication *Application*

10. Jackie wants to send a basketball with a volume of 7238 cm^3 to her friend, Maggie, for her birthday. Jackie wants to find the smallest box needed to mail the gift.

a) Find the radius of the basketball, to one decimal place.

b) Determine the dimensions and surface area of the smallest box that the basketball will fit into.

CALVIN AND HOBBES © 1986 Watterson. Reprinted with permission of UNIVERSAL PRESS SYNDICATE. All rights Reserved.

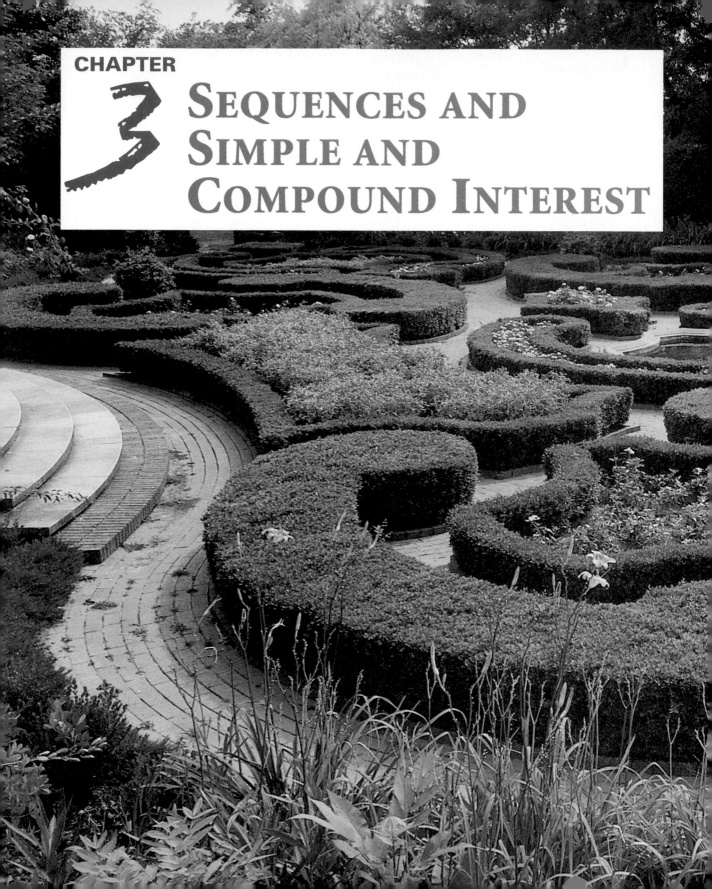

CHAPTER 3

SEQUENCES AND SIMPLE AND COMPOUND INTEREST

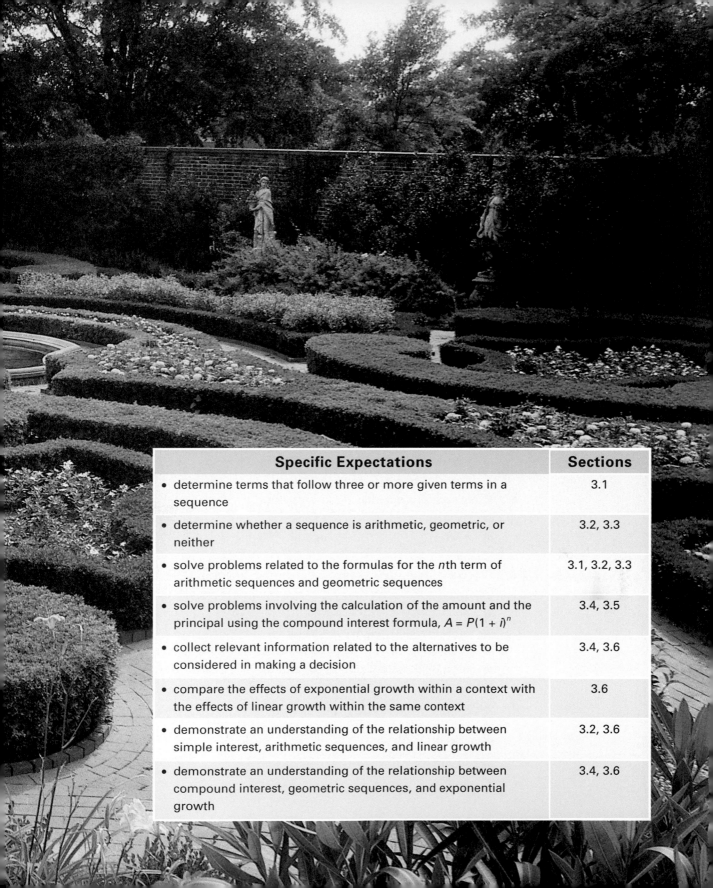

Specific Expectations	Sections
• determine terms that follow three or more given terms in a sequence	3.1
• determine whether a sequence is arithmetic, geometric, or neither	3.2, 3.3
• solve problems related to the formulas for the nth term of arithmetic sequences and geometric sequences	3.1, 3.2, 3.3
• solve problems involving the calculation of the amount and the principal using the compound interest formula, $A = P(1 + i)^n$	3.4, 3.5
• collect relevant information related to the alternatives to be considered in making a decision	3.4, 3.6
• compare the effects of exponential growth within a context with the effects of linear growth within the same context	3.6
• demonstrate an understanding of the relationship between simple interest, arithmetic sequences, and linear growth	3.2, 3.6
• demonstrate an understanding of the relationship between compound interest, geometric sequences, and exponential growth	3.4, 3.6

Get Ready...

1. Find the next two terms in each pattern.
   a) 1, 3, 5, 7, ?, ?
   b) 1, 2, 4, 8, ?, ?
   c) 1, −1, −3, −5, ?, ?
   d) $1, \frac{1}{2}, \frac{1}{3}, \frac{1}{4}$, ?, ?

2. Substitute to evaluate each.
   a) $3n + 5$; $n = 6$
   b) $5x − 8$; $x = 10$
   c) $y^2 − 1$; $y = 6$
   d) 2^n; $n = 5$

3. Substitute to evaluate each. Round to two decimal places, if necessary.
   a) $200(1.04)^n$; $n = 5$
   b) $4n^2 − 8$; $n = 3$
   c) $(1 + i)^5$; $i = 0.03$
   d) 1.03^{-n}; $n = 8$
   e) $(1 + i)^{-4}$; $i = 0.02$
   f) $A(1.05)^{-6}$; $A = 300$

4. Write an algebraic expression in terms of n to represent each phrase.
   a) three more than the number
   b) half the number
   c) eight less than the number
   d) the square of the number
   e) one less than double the number
   f) half the square of the number

5. Write each as a decimal.
   a) 34%
   b) 9%
   c) 0.8%
   d) 6.9%
   e) 11.75%
   f) 8.25%

6. Calculate the simple interest on each investment. Use the simple interest formula, $I = Prt$. Remember, per annum means per year, or annually.
   a) $865 invested at 10% per annum for 3 years
   b) $800 invested at 8% per annum for 1.5 years
   c) $500 invested at 3.9% per annum for 9 months
   d) $30 000 invested at 6.5% per annum for 16 months

7. Solve each formula for the given variable.
   a) $A = lw$ for w
   b) $P = 2l + 2w$ for l
   c) $I = Prt$ for r

8. Solve. Then, check by substitution.

a) $4x = 44$

b) $\dfrac{m}{-2} = 35$

c) $b - 10 = 35$

d) $3m + 14 = -4$

e) $-2x - 4 = -10$

f) $0.4y + 12.8 = 10$

9. Evaluate each. Round to two decimal places.

a) 1.06^{12}

b) 1.0032^{15}

c) 1.05^{-10}

d) 1.006^{-12}

e) $500(1.02)^{10}$

f) $450(1.07)^{-5}$

CASE STUDY

Throughout this chapter, you will learn how to calculate simple and compound interest on money borrowed and invested. In some sections of the chapter, you will solve problems related to the Case Study described below. At the end of the chapter, in the Case Study Wrap-Up on page 113, you will be asked to write a report on the Case Study. Keep five or six pages of your notebook free for work related to the Case Study. You may also keep your work in a Case Study Portfolio.

A young couple, Aaron and Selma, have two children: Jacob, who is 8 years old, and Mercedes, who is 5 years old. They recently inherited $150 000 and are planning to invest most of it. They will use whatever is left over for day-to-day expenses.

They plan to invest $25 000 for each child's education immediately, so that the money will grow until each child is 18 years old. They predict that they will need $30 000 in 3 years for a new car. As well, they are planning a special vacation in 5 years. They estimate that it will cost $15 000. They will then invest half of what is left over for a "rainy day" or unexpected expenses, such as a major repair on the house. The rest will be kept for current needs, such as paying off credit card debts and day-to-day expenses.

Christophe operates a business installing interlocking bricks. His favourite pattern uses two colours of bricks, grey and brown, in this sequence: 2 grey bricks in the first row, 4 grey bricks in the second row, 6 in the third row, and so on. To predict the number of grey bricks in a specific row, Christophe could skip count by two. Alternatively, he could develop a formula to quickly calculate the number of grey bricks in a specific row.

A **sequence** is an ordered list of terms. In most sequences, the terms are related to each other, and form a predictable pattern. In number sequences, this relationship, or pattern, can be expressed both in words and as a formula.

DISCOVER

Patterns in Sequences

For each sequence below,

a) continue the pattern, showing the next two terms

b) describe the pattern in words

1.

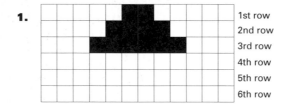

1st row
2nd row
3rd row
4th row
5th row
6th row

2. $2, 5, 8,$ ⬚, ⬚   **3.** $\dfrac{1}{2}, \dfrac{1}{3}, \dfrac{1}{4},$ ⬚, ⬚   **4.** $1, 4, 9,$ ⬚, ⬚   **5.** $5, 10, 20,$ ⬚, ⬚

Each term in a sequence, t_n, can be expressed as a mathematical formula in terms of the term number, n, where n is a natural number $(1, 2, 3, \ldots)$.

EXAMPLE 1

Determine the Terms Given a Description of the Sequence

Determine the first five terms of a sequence for the following description:
The first term is 7 and every term is 3 more than the previous term.

Solution

$t_1 = 7$

$t_2 = 7 + 3$ Add 3 to the 1st term.
$t_2 = 10$

$t_3 = 10 + 3$ Add 3 to the 2nd term.
$t_3 = 13$

$t_4 = 13 + 3$ Add 3 to the 3rd term.
$t_4 = 16$

$t_5 = 16 + 3$ Add 3 to the 4th term.
$t_5 = 19$

The first five terms of the sequence are 7, 10, 13, 16, and 19.

EXAMPLE 2

Determine the Terms Given the Sequence Formula

Determine the first four terms of the sequence defined by each formula.

a) $t_n = 2n$ **b)** $t_n = n^2$ **c)** $t_n = 4 - 3(n - 1)$

Solution

For each formula, substitute values for n from 1 to 4, and then, simplify.

a) $t_n = 2n$

| $n = 1$ | $n = 2$ | $n = 3$ | $n = 4$ |

$t_1 = 2(1)$ $t_2 = 2(2)$ $t_3 = 2(3)$ $t_4 = 2(4)$
$t_1 = 2$ $t_2 = 4$ $t_3 = 6$ $t_4 = 8$

The first four terms of the sequence defined by $t_n = 2n$ are 2, 4, 6, and 8.

b) $t_n = n^2$

| $n = 1$ | $n = 2$ | $n = 3$ | $n = 4$ |

$t_1 = 1^2$ $t_2 = 2^2$ $t_3 = 3^2$ $t_4 = 4^2$
$t_1 = 1$ $t_2 = 4$ $t_3 = 9$ $t_4 = 16$

The first four terms of the sequence defined by $t_n = n^2$ are 1, 4, 9, and 16.

c) $t_n = 4 - 3(n - 1)$

$n = 1$	$n = 2$	$n = 3$	$n = 4$
$t_1 = 4 - 3(1 - 1)$	$t_2 = 4 - 3(2 - 1)$	$t_3 = 4 - 3(3 - 1)$	$t_4 = 4 - 3(4 - 1)$
$t_1 = 4 - 3(0)$	$t_2 = 4 - 3(1)$	$t_3 = 4 - 3(2)$	$t_4 = 4 - 3(3)$
$t_1 = 4 - 0$	$t_2 = 4 - 3$	$t_3 = 4 - 6$	$t_4 = 4 - 9$
$t_1 = 4$	$t_2 = 1$	$t_3 = -2$	$t_4 = -5$

The first four terms of the sequence defined by $t_n = 4 - 3(n - 1)$ are 4, 1, −2, and −5.

EXAMPLE 3

Develop a Formula Given the Sequence

Develop a formula for t_n in each sequence:

a) 2, 3, 4, 5, ... **b)** 2, 4, 8, 16, ... **c)** 9, 7, 5, 3, ...

Solution

Look for a relationship between the term numbers and the term values.

a) 2, 3, 4, 5, ...

$t_1 = 2$	$t_2 = 3$	$t_3 = 4$	$t_4 = 5$
$t_1 = 1 + 1$	$t_2 = 2 + 1$	$t_3 = 3 + 1$	$t_4 = 4 + 1$

Each term is 1 more than the term number: $t_n = n + 1$

A formula for the sequence is $t_n = n + 1$.

b) 2, 4, 8, 16, ...

$t_1 = 2$	$t_2 = 4$	$t_3 = 8$	$t_4 = 16$
$t_1 = 2^1$	$t_2 = 2^2$	$t_3 = 2^3$	$t_4 = 2^4$

Each term is a power of 2 and the term number is the same as the exponent: $t_n = 2^n$

A formula for the sequence is $t_n = 2^n$.

c) 9, 7, 5, 3, ...

$t_1 = 9$	$t_2 = 7$	$t_3 = 5$	$t_4 = 3$
$t_1 = 9 - 0$	$t_2 = 9 - 2$	$t_3 = 9 - 4$	$t_4 = 9 - 6$
$t_1 = 9 - 2(0)$	$t_2 = 9 - 2(1)$	$t_3 = 9 - 2(2)$	$t_4 = 9 - 2(3)$
$t_1 = 9 - 2(1 - 1)$	$t_2 = 9 - 2(2 - 1)$	$t_3 = 9 - 2(3 - 1)$	$t_4 = 9 - 2(4 - 1)$

The number in brackets is 1 less than the term number: $t_n = 9 - 2(n - 1)$

A formula for the sequence is $t_n = 9 - 2(n - 1)$ or $t_n = 11 - 2n$.

	EXAMPLE 4	**Interlocking Brick Patterns**

EXAMPLE 4

Interlocking Brick Patterns

Recall Christophe's favourite brick pattern described on page 70.

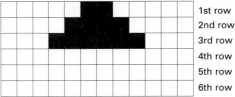

1st row
2nd row
3rd row
4th row
5th row
6th row

a) Develop a formula to calculate the number of grey bricks in a specific row.

b) Use the formula to calculate the number of grey bricks required for the 20th row.

Solution

a) List the sequence: 2, 4, 6, 8, …

Let t_n represent the number of grey bricks in row n:

$t_1 = 2$	$t_2 = 4$	$t_3 = 6$	$t_4 = 8$
$t_1 = 2(1)$	$t_2 = 2(2)$	$t_3 = 2(3)$	$t_4 = 2(4)$

The value of each term is 2 times the term number: $t_n = 2n$

A formula for calculating the number of grey bricks in a specific row is $t_n = 2n$, where n represents the row number.

b) If $t_n = 2n$ and $n = 20$, then
$$t_{20} = 2(20)$$
$$t_{20} = 40$$

In the 20th row, there are 40 bricks.

KEY CONCEPTS

- A sequence is an ordered list of individual terms.

- In many cases, each term in a sequence, t_n, can be modelled with a mathematical formula that is expressed using the term number, n.

- If a sequence is modelled by a formula, you can determine the individual terms of the sequence by substituting values for n, beginning with 1, and then, simplifying.

- To develop a formula for a sequence, follow these steps:
  Step 1: Examine the terms in the sequence to determine the relationship between the term values and term numbers.
  Step 2: Describe the relationship in words.
  Step 3: Translate the description into a formula.

1. For the following sequence, describe the relationship between the term numbers and term values.

$$t_1 = 2(1) - 1 \qquad t_2 = 2(2) - 1 \qquad t_3 = 2(3) - 1$$

2. Explain why 5, 12, 8, 132, 15, 23, 45 cannot be defined by a formula.

PRACTISE

(A) 1. Describe the pattern in each sequence. Determine the next two terms.

a)

b) 9, 5, 1, −3, …   **c)** 3, 6, 12, 24, …   **d)** 1, −1, 1, −1, …

2. Determine the first five terms of the sequence described by each formula.

a) $t_n = 5n - 1$ **b)** $t_n = n^3$

c) $t_n = 5(n - 1)$ **d)** $t_n = \dfrac{n-1}{n+1}$

3. Complete each sequence in two different ways.

a) 2, **?**, 8, **?**   **b)** 10, **?**, 1000, **?**

4. For each sequence,
i) determine possible missing terms
ii) describe the pattern

a) 5, **?**, **?**, 23   **b)** 5, **?**, **?**, **?**, 23

c) 3, **?**, **?**, 243   **d)** 3, **?**, **?**, **?**, 243

5. For each sequence,
i) describe the relationship between the term numbers and term values
ii) develop a formula for t_n

a) 5, 7, 9, 11, …   **b)** 3, 6, 9, 12, …

c) $1^2 + 1, 2^2 + 1, 3^2 + 1, 4^2 + 1, \ldots$ **d)** $\dfrac{1}{3}, \dfrac{1}{4}, \dfrac{1}{5}, \dfrac{1}{6}, \ldots$

6. **Stadium seating** A stadium has 30 seats in the front row, 34 in the second row, 38 in the third, and so on. There are 50 rows altogether.
  a) Determine the first five terms of the sequence of numbers of seats.
  b) Write a formula to represent the number of seats in the nth row.
  c) Use the formula to calculate the number of seats in the last row.

B 7. **Pizza toppings** The cost of a large pizza is $9.00, plus $3.50 per topping.
  a) Express the cost of a pizza with any number of toppings as a list of terms in a sequence.
  b) Develop a formula for calculating the cost of a pizza with n toppings.
  c) What is the cost of a pizza with 6 toppings?
  d) How many toppings are there on a pizza that costs $19.50?

8. **Application** A fence has 4 posts and 9 rails.
How many rails would there be if there were
  a) 6 posts?
  b) 8 posts?
  c) n posts?
  d) 100 posts?

9. **Pay raise** Tuyet recently began a part-time job that pays $11.00/h. She has been promised a raise of $0.25/h every month for the next year.
  a) Express Tuyet's hourly wage during each month of the next year as a list of terms in a sequence.
  b) Develop a formula for calculating her hourly wage for month n.
  c) If this continues the following year, how long will it take for Tuyet to earn $16.75/h?

10. **Communication**
  a) Create three different sequences.
  b) Describe each sequence in words.
  c) Develop a formula for t_n in each sequence.

11. **Problem Solving**
  a) Create two different sequences that begin with 1, 2.
  b) Develop a formula for t_n in each sequence, if possible.
  c) If a formula is not possible, explain why.

C **12.** A sequence can also be defined by a formula that describes how each term relates to the term before it. This is called a recursion formula. An example is $t_1 = 3$, $t_n = t_{n-1} - 5$. To determine the next term, substitute the previous term:

If $t_1 = 3$ and $t_n = t_{n-1} - 5$, then, $t_2 = t_{2-1} - 5$
$$t_2 = t_1 - 5$$
$$t_2 = 3 - 5$$
$$t_2 = -2$$

Determine the next three terms.

13. **Problem Solving** Develop a recursion formula for a sequence that begins with $t_1 = 9$. You may use any mathematical operation. Describe your formula in words.

14. **Fibonacci** A famous sequence that uses a recursion formula is the Fibonacci sequence: 1, 1, 2, 3, 5, 8, 13, …
   a) Write the first 15 terms of the sequence. (Hint: To determine the pattern, look at more than one previous term.)
   b) Develop a recursion formula for the sequence.
   c) Find two different patterns in the terms of the Fibonacci sequence. Describe the patterns.
   d) Go to *www.school.mcgrawhill.ca/resources/* and follow the links to find out more about Fibonacci sequences.

See page 409 in the Technology Appendix for specific instructions.

15. **Technology** A graphing calculator can be used to determine a formula for t_n in an arithmetic sequence. For example, for the sequence 8, 11, 14, 17, …:

The Stat List Editor:

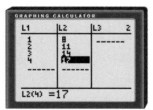

The Linear Regression Instruction:

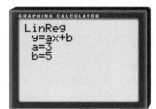

The formula is $t_n = 3n + 5$.

Determine the formula for each sequence.
   a) 14, 20, 26, …
   b) 23, 17, 11, …
   c) 44, 47, 50, …

3.2 | Arithmetic Sequences and Simple Interest

Christophe needed some equipment for his landscaping business. He borrowed $1000 from a bank. Simple interest is charged on the loan at 9%. Christophe plans to pay off the loan in a lump sum at the end of 1 year. He uses a table to keep track of how much he owes each month. Instead, Christophe could create a formula to calculate how much he owes each month.

DISCOVER

Common Differences

1. Copy and complete the following table.

	Sequence	Differences			
		$t_2 - t_1$	$t_3 - t_2$	$t_4 - t_3$	$t_5 - t_4$
a)	2, 5, 8, 11, 14, …				
b)	5, 10, 15, 20, 25, …				
c)	9, 7, 5, 3, 1, …				

2. What did you notice about the differences in sequence a)? sequence b)? sequence c)?

Each sequence in the Discover is an **arithmetic sequence**. Each term in an arithmetic sequence is found by adding the same number to the term before it. This constant number is called the **common difference**. The common difference can be positive, negative, a fraction, or a decimal.

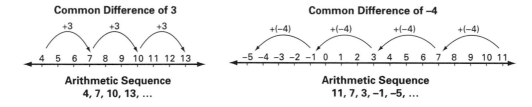

EXAMPLE 1

Develop a Formula Given the Sequence

a) Determine if the sequence 4, 11, 18, 25, 32, … is arithmetic.
b) Develop a formula for t_n in the sequence.
c) Determine the 20th term.

Solution

a) 4, 11, 18, 25, 32, …

Determine if there is a common difference:

$t_1 = 4, t_2 = 11, t_3 = 18, t_4 = 25, t_5 = 32$

$t_2 - t_1 = 11 - 4$	$t_3 - t_2 = 18 - 11$	$t_4 - t_3 = 25 - 18$	$t_5 - t_4 = 32 - 25$
$= 7$	$= 7$	$= 7$	$= 7$

There is a common difference of 7, so, the sequence is arithmetic.

b) Look for a relationship between the term numbers and the term values:

$t_1 = 4$	$t_2 = 11$	$t_3 = 18$	$t_4 = 25$
$t_1 = 4 + 0(7)$	$t_2 = 4 + 1(7)$	$t_3 = 4 + 2(7)$	$t_4 = 4 + 3(7)$
$t_1 = 4 + (1-1)(7)$	$t_2 = 4 + (2-1)(7)$	$t_3 = 4 + (3-1)(7)$	$t_4 = 4 + (4-1)(7)$

The coefficient of 7 is one less than n: $t_n = 4 + (n-1)(7)$
A formula for t_n in the sequence is $t_n = 4 + (n-1)(7)$.

c) Use the formula for t_n:

$t_n = 4 + (n-1)(7)$
$t_{20} = 4 + (20-1)(7)$ Substitute $n = 20$.
$t_{20} = 4 + (19)(7)$
$t_{20} = 137$

The 20th term is 137.

Alternatively, the sequence function of a graphing calculator could be used to find the nth term. (See page 409 in the Technology Appendix.)

```
GRAPHING CALCULATOR
seq(4+(N-1)7,N,2
0,20)
            {137}
```

EXAMPLE 2

Develop a Formula for Any Arithmetic Sequence

An arithmetic sequence has a first term of a and a common difference of d. Develop a formula for t_n in the sequence.

Solution

List the sequence and look for a relationship between the term numbers and the term values:

$t_1 = a$ $t_2 = a + d$ $t_3 = a + 2d$ $t_4 = a + 3d$

$t_1 = a + (1 - 1)d$ $t_2 = a + (2 - 1)d$ $t_3 = a + (3 - 1)d$ $t_4 = a + (4 - 1)d$

The coefficient of d is one less than n: $t_n = a + (n - 1)d$

A formula for t_n in the arithmetic sequence is $t_n = a + (n - 1)d$.

The formula $t_n = a + (n - 1)d$ can be used to find the formula for t_n in any arithmetic sequence, where a is the first term and d is the common difference.

EXAMPLE 3

Use $t_n = a + (n - 1)d$ to Develop a Formula for t_n in a Sequence

a) Develop a formula for t_n in the sequence 12, 7, 2, −3, ...

b) Determine the 100th term.

Solution

a) Determine if the sequence is arithmetic:

$t_2 - t_1 = 7 - 12$ $t_3 - t_2 = 2 - 7$ $t_4 - t_3 = -3 - 2$

        $= -5$ $= -5$ $= -5$

There is a common difference, so, 12, 7, 2, −3, ... is an arithmetic sequence.

Use the formula for t_n in any arithmetic sequence, $t_n = a + (n - 1)d$:

$t_n = a + (n - 1)d$ $a = 12, d = -5$

$t_n = 12 + (n - 1)(-5)$

$t_n = 12 - 5n + 5$ Simplify.

$t_n = 17 - 5n$

A formula for the sequence is $t_n = 17 - 5n$.

b) Use the formula for t_n in the sequence:

$t_n = 17 - 5n$ $n = 100$

$t_{100} = 17 - 5(100)$

$t_{100} = -483$

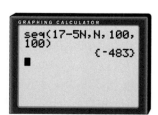

GRAPHING CALCULATOR

seq(17-5N,N,100, 100)
           {-483}

The 100th term in the sequence is −483.

| EXAMPLE 4 | **Relate Simple Interest and Arithmetic Sequences** |

Relate Simple Interest and Arithmetic Sequences

Recall Christophe's loan of $1000 described on page 77.

a) Create a table of values to show the amount owed after each month for the first 4 months.

b) Write the sequence of the amount owed at the end of each month. Describe the sequence.

c) Develop a formula to calculate the amount owed after n months.

d) What is owed after 11 months?

Did You Know?

The Chinese were the first to use paper money. Prior to that, coins made of heavy iron were used. People would sometimes leave their heavy coins with merchants who issued them paper receipts— these receipts eventually became official currency.

Solution

a) Use the simple interest formula to determine the interest owed each month:

$I = Prt$ $P = 1000, r = 0.09$ (9%)

$I = (1000)(0.09)\left(\dfrac{1}{12}\right)$ Use $\dfrac{1}{12}$ for t.

$I = 7.5$

$7.50 interest is owed each month.

Create a table:

Month	Interest Owed $ ($I = Prt$)	Amount Owed $ ($A = P + I$)
1	7.50	1007.50
2	15.00	1015.00
3	22.50	1022.50
4	30.00	1030.00

b) 1007.50, 1015.00, 1022.50, 1030.00

The amount owed increases by $7.50 each month. This forms an arithmetic sequence.

c) Use the formula for t_n in any arithmetic sequence:

$t_n = a + (n - 1)d$ $a = 1007.50, d = 7.50$

$t_n = 1007.50 + (n - 1)7.50$ Use A_n to represent the amount at the end

$A_n = 1000 + 7.50n$ of month n, and then, simplify.

A formula is $A_n = 1000 + 7.50n$, where A is the amount owed and n is the number of months.

d) Use the formula $A_n = 1000 + 7.50n$:

$A_n = 1000 + 7.50n$ $\quad\quad n = 11$

$A_{11} = 1000 + 7.50(11)$

$A_{11} = 1082.50$

After 11 months, Christophe owes $1082.50.

KEY CONCEPTS

- A sequence that has a common difference between consecutive terms is an arithmetic sequence.

- The formula $t_n = a + (n - 1)d$ can be used to develop a formula for the nth term, t_n, in any arithmetic sequence, where

  n is the term number

  a is the first term

  d is the common difference

- Simple interest is an example of an arithmetic sequence.

DISCUSS THE CONCEPTS

1. Describe how to tell if a sequence is an arithmetic sequence.

2. Explain why simple interest is an arithmetic sequence.

3. Does the formula $t_n = 11 + 4(n - 1)$ represent an arithmetic sequence? Why or why not?

PRACTISE

A **1.** Determine whether each sequence is arithmetic or not. If it is arithmetic, state the common difference. If it is not arithmetic, explain how you know.

a) 4, 9, 14, …
b) 26, 15, 4, …
c) 6, 10, 15, …

d) 5, 10, 20, …
e) $\dfrac{2}{3}, 1, \dfrac{4}{3}, \dots$
f) 2, 5, 1, 4, 0, …

2. For each arithmetic sequence,

i) develop and simplify a formula for t_n

ii) find the value of the indicated term

a) first term = 3, common difference = 6; $t_{12} = $ **?**

b) first term = 10, common difference = -4; $t_8 = $ **?**

c) first term = -20, common difference = 9; $t_{25} = $ **?**

3. For each sequence, develop a formula for t_n. Then, determine the 15th term.
   a) 7, 10, 13, …
   b) 5, −2, −9, …
   c) 1, 23, 45, …
   d) −1, 0.5, 2, …
   e) 100, 95.2, 90.4, …
   f) $108.50, $117.00, $125.50, …

4. For each sequence, determine the first five terms. Then, determine the values of a and d.
   a) $t_n = 5 + (n - 1)(-3)$
   b) $t_n = -11 + (n - 1)(2)$
   c) $t_n = 8n - 7$

APPLY THE CONCEPTS

5. **Investment** A $100 investment grows at 6% simple interest.
   a) Develop a formula to calculate the amount after n months.
   b) What is the amount after 7 months?

B **6.** **Animal pens** A farmer is using panels to create a single row of pens to hold animals.
   a) How many panels are needed to make 1 pen? 2 pens? 3 pens?
   b) How many panels are needed to make n pens?
   c) How many panels are needed to make 10 pens?
   d) Suppose the farmer uses a double row of pens. How many panels are needed to make
      i) 4 double pens? **ii)** n double pens? **iii)** 10 double pens?

3 double pens

   e) Which uses fewer panels to create the same number of pens, a single row of pens or a double row of pens? Explain.

7. **Astronomy** Some comets travel in an orbit that follows a predictable pattern. The sequence for each comet below shows the years the comet passed close enough to Earth to be seen.
   Encke's Comet: 1994, 1997, 2000, …
   Faye's Comet: 1985, 1992, 1999, …
   Halley's Comet: 1834, 1910, 1986, …
   a) Determine the years of the next three sightings.
   b) Develop a formula to determine the years each comet passed close to Earth.

8. **Salary increase** Christophe's landscaping business hired a management trainee. She will receive a salary of $2500 per month to start. She will get a raise of $200 per month every 2 months for an 18-month training period.
   a) Develop a formula to calculate the trainee's monthly salary during any 2-month period.
   b) What is the trainee's monthly salary during the fifth 2-month period?
   c) What is the trainee's monthly salary at the end of the training period?

9. **Application** Rona purchased a new sound system on February 1. She is to pay $300 down on February 1, and then, 24 monthly payments of $75, beginning on March 1. Use an arithmetic sequence formula to determine how much
   a) has been paid on December 1 of the first year
   b) has been paid on February 1 of the second year
   c) Rona still owes on January 1 of the second year

10. **Communication** Explain how simple interest and arithmetic sequences are related. Use an example to illustrate.

11. **Thinking** Is it always more efficient to use a formula to solve an arithmetic sequence problem? Explain why or why not.

12. **Summer Olympics** The first modern Summer Olympics were held in 1896. The second were held in 1900, the third in 1904, and so on.
   a) Develop a formula to determine the year of the *n*th Summer Olympics.
   b) Which Summer Olympics will occur in 2024?
   c) Which Summer Olympics will occur in 2100?
   d) Which Summer Olympics were held in Montreal in 1976?
   e) There were a number of times when the Summer Olympics were not held. Go to *www.school.mcgrawhill.ca/resources/* and follow the links to find out when and why.

EXTEND THE CONCEPTS

13. **Problem Solving** Determine the number of terms in each sequence without listing the terms.
   a) 2, 5, 8, …, 299
   b) 9, 5, 1, …, −251
   c) −7, −2, 3, …, 198
   d) −3, −5, −7, …, −401

3.3 | Geometric Sequences

E. coli is a type of bacteria that is studied by scientists. They create bacterial cultures to see how the bacteria reproduce in response to different treatments. Each bacterium in an E. coli culture reproduces by splitting into 2, into 4, into 8, into 16, and so on. This forms a special type of sequence.

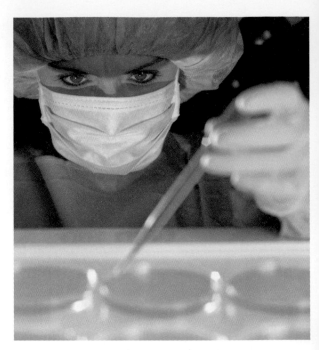

DISCOVER

Common Ratios

1. Copy and complete the following table.

	Sequence	Ratios			
		$t_2 \div t_1$	$t_3 \div t_2$	$t_4 \div t_3$	$t_5 \div t_4$
a)	3, 6, 12, 24, 48, ...				
b)	2, −10, 50, −250, 1250, ...				
c)	512, 256, 128, 64, 32, ...				

2. What did you notice about the ratios in sequence a)? sequence b)? sequence c)?

Each sequence in the Discover is a **geometric sequence**. Each term in a geometric sequence is found by multiplying the term before it by the same number. This constant number is called the **common ratio**. The common ratio can be positive, negative, a fraction, or a decimal.

Common Ratio of 3

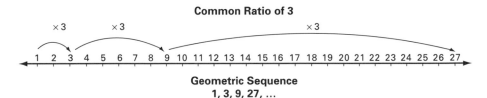

Geometric Sequence
1, 3, 9, 27, ...

EXAMPLE 1

Develop a Formula Given the Sequence

An E. coli bacterium splits into 2 bacteria, then into 4, then into 8, and so on.

a) Determine if the E. coli sequence is geometric.

b) Develop a formula for t_n in the sequence.

c) Determine the 12th term.

d) If the bacteria split every 5 min, how many are there after 40 min?

Solution

a) List the sequence and then, determine if there is a common ratio:

$t_1 = 1,\ t_2 = 2,\ t_3 = 4,\ t_4 = 8$

$$t_2 \div t_1 = 2 \div 1 \qquad\qquad t_3 \div t_2 = 4 \div 2 \qquad\qquad t_4 \div t_3 = 8 \div 4$$
$$= 2 \qquad\qquad\qquad\qquad = 2 \qquad\qquad\qquad\qquad = 2$$

There is a common ratio of 2, so, the sequence is geometric.

b) Look for a relationship between the term numbers and the term values:

$$t_1 = 1 \qquad\quad t_2 = 2 \qquad\quad t_3 = 4 \qquad\quad t_4 = 8$$
$$t_1 = 1 \qquad\quad t_2 = 2 \qquad\quad t_3 = 2 \times 2 \qquad\quad t_4 = 2 \times 2 \times 2$$
$$t_1 = 2^{1-1} \qquad t_2 = 2^{2-1} \qquad t_3 = 2^{3-1} \qquad t_4 = 2^{4-1}$$

The exponent is 1 less than the term number: $t_n = 2^{n-1}$

A formula for t_n in the sequence is $t_n = 2^{n-1}$.

c) Use the formula for t_n:

$$t_n = 2^{n-1} \qquad n = 12$$
$$t_{12} = 2^{12-1}$$
$$t_{12} = 2^{11}$$
$$t_{12} = 2048$$

The 12th term is 2048.

Alternatively, the sequence function of a graphing calculator could be used to find the nth term. (See page 409 in the Technology Appendix.)

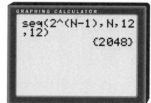

GRAPHING CALCULATOR

seq(2^(N–1),N,12 ,12)
                    {2048}

d) Determine the term number after 40 min:

Time (min)	0	5	10	15	20	25	30	35	40
Term Number	1	2	3	4	5	6	7	8	9

$$t_n = 2^{n-1} \qquad n = 9$$
$$t_9 = 2^{9-1}$$
$$t_9 = 2^8$$
$$t_9 = 256$$

There are 256 bacteria after 40 min.

EXAMPLE 2

Develop a Formula for Any Geometric Sequence

A geometric sequence has a first term of a and a common ratio of r. Develop a formula for t_n in the sequence.

Solution

List the sequence, and then, look for a relationship between the term numbers and the term values:

$$t_1 = a \qquad\qquad t_2 = a \times r \qquad\qquad t_3 = a \times r \times r \qquad\qquad t_4 = a \times r \times r \times r$$
$$t_1 = a \times r^0 \qquad t_2 = a \times r^1 \qquad t_3 = a \times r^2 \qquad\qquad t_4 = a \times r^3$$
$$t_1 = a \times r^{1-1} \qquad t_2 = a \times r^{2-1} \qquad t_3 = a \times r^{3-1} \qquad t_4 = a \times r^{4-1}$$

The exponent of r is 1 less than the term number: $t_n = ar^{n-1}$

A formula for t_n in a sequence with a first term of a and a common ratio of r is $t_n = ar^{n-1}$.

The formula $t_n = ar^{n-1}$ can be used to find the formula for t_n in any geometric sequence.

EXAMPLE 3

Use $t_n = ar^{n-1}$ to Develop a Formula for t_n in a Sequence

a) Develop a formula for t_n in the sequence $35, -175, 875, -4375, \ldots$.
b) Determine the 8th term.

Solution

a) Determine if the sequence is geometric:

$$t_2 \div t_1 = -175 \div 35 \qquad t_3 \div t_2 = 875 \div (-175) \qquad t_4 \div t_3 = -4375 \div 875$$
$$= -5 \qquad\qquad\qquad = -5 \qquad\qquad\qquad\qquad = -5$$

There is a common ratio of -5, so, the sequence is geometric.

Use the formula $t_n = ar^{n-1}$:

$$t_n = ar^{n-1} \qquad a = 35, r = -5$$
$$t_n = 35(-5)^{n-1}$$

A formula for t_n in the sequence is $t_n = 35(-5)^{n-1}$.

b) Use the formula for t_n:
$$t_n = 35(-5)^{n-1} \quad n = 8$$
$$t_8 = 35(-5)^{8-1}$$
$$t_8 = -2\,734\,375$$

The 8th term in the sequence is $-2\,734\,375$.

EXAMPLE 4

Common Ratio Between 0 and 1

a) Develop a formula for t_n in the following geometric sequence:
390 625, 78 125, 15 625, …

b) Determine the 12th term.

Solution

a) Determine the common ratio:

$$t_2 \div t_1 = 78\,125 \div 390\,625 \qquad\qquad t_3 \div t_2 = 15\,625 \div 78\,125$$
$$= 0.2 \qquad\qquad\qquad\qquad\qquad = 0.2$$

The common ratio is 0.2.

Use the formula $t_n = ar^{n-1}$:

$$t_n = ar^{n-1} \qquad\qquad a = 390\,625, r = 0.2$$
$$t_n = 390\,625(0.2)^{n-1}$$

A formula for t_n in the sequence is $t_n = 390\,625(0.2)^{n-1}$.

b) Use the formula for t_n:

$$t_n = 390\,625(0.2)^{n-1} \quad n = 12$$
$$t_{12} = 390\,625(0.2)^{12-1}$$
$$t_{12} = 0.008$$

The 12th term is 0.008.

KEY CONCEPTS

• A sequence that has a common ratio between consecutive terms is a geometric sequence.

• The formula $t_n = ar^{n-1}$ can be used to develop a formula for the nth term, t_n, in any geometric sequence, where

  n is the term number

  a is the first term

  r is the common ratio

DISCUSS THE CONCEPTS

1. Describe the differences between arithmetic sequences and geometric sequences.

2. Explain how to find the common ratio in each sequence:
   a) 4, 12, 36, ... **b)** 120, 60, 30, ... **c)** 50, −200, 800, ...

3. Explain how you would find the 20th term in the sequence in question 2, part a).

PRACTISE

A 1. Write the first four terms of each geometric sequence.
   a) first term = 1, common ratio = 4
   b) first term = 200, common ratio = 0.5
   c) first term = 10, common ratio = −3
   d) first term = 240, common ratio = −0.5

2. Determine whether each sequence is arithmetic, geometric, or neither. Give a reason for each.
   a) 2, 8, 32, ... **b)** 2, 6, 10, ... **c)** 2, 6, 24, ...
   d) 5, −15, 45, ... **e)** $12, 3, \dfrac{3}{4}, ...$ **f)** 20, 16, 12, ...

3. For each geometric sequence,
   i) develop and simplify a formula for t_n
   ii) find the value of the indicated term
   a) $a = 3, r = 6; t_{10} = $?
   b) $a = 10, r = −4; t_8 = $?
   c) $a = −20, r = 0.5; t_{15} = $?

4. Develop a formula for t_n. Then, determine the term. Round to four decimal places, if necessary.
   a) $7, 14, 28, ...; t_{12}$ **b)** $3, −6, 12, ...; t_{12}$
   c) $1, 0.5, 0.25, ...; t_{10}$ **d)** $−5, −20, −80, ...; t_{12}$
   e) $20\ 000\ 000, −2\ 000\ 000, 200\ 000, ...; t_8$ **f)** $1000, 100, 10, ...; t_7$

5. For each geometric sequence, determine the first five terms. Then, determine the values of a and r.
   a) $t_n = 8 \times 3^{n-1}$
   b) $t_n = 5120 \times 0.5^{n-1}$

6. **Bacteria** A culture begins with 10 bacteria. Each bacterium splits into two every minute.
  a) Develop a formula to calculate the number of bacteria after n minutes.
  b) How many bacteria are there after 20 min?

B **7.** **Phone tree** A fan-out calling system is used to spread news quickly to a large number of people. For instance, it is used to contact volunteers for disaster relief. Suppose, in stage 1 of calling, the first person calls 4 people. Then, each of those people calls 2 people in stage 2. In stage 3, each of those people calls 2 people, and so on.
  a) How many people will be called during stage 7?
  b) At stage 7, how many people will have been called altogether?

8. **Tennis tournament** A tennis tournament begins with 512 players. If a player wins round 1, the player continues to round 2. If the player loses, the player drops out of the tournament. This continues for each round.
  a) Develop a formula to calculate the number of players left in the nth round.
  b) How many players will be playing in the 7th round?

9. **Application** You have two natural parents (P), four natural grandparents (GP), eight natural great-grandparents (GGP), and so on. How many ancestors do you have
  a) in the 6th generation past?
  b) in the 8th generation past?
  c) altogether in the past 8 generations?

Your Ancestors

Generation 4 GGP GGP GGP GGP GGP GGP GGP GGP

Generation 3   GP   GP   GP   GP

Generation 2   P   P

Generation 1   YOU

10. **Communication** Create and solve a geometric sequence problem that uses the formula $t_n = ar^{n-1}$ in its solution.

11. **Application** A rubber ball bounces to $\frac{5}{8}$ of its previous height. The ball is dropped from a height of 16 m. Use what you have learned in this section to determine how high the 6th bounce will be.

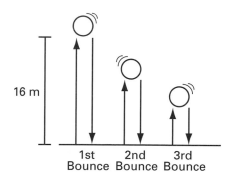

16 m

1st   2nd   3rd
Bounce Bounce Bounce

12. a) Follow these steps to see the shape formed by the sequence defined by $t_n = 2^n$.

Step 1: Place the tip of your pencil on a piece of grid paper, about 10 squares from the left and 20 squares from the bottom of the paper. Ensure the pencil is on an intersection of grid lines.

Step 2: Draw a line to the right the number of grid spaces equal to the difference between the first and second terms of the sequence.

Step 3: Turn 90° clockwise and draw a line the number of grid spaces equal to the difference between the second and third terms.

Step 4: Turn 90° clockwise and draw a line the number of grid spaces equal to the difference between the third and fourth terms.

Step 5: Continue in this way until you run off the paper.

b) Describe the shape formed.

c) Predict the shape formed by the sequence defined by $t_n = 4 + (n-1)(7)$. Then, repeat the steps.

d) Compare the shapes. Explain why they are different.

C 13. Problem Solving A camera has an opening that lets light in to expose the film. You can adjust the size of the opening (the F-stop) and the length of time it is open (the shutter speed) to allow in a specific amount of light. The numbers listed below are what appear on the camera. However, many of the numbers are rounded. The exact numbers form a geometric sequence. The first two numbers in each sequence are exact. Rewrite each sequence using exact numbers. Round F-stops to two decimal places, if necessary.

a) Shutter speeds (in seconds): $2, 1, \dfrac{1}{2}, \dfrac{1}{4}, \dfrac{1}{8}, \dfrac{1}{15}, \dfrac{1}{30}, \dfrac{1}{60}, \dfrac{1}{125}, \dfrac{1}{250}, \dfrac{1}{500}, \dfrac{1}{1000}$

b) F-stops: 1.4, 2, 2.8, 4, 5.6, 8, 11, 16, 22

EXTEND THE CONCEPTS

14. Problem Solving Determine the number of terms in each sequence without listing the terms.

a) 2, 4, 8, …, 16 777 216

b) 1, 5, 25, …, 244 140 625

15. Thinking A paradox is a situation that seems possible but is impossible. For example, the following is a paradox:

A runner set out to run 8 km at a constant speed. He reached the halfway point (with 4 km remaining). He then reached the next halfway point (with 2 km remaining). He then reached the next halfway point (with 1 km remaining). He continued on in this way.

a) Why is this a paradox?

b) How is this related to sequences?

3.4 | Compound Interest

Often, when money is borrowed or invested, the interest is added on to the principal after a set period of time. Then, after the same period of time, interest is calculated again. However, this time it is calculated on the new amount, which includes the principal and interest. This continues until the loan or investment is finished. This type of interest is **compound interest**.

Current High Yield Certificates

Account		Annual Rate
7 Month	$2,500 minimum. Daily compounding. Interest paid quarterly and at maturity. Interest may be deferred until maturity.	**3.80**%c
***12 Month**	$2,500 minimum. Daily compounding. Interest paid quarterly and at maturity. Interest may be deferred until maturity.	**4.25**%
***24 Month**	$2,500 minimum. Daily compounding. Interest paid quarterly and at maturity.	**4.75**%
Non-gift Rate ***3 Year**	$2,500 minimum. Daily compounding.	**5.60**%
***4 Year**	$2,500 minimum. Daily compounding.	**6.00**%
***5 Year**	$2,500 minimum. Daily compounding.	**6.50**%

DISCOVER

Calculate Compound Interest

A $1000 investment earns interest at 6% per annum, compounded annually. Calculate the amount of the investment after 7 years.

$1000 at 6% per annum, compounded annually, for 7 years is $ [?]

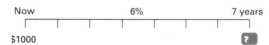

Now   6%   7 years

$1000   [?]

Complete either **Method 1** or **Method 2**, and then, answer questions 1 to 3.

See page 405 for specific spreadsheet instructions.
Method 1: Use a spreadsheet

Follow these steps to use a spreadsheet to automatically calculate the amount of the investment each year for 7 years.

Step 1: In cells A1, B1, and C1, enter the column headings, as shown. Widen the columns, if necessary.

	A	B	C	
1	Year Number	Interest (%)	Amount ($)	
2	0	0	1000	
3				

Step 2: Format columns B and C to 2 decimal places and column A to 0 decimal places.

Step 3: In cells A2, B2, and C2, enter the values **0, 0**, and **1000**.

Step 4: In cell A3, enter the formula **=A2+1**. Then, copy it into cells A4 to A9.

Step 5: In cell B3, enter the formula **=C2*0.06**. Then, copy it into cells B4 to B9.

Step 6: In cell C3, enter the formula **=C2+B3**. Then, copy it into cells C4 to C9.

Did You Know?

The first mechanical calculator was invented by Blaise Pascal in 1642. Mechanical calculators were used until the introduction of the modern electronic calculator in the 1960s.

Method 2: Use a calculator

Follow these steps to use a calculator and the formula $A = 1000(1.06)^n$, where A is the amount after n years, to calculate the amount of the investment each year for 7 years.

Step 1: Set up a table of values as shown.

Number of Years	Amount ($)
0	1000.00
1	
2	
3	
4	
5	
6	
7	

Step 2: Calculate $1000(1.06)^1$. Enter the result under **Amount** for year 1.

Step 3: Calculate $1000(1.06)^2$. Enter the result under **Amount** for year 2.

Step 4: Continue on to complete the table.

1. Explain what you did and why in each step of **Method 1** or **Method 2** of the Discover.

2. **a)** Describe how the amount has grown over the 7 years.
b) Has it grown at a constant rate or in a different manner? Explain.

3. What type of sequence do the terms in the **Amount** column form? Explain.

The formula $A = P(1 + i)^n$ is used to determine the amount, or final amount of an investment or loan, where
- A is the amount, or final amount
- P is the principal, or initial amont
- i is the interest rate per compounding period
- n is the number of compounding periods

Note that all interest rates in Canada, unless stated otherwise, are annual, or yearly. An investment such as $10 000 at 5% per annum, compounded quarterly would be described as $10 000 at 5%, compounded quarterly.

EXAMPLE 1

Determine the Values of the Compound Interest Formula Variables

Determine the values of P, n, and i in the formula $A = P(1 + i)^n$ for each.
a) Nasir invested $500 for 5 years at 8%, compounded semi-annually.
b) Arezo borrowed $300 for 3 years at 5%, compounded quarterly.
c) Diane invested $1500 for 2 years at 7%, compounded monthly.

Solution
a) $500 for 5 years at 8%, compounded semi-annually

Compounded **semi-annually** means 2 times a year.
2 times the number of years at $\frac{1}{2}$ the annual interest rate

$$P = 500 \qquad n = 5 \times 2 \qquad i = 0.08 \div 2$$
$$n = 10 \qquad i = 0.04$$

b) $300 for 3 years at 5%, compounded quarterly

Compounded **quarterly** means 4 times a year.
4 times the number of years at $\frac{1}{4}$ the annual interest rate

$$P = 300 \qquad n = 3 \times 4 \qquad i = 0.05 \div 4$$
$$n = 12 \qquad i = 0.0125$$

c) $1500 for 2 years at 7%, compounded monthly

Compounded monthly means 12 times a year.
12 times the number of years at $\frac{1}{12}$ the annual interest rate.

$$P = 1500 \qquad n = 2 \times 12 \qquad i = 0.07 \div 12$$
$$n = 24 \qquad i \doteq 0.005\ 83$$

EXAMPLE 2

Calculate the Amount of an Investment

Cora invested $500 at 5%, compounded quarterly, for 2 years. What will the investment be worth at the end of the 2-year term?

Solution

Draw a time line diagram to organize the information:

$500 at 5%, compounded quarterly, for 2 years is $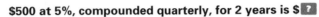

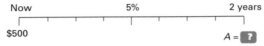

Use the formula $A = P(1 + i)^n$:
Determine the values of the variables:

$A =$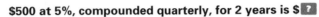
$P = 500$ The principal is $500.
$n = 8$ quarterly, or 4 times a year, for 2 years is 8
$i = 0.0125$ 5%, compounded 4 times a year is $0.05 \div 4$

Use the formula:
$A = P(1 + i)^n$ Substitute for P, n, and i.
$A = 500(1 + 0.0125)^8$
$A = 500(1.0125)^8$ Simplify.
$A \doteq 552.24$

The investment will be worth $552.24 at the end of the 2-year term.

Alternatively, a finance application of a graphing calculator
could be used to find the final amount, or future value (FV).
(See page 413 in the Technology Appendix.)

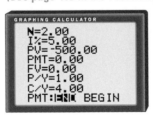

EXAMPLE 3

Calculate the Amount and Interest for a Loan

Calculate the amount and interest paid on a $700 loan, after 3 years, at 6%, compounded semi-annually.

Solution

Draw a time line diagram to organize the information:

$700 at 6%, compounded semi-annually, for 3 years is $?

```
Now                      6%              3 years
 ├────┬────┬────┬────┬────┤
$700                              A = ?
```

Use the formula $A = P(1 + i)^n$:

$A = $?

$P = 700$ The principal is $700.

$n = 6$ semi-annually, or 2 times a year, for 3 years is 6

$i = 0.03$ 6%, compounded 2 times a year is 0.06 ÷ 2

$A = P(1 + i)^n$ Substitute for P, n, and i.

$A = 700(1.03)^6$ Do the step $700(1 + 0.03)^6 = 700(1.03)^6$ mentally.

$A \doteq 835.84$

Calculate the interest paid by subtracting the principal from the amount:

$I = A - P$

$I = 835.84 - 700.00$

$I = 135.84$

The amount after 3 years will be $835.84. The interest paid will be $135.84.

KEY CONCEPTS

- The formula $A = P(1 + i)^n$ is used to calculate the amount, or final amount of a loan or an investment, where

    A is the amount, or final amount

    i is the interest rate per compounding period

    P is the principal, or initial amount

    n is the number of compounding periods

- To calculate the value of i, use $i = r \div N$, where r is the annual interest rate and N is the number of compounding periods per year.

- To calculate the value of n, use $n = yN$, where y is the number of years and N is the number of compounding periods per year.

- Compound interest is an example of a geometric sequence.

DISCUSS THE CONCEPTS

1. Tasha borrowed $250 at 9%, compounded quarterly, for a term of 3 years. Describe how to determine the values of i and n in order to use the compound interest formula.

2. Peta invested $100 for 10 years with simple interest charged at 10%. Kyle invested $100 for 10 years at 10%, compounded annually. Who made the better investment? Explain.

3. $800 is invested for a 3-year term at 6%, compounded annually. The amount of the investment at the end of each year is $800(1.06)$, $800(1.06)^2$, and $800(1.06)^3$. What kind of sequence do these values form? Explain how you know.

PRACTISE

A 1. Evaluate. Round to two decimal places.
   a) $1000(1.01)^8$
   b) $490(1.05)^{12}$
   c) $5000(1.0025)^{50}$
   d) $1200(1.04)^6$

2. List the calculator keystrokes you used to evaluate $5000(1.0025)^{50}$.

3. For each, state the values of P, n, and i.
   a) a $600 loan at 8%, compounded quarterly, for 5 years
   b) a $2000 investment at 3%, compounded monthly, for 2 years
   c) a $750 investment at 10%, compounded annually, for 8 years
   d) a $1000 loan at 7%, compounded semi-annually, for 1.5 years

4. Write each in the form $A = P(1 + i)^n$.
   a) $500 at 6%, compounded monthly, for 2 years
   b) $2500 at 9%, compounded semi-annually, for 3 years
   c) $10 000 at 6%, compounded quarterly, for 20 years
   d) $375 at 3%, compounded monthly, for 10 years

APPLY THE CONCEPTS

5. Borrowing money Tera borrowed $2000 at 10%, compounded semi-annually, for a 2-year term. She will pay back the loan in 2 years.
   a) How much will Tera have to pay back?
   b) How much of what she pays back will be interest?

B **6. Long-term investments** When Bill was born, his parents invested $2000 at 6%, compounded quarterly.

    a) What will the investment be worth on Bill's 18th birthday?

    b) How much interest will have been earned?

7. Small business loans A small business loan of $3000, at 9%, compounded monthly, must be repaid after 2 years.

    a) How much must be repaid?

    b) How much interest will have been paid?

8. Population growth A town has a population of 12 000 people. It has a projected growth rate of 1% per year for the next 10 years.

    a) What is the projected population in 10 years?

    b) How does this situation relate to compound interest?

9. Application For the past 10 years, a certain mutual fund has grown at an average rate of 14.8% per year, compounded annually. Helen has decided to invest $2000 in the fund. If the trend continues, what will her investment be worth in 5 years?

10. Salary increase According to Tammy's latest contract, her annual salary is to increase by 3.5% per year for the next 3 years. Her current salary is $35 500. What will her salary be in 3 years?

11. Spreadsheet

    a) Use a spreadsheet to show the growth of a $2000 investment over a 2-year term, at 6%, compounded semi-annually.

    b) Describe how the amount has grown.

12. Communication Design a compound interest problem that uses $A = 2000(1.025)^8$ in its solution.

13. Landscaping Christophe needs to borrow $20 000 to expand his landscaping business. One bank offers an interest rate of 10.5%, compounded semi-annually, for 5 years. Another bank offers an interest rate of 10%, compounded quarterly, for 5 years.

    a) Which loan should Christophe choose? Explain.

    b) What is the difference in interest to be paid between the two loans?

14. Problem Solving A $500 investment earns interest at 6%, compounded quarterly, for 8 years. How much interest will be earned in the final year of the 8-year term?

15. Comparing interest Firosha plans to invest $5000 for 1 year. She can invest at 5% simple interest or at 4.5%, compounded monthly. Which is the better investment? Explain.

16. Gus invested $1350 at 4%, compounded semi-annually, for 6 years.
   a) What will his investment be worth after 5 years?
   b) What will his investment be worth after 6 years?
   c) How much interest will be earned during the 6th year?
   d) How much interest will be earned altogether?

17. Geometric sequences
   a) Describe how the compound interest formula is related to the geometric sequence formula, $t_n = ar^{n-1}$.
   b) How would you determine the common ratio in a compound interest sequence?
   c) Calculate the common ratios of several different compound interest sequences. What do you notice?

18. Recall the young couple, Aaron and Selma, and their investment plans, as described on page 69. They plan to invest $25 000 for each child's education immediately, so that the investment will grow until each child is 18 years old.
   a) Contact a financial institution or go to *www.school.mcgrawhill/resources/* and follow the links to research interest rates for risk-free, long-term investments for which interest is compounded, such as term deposits and guaranteed investment certificates (GICs).
   b) Determine how much money there will be for Mercedes' education.
   c) Determine how much money there will be for Jacob's education.
   d) Describe any difficulties you had in completing parts a) to c).

19. Problem Solving Saram invested $1250 at 4%, compounded semi-annually, for 3 years. She then re-invested at 6%, compounded quarterly, for 5 more years. What will her investment be worth at the end of the 8 years?

3.5 | Present Value

A student will need $3000 to pay for college tuition next year. A small business will need $10 000 to upgrade computer equipment in 2 years. In each situation, it is necessary to calculate the principal, or **present value**, that must be invested today in order to have a specific amount later.

DISCOVER

Determine the First Term of a Geometric Sequence

To determine the value of any term, t_n, in a geometric sequence, you can use the formula $t_n = ar^{n-1}$.

Suppose you want to determine the first term of a sequence, a. You can do this if you know the last term, the number of terms, and the common ratio. You can use the same formula, but rearranging it will make it easier to use:

$$t_n = ar^{n-1}$$ Rearrange the formula to solve for a.

$$\frac{t_n}{r^{n-1}} = \frac{a \times r^{n-1}}{r^{n-1}}$$ Divide both sides by r^{n-1}.

$$a = \frac{t_n}{r^{n-1}}$$ t_n is the last term, r is the common ratio, and n is the number of terms.

1. In each geometric sequence, use the rearranged formula to determine the value of the first term.

   a) The last term is 160, the common ratio is 2, and there are 6 terms.

   b) The last term is 486, the common ratio is 3, and there are 5 terms.

2. Describe how you could check if your answers in question 1 are correct.

Determining the principal, or present value, of an investment that has compounding interest is like determining the first term in a geometric sequence. You can use the formula $A = P(1 + i)^n$ to find the principal, or present value of an investment (the first term), if you know
- the final amount (the last term)
- the number of compounding periods (the number of terms)
- the interest rate per compounding period (the common ratio)

EXAMPLE 1

Calculate Present Value Two Ways

What principal must be invested today in order to grow to $2000 in 5 years, at 6%, compounded annually?

Solution

Draw a time line diagram to organize the information:

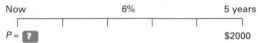

$$ \$\boxed{?} \text{ at 6\%, compounded annually,} $$
$$ \text{for 5 years is \$2000} $$

Now		6%		5 years

$P = \boxed{?}$ $2000

Determine the values of the variables:

$A = 2000$ $P = \boxed{?}$ $i = 0.06$ $n = 5$

Method 1: Use $A = P(1 + i)^n$

$A = P(1+i)^n$ Substitute for A, n, and i.

$2000 = P(1.06)^5$ Solve for P.

$\dfrac{2000}{1.06^5} = \dfrac{P(1.06)^5}{1.06^5}$ Evaluate.

$P = \dfrac{2000}{1.06^5}$

$P \doteq 1494.52$

A principal of $1494.52 must be invested today at 6%, compounded annually, in order to grow to $2000 in 5 years.

Method 2: Use $P = A(1 + i)^{-n}$

Rearrange the formula $A = P(1 + i)^n$ first:

$A = P(1+i)^n$

$\dfrac{A}{(1+i)^n} = \dfrac{P(1+i)^n}{(1+i)^n}$ Solve for P.

$P = \dfrac{A}{(1+i)^n}$ Rewrite using a negative exponent (remember, $\dfrac{1}{(1+i)^n} = (1+i)^{-n}$

$P = A(1+i)^{-n}$

Use the rearranged formula:

$P = A(1 + i)^{-n}$ Substitute for A, n, and i.

$P = 2000(1.06)^{-5}$ Evaluate.

$P \doteq 1494.52$

A principal of $1494.52 must be invested today at 6%, compounded annually, in order to grow to $2000 in 5 years.

In Example 1, both methods, using $A = P(1 + i)^n$ and using $P = A(1 + i)^{-n}$, worked well. However, for more complex problems, using $P = A(1 + i)^{-n}$ is quicker and easier.

When you use the formula $P = A(1 + i)^{-n}$ to determine present value, use PV instead of P:

$PV = A(1 + i)^{-n}$ where
- PV is the present value, or principal
- A is the final amount
- i is the interest rate per compounding period
- n is the number of compounding periods

EXAMPLE 2

Use $PV = A(1 + i)^{-n}$ to Calculate Present Value

Abi and Niera plan to invest some money on the birth of their granddaughter, so that there will be $10 000 on her 16th birthday. They will invest their money at 8%, compounded semi-annually. How much do they need to invest today?

Solution

Draw a time line diagram to organize the information:

$? at 8%, compounded semi-annually, for 16 years is $10 000

Now   8%   16 years

$PV = ?$ $10 000

Use the formula $PV = A(1 + i)^{-n}$:
Determine the values of the variables:

$PV = ?$

$A = 10\ 000$

$i = 0.04$ 8%, compounded semi-annually, or 2 times a year is $0.08 \div 2$

$n = 32$ 2 times a year, for 16 years is 32

Use the formula:

$PV = A(1 + i)^{-n}$ Substitute for A, n, and i.

$PV = 10\ 000(1.04)^{-32}$ Evaluate.

$PV \doteq 2850.58$

They need to invest $2850.58 today to have $10 000 in 16 years.

EXAMPLE 3

Discount the Value of a Debt

Seth needs to pay off a $1000 debt in 1 year. His creditor, the bank, is willing to accept payment today, discounted at an interest rate of 9%, compounded monthly. How much is his creditor willing to accept today?

Solution

Determining the discounted value of a debt is like determining the present value of an investment.

Draw a time line diagram to organize the information:

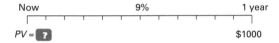

**$[?] at 9%, compounded monthly,
for 1 year is $1000**

Now   9%   1 year

$PV = [?]$ $1000

Use the formula $PV = A(1 + i)^{-n}$:
Determine the values of the variables:

$PV = [?]$
$A = 1000$
$n = 12$ monthly, or 12 times a year, for 1 year is 12
$i = 0.0075$ 9%, 12 times a year is $0.09 \div 12$

Use the formula:
$PV = A(1 + i)^{-n}$
$PV = 1000(1.0075)^{-12}$
$PV \doteq 914.24$

Seth's creditor is willing to accept $914.24 today.

Alternatively, a finance application of a graphing calculator, could be used to find present value (PV). (See page 413 in the Technology Appendix.)

KEY CONCEPTS

- To find the present value, or principal of an investment or loan, use the formula $PV = A(1 + i)^{-n}$, where
  - PV is the present value, or principal
  - A is the final amount
  - i is the interest rate per compounding period
  - n is the number of compounding periods

- Determining the discounted value of a debt is like determining the present value of an investment.

DISCUSS THE CONCEPTS

1. In Examples 1 and 2, the present value is less than the final amount. Explain why.

2. **a)** Describe an investment for which the present value could be calculated using $1500(1.02)^{-12}$.
   b) Describe the keystrokes you would use on a calculator to evaluate $1500(1.02)^{-12}$.

3. Explain how the present value of an investment is like the first term in a geometric sequence.

4. Explain how finding the discounted value of a debt is like finding the present value of an investment.

PRACTISE

A 1. Evaluate each. Round to two decimal places.
   a) $300(1.02)^{-8}$
   b) $675(1.005)^{-20}$
   c) $1000(1.04)^{-12}$
   d) $15\,000(1.06)^{-8}$
   e) $2500(1.0125)^{-10}$
   f) $500(1.0625)^{-5}$

2. Find the present value.
   a) $500 required in 3 years invested at 6%, compounded monthly
   b) $800 required in 4 years invested at 5%, compounded quarterly

3. Find the discounted value.
   a) $2000 debt due in 10 years, discounted at 7%, compounded annually
   b) $1500 debt due in 5 years, discounted at 8%, compounded semi-annually

4. Transportation costs Juan wants to save enough money to buy an $8000 motorcycle in 4 years. He plans to invest his money at 7%, compounded quarterly. How much does he need to invest today?

5. Debt payment A debt payment of $5000 is due in 2 years. The creditor will accept payment today at a discounted interest rate of 10%, compounded quarterly. If the payment was made today, how much would it be?

B 6. One million dollars Liza would like to be a millionaire by the time she is 45 years old. She is now 18 years old. How much does she need to invest today, at 6%, compounded semi-annually?

7. Debt payment Jessica owes $1500. The debt is to be paid in one lump sum in 18 months. Her creditor will discount the debt at 12%, compounded monthly, if she pays today. What is the value of the debt today?

8. Mutual funds A bank is advertising a mutual fund with a 10.3% average yearly growth rate over the past 5 years. If an investment in the fund is worth $9795.55 today, what would the initial investment have been 5 years ago?

9. Application/Communication A city has 128 000 residents. The average yearly growth rate over the past 10 years has been 1.4%.
a) What was the population 10 years ago?
b) How is this problem like determining the present value of an investment?

10. Recall the young couple, Aaron and Selma, and their investment plans, as described on page 69. They predict that they will need $30 000 in 3 years to buy a car. And, they are planning a special vacation in 5 years. They estimate that it will cost $15 000.
a) In question 18 on page 98, you researched risk-free, long-term investments for which interest is compounded, such as term deposits and guaranteed investment certificates (GICs). Decide which investments are suitable for Aaron and Selma's car and vacation investments.
b) Determine how much they must invest today to pay for their car in 3 years.
c) Determine how much they must invest today to pay for their vacation in 5 years.

11. Communication

   a) Design and solve a present value problem that uses the formula $PV = A(1 + i)^{-n}$ in its solution.

   b) Trade problems with a classmate to check if your solutions are correct.

12. Application Mai wants to start a hair-styling business in 3 years. She figures that she will need $10 000 to start. One bank offers her a term deposit with interest at 6%, compounded semi-annually. Another bank offers her a term deposit with interest at 5.75%, compounded quarterly. Which term deposit should she invest in today? Explain.

13. Comparison

   a) Which investment is worth more today?
   Investment A at 4%, compounded semi-annually, worth $5000 in 8 years
   Investment B at 6%, compounded quarterly, worth $6500 in 10 years

   b) How much more is one investment worth than the other?

ACHIEVEMENT Check Knowledge/Understanding Thinking/Inquiry/Problem Solving Communication Application

14. John is owed $2000 in 3 years. He accepts payment today at a discounted interest rate of 6%, compounded semi-annually. He immediately invests the payment at 7%, compounded quarterly, for 3 years. How much will he have in 3 years?

EXTEND THE CONCEPTS

C 15. Technology Use a spreadsheet to show the change in value of an amount of $5000 due in 3 years, discounted at an interest rate of 4%, compounded semi-annually.

16. Geometric sequences

   a) Use the formula for t_n in any geometric sequence, $t_n = ar^{n-1}$, to calculate the number of terms, n, in each sequence.

   i) The last term is 270, the first term is 10, and the common ratio is 3.

   ii) The last term is 512, the first term is 2, and the common ratio is 2.

   b) Explain how you could check to see if your answers to part a) are correct.

3.6 Linear and Exponential Growth

Many things grow—children, plants, investments, populations, and so on. However, things grow following different patterns. If you were to draw a graph of your height on each birthday since you were born, you would be able to see the shape, or pattern, of your growth. A graph of the value of an investment over time would have a different growth pattern.

DISCOVER

Compare Investment Growth Patterns

Investment A: $100 at 10% simple interest, for 5 years
Investment B: $100 at 10% compounded annually, for 5 years

One way to compare the growth of these investments is to compare their graphs.

1. a) Copy and complete these two tables of values.

- Simple interest is calculated each year on the principal.
- The amount for each year is the principal plus the interest earned so far.

- Use the compound interest formula to complete the amount for each year.
- Calculate $100(1.10)^1$ for year 1, $100(1.10)^2$ for year 2, and so on. Round to the whole dollar, if necessary.

Simple Interest	
Year	Amount ($)
0	100
1	
2	
3	
4	
5	

Compound Interest	
Year	Amount ($)
0	100
1	
2	
3	
4	
5	

b) From the tables of values, predict the shape of each graph.

2. a) Graph both investments on the same set of axes. Set up your axes as shown here.

b) How are the growth patterns the same? different?

3) Why do you think the two investments have different growth patterns?

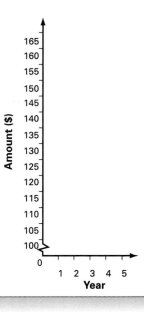

EXAMPLE 1

Analyze Linear Growth

Identify the type of growth shown by the sequence 4, 7, 10, 13, ….

Solution

Step 1: Analyze the pattern in the sequence 4, 7, 10, 13, …:

$$7 - 4 = 3 \qquad 10 - 7 = 3 \qquad 13 - 10 = 3$$

There is a common difference, so, the growth is constant and the sequence is arithmetic.

Step 2: Develop and then, analyze the formula for t_n in the sequence 4, 7, 10, 13, …:

$t_n = a + (n-1)d \qquad a = 4$ and $d = 3$
$t_n = 4 + (n-1)(3)$
$t_n = 4 + 3n - 3 \qquad$ Simplify.
$t_n = 3n + 1$

The formula is a linear equation.

Step 3: Create and then, analyze a graph of the sequence 4, 7, 10, 13, …:

Graph the relationship between the term numbers and term values.

The points of the graph form a straight line, or have a linear pattern.

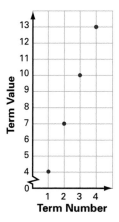

Step 4: Identify the type of growth:

The sequence 4, 7, 10, 13, … shows **linear growth** because
- the consecutive terms have a common difference, so, the growth is constant—the sequence is arithmetic
- the formula for t_n in the sequence is a **linear equation**
- the points of the graph of the sequence form a straight line, or are linear

EXAMPLE 2

Analyze Exponential Growth

Identify the type of growth shown by $1000 invested at 6%, compounded semi-annually, for 3 years.

Solution

Step 1: Create a table of values for the investment and analyze the pattern in the sequence of the amounts:

Compounding Period (n)	Amount ($) $A_n = 1000(1.03)^n$	Common Ratio
0	$1000(1.03)^0 = 1000.00$	
1	$1000(1.03)^1 = 1030.00$	1.03
2	$1000(1.03)^2 = 1060.90$	1.03
3	$1000(1.03)^3 \doteq 1092.73$	1.03
4	$1000(1.03)^4 \doteq 1125.51$	1.03
5	$1000(1.03)^5 \doteq 1159.28$	1.03
6	$1000(1.03)^6 \doteq 1194.05$	1.03

At the end of each interest period, the amount increases by a common ratio of 1.03, so, the amounts form a geometric sequence. Because there is not a common difference, the growth is not constant, or linear.

Step 2: Analyze the formula for A_n for the investment:

$A_n = 1000(1.03)^n$ is an exponential sequence because it has a variable exponent.

Step 3: Create and then, analyze a graph of the investment:

Graph the relationship between the compounding periods and amounts.

The graph is non-linear. It forms an upward curve.

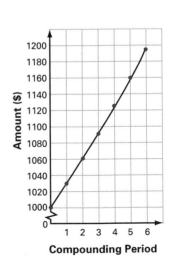

Compounding Period

Step 4: Identify the type of growth:

The investment shows **exponential growth** because
- the consecutive terms have a common ratio, not a common difference, so, the growth is not constant, or linear—the sequence is geometric
- the formula for A_n for the investment is an **exponential equation**
- the graph of the sequence forms an upward exponential curve

KEY CONCEPTS

- The following is evidence of linear growth:
  a common difference between consecutive terms—an arithmetic sequence
  a linear equation
  a straight line, or linear graph

- The following is evidence of exponential growth:
  a common ratio between consecutive terms—a geometric sequence
  an exponential equation
  a graph with an exponential curve

- A simple interest investment is an example of linear growth.

- A compound interest investment is an example of exponential growth.

DISCUSS THE CONCEPTS

1. Explain how you would determine the type of growth for each sequence.
   a) 20, 35, 50, …
   b) 100, 150, 225, …
   c) 50, 100, 300, …

2. The graph of an arithmetic sequence is linear. Explain why.

3. The graph of a geometric sequence is curved. Explain why.

A **1.** **a)** Create an arithmetic sequence with a first term of 2.

b) Predict what a graph of the relationship between the term numbers and the term values would look like. Explain your prediction.

2. **a)** Create a geometric sequence with a first term of 2.

b) Predict what a graph of the relationship between the term numbers and the term values would look like. Explain your prediction.

B Application *For questions 3 to 7, complete the following:*

a) Create a table of values.

b) Determine the relationship between consecutive terms.

c) Determine a formula for t_n in the sequence, if possible.

d) Draw a graph.

e) Classify the type of growth as linear, exponential, or other, and explain.

3. **Art investments** A painting that cost $1000 is expected to increase in value by 12% each year for the next 6 years.

4. **Simple interest** Simple interest is charged on a $2000 loan at a rate of 9% per annum. The loan is for 1 year but the amount owing is calculated at the end of each month.

5. **Compound interest** A $650 investment earns interest at 6%, compounded quarterly. The money is invested for 2 years.

6. **Pediatrics** A child's height is measured and recorded every 6 months, for 3 years, by her doctor. The heights were 21 cm, 23 cm, 28 cm, 31 cm, 34 cm, and 38 cm.

7. **Television viewing** The audience shares of a particular TV show over the first 5 weeks of the season were 12%, 15%, 18%, 21%, and 24%.

8. **Communication** Based on your answers for question 4, what type of growth is modelled by a simple interest loan? Explain how you know.

9. **Communication** Based on your answers for question 5, what type of growth is modelled by a compound interest investment? Explain how you know.

10. Recall Aaron and Selma, and their investment plans, as described on page 69. They plan to make the following investments:

- $25 000 for each child's education (see question 18 on page 98)
- an investment that will grow to $30 000 in 3 years to buy a car (see question 10 on page 104)
- an investment that will grow to $15 000 in 5 years for a vacation (see question 10 on page 104)

Then, they will invest half of what is left over for a "rainy day" or unexpected expenses, such as a major repair on the house. The rest will be kept for current needs, such as paying off credit card debts and day-to-day expenses.

a) How much do they have altogether for their "rainy day" investment and for current needs?

b) How much will they have for their "rainy day" investment?

c) Contact a financial institution or go to *www.school.mcgrawhill.ca/resources/* and follow the links to find the current interest rates for short-term, risk-free investments. Choose an investment that is suitable for their "rainy day" investment that has a term of 1 year or less and has compounding interest. Explain why you chose that investment.

d) Create a table of values and a graph to show the growth of their "rainy day" investment over a 10-year period. Describe the growth.

EXTEND THE CONCEPTS

C **11.** **Application** Canada's population every 20 years since 1861 is shown.

Year	1861	1881	1901	1921	1941	1961	1981	2001
Population (millions)	3.230	4.325	5.371	8.788	11.507	18.238	25.820	31.051

a) Approximately what type of growth is shown by these statistics? Explain.

b) Develop a formula that could be used to estimate the population every 20 years.

c) Use the formula to estimate the population in 2021.

CAREER PROFILE

Horticulture and Landscaping Technician

A horticulture and landscaping technician can find work in many industries. One example is as a golf course landscaper. This requires more knowledge about horticulture and landscaping than most people think. The greens must be irrigated and fertilized, and gardens and pathways must be looked after.

A career in horticulture and landscaping could also lead to self-employment. After working for a landscaping company, you may decide to start your own business.

A career as a horticulture and landscaping technician involves a 2-year program that covers theoretical and practical training. The admission requirements at Algonquin College in Nepean, Ontario are an Ontario Secondary School Diploma with Mathematics and English at the Academic or Applied Level. Students that have Mathematics and/or English at the Essentials Level must write a test to determine if they can succeed in the program. Go to

 www.school.mcgrawhill.ca/resources/ and follow the links to find out more about these courses offered at Algonquin College.

1. A career in landscaping is usually seasonal.
   a) Discuss the meaning of seasonal. List other seasonal careers.
   b) To be employed all year long, what other related employment could a landscaper consider?

2. Suppose you decide to start your own landscaping business.
   a) You must consider the start-up costs. Make a list of items that a landscaper might need.
   b) List the mathematical skills that you have learned in this chapter that would be useful in running your own business. Explain why you would need each skill.
   c) Other mathematical skills would also be required, for example, measuring area and perimeter. List other mathematical skills that you think would be required for landscaping. Explain why you would need each skill.

CASE STUDY WRAP-UP

A young couple, Aaron and Selma, have two children: Jacob, who is 8 years old, and Mercedes, who is 5 years old. They recently inherited $150 000 and are planning to invest most of it, using whatever is left over for day-to-day expenses.

They plan to invest $25 000 for each child's education immediately, so that the money will grow until each child is 18 years old. They predict that they will need $30 000 in 3 years for a new car. As well, they are planning a special vacation in 5 years. They estimate that it will cost $15 000. They will then invest half of what is left over for a "rainy day" or for an unexpected expense, such as a major repair on the house. The rest will be kept for current needs, such as paying off credit card debts and day-to-day expenses.

Throughout this chapter, you have solved problems related to the Case Study. You are now ready to prepare a report for Aaron and Selma, which answers the following questions:
a) How much will they have for each child's education at age 18?
b) How much should they invest today in order to buy a car in 3 years?
c) How much should they invest today for a vacation in 5 years?
d) How much will they have for a "rainy day" and for day-to-day expenses?
e) How will their "rainy day" investment grow over the next 10 years?

When preparing your report,
- refer to the Case Study questions on pages 98, 104, and 111
- provide complete solutions, including all calculations
- justify, or explain, your answers
- include a list of any materials you used, all your original data, your sources of information, and any formulas, tables, and graphs that you used or created
- use technology, where appropriate

*R*eview

3.1 Sequences, pages 70–76

1. For each sequence, describe the pattern and then, determine the next two terms.

   a) 4, 7, 10, …   **b)** 96, 48, 24, …

2. What are the first five terms of the sequence defined by each formula?

   a) $t_n = 3n - 2$ **b)** $t_n = n^2 + 1$

3. Develop a formula for t_n in the following sequence: $\dfrac{2}{3}, \dfrac{2}{4}, \dfrac{2}{5}, \ldots$

3.2 Arithmetic Sequences and Simple Interest, pages 77–83

4. For each sequence,

   i) explain how you know it is arithmetic

   ii) develop a formula for t_n

   iii) determine the 16th term

   a) 7, 11, 15, …   **b)** 4, −3, −10, …

5. An arithmetic sequence is defined by $t_n = -5n + 3$.

   a) Determine the first five terms in the sequence.

   b) What are the values of a and d?

6. In her new job, Sukitha earns $9.85/h. She will receive a $0.25/h raise every month for the next 6 months.

   a) Develop a formula for Sukitha's hourly wage during the nth month.

   b) What will her hourly wage be during the 5th month?

3.3 Geometric Sequences, pages 84–90

7. For each sequence,

   i) explain how you know it is geometric

   ii) develop a formula for t_n

   iii) determine the 9th term

   a) 9, 18, 36, …   **b)** 13 122, −4374, 1458, …

8. A geometric sequence is defined by $t_n = 5(-3)^{n-1}$.

   a) Determine the first five terms in the sequence.

   b) What are the values of a and r?

9. a) Develop a formula for the frequency of the E note in the nth octave.

b) What is the frequency of the E note in the 7th octave?

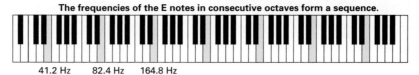

The frequencies of the E notes in consecutive octaves form a sequence.

41.2 Hz   82.4 Hz   164.8 Hz

3.4 Compound Interest, pages 91–98

10. a) What type of sequence does compound interest create? Explain how you know.

b) Provide an example of a compound interest sequence.

c) How is compound interest different from simple interest?

11. $800 was invested at 8%, compounded quarterly, for 3 years.

a) Write the investment in the form $A = P(1 + i)^n$.

b) Explain how you determined the values of the variables P, i, and n in part a).

12. Paula borrowed $3000, at 9%, compounded semi-annually, for 4 years.

a) How much will she have to repay?

b) How much of what she will repay is interest?

3.5 Present Value, pages 99–105

13. The present value of an investment can be represented by $5000(1.06)^{-10}$.

a) What do you know about the investment?

b) What keystrokes would you use on a calculator to evaluate $5000(1.06)^{-10}$?

14. $2000 is needed in 6 years. How much would have to be invested today at 4%, compounded quarterly? Explain how you solved the problem.

15. Gary owes $2000 that must be repaid in 5 years. The bank will accept payment today at a discounted interest rate of 5%, compounded semi-annually. How much will Gary have to pay back if he pays today?

3.6 Linear and Exponential Growth, pages 106–111

16. A $650 investment earns interest at 5%, compounded semi-annually, for 6 years.

a) Analyze the growth of this investment by investigating its sequence, formula, and graph.

b) Classify the type of growth. Justify your answer.

17. a) Describe an investment that shows linear growth.

b) Explain how you know it is linear.

Practice Test

Achievement Chart Category Connections

Category	Knowledge/Understanding	Thinking/Inquiry/Problem Solving	Communication	Application
Questions	1–12	6, 9, 12	1, 2, 5, 6, 9, 12	3–5, 7–12

1. **i)** Describe the pattern in each sequence in words.

   ii) Write the next two terms.

   iii) Describe the relationship between the term numbers and the term values.

   a) 4, 10, 16, …

   b) $3^4, 4^5, 5^6, …$

   c) 7, 0, −7, −14, …

2. Identify each sequence as arithmetic, geometric, or neither. Give a reason for each.

   a) 5, 7, 10, 14, …

   b) 2, 7, 12, …

   c) m, dm, cm, mm, …

3. Determine the first five terms of the sequence defined by each formula.

   a) $t_n = \dfrac{1}{n+3}$

   b) $t_n = 2 \times 3^{n-1}$

   c) $t_n = 7n - 2$

4. Develop a formula for t_n in each sequence. Then, determine each term.

   a) −2, 2, 6, …; t_{12}

   b) −4, 12, −36, …; t_{12}

   c) 2187, 729, 243, …; t_8

5. Determine the term in each sequence. Explain what you did.

   a) t_{50} in 7, 11, 15, 19, …

   b) t_{21} in −2, 6, −18, 54, …

6. **a)** Create a sequence that is neither geometric nor arithmetic.

   b) Explain why it is neither type of sequence.

7. Determine the value of $2500 invested at 5%, compounded semi-annually, after 7 years.

8. Jason borrowed $5000 at 9%, compounded monthly, for 3 years. How much must he repay? How much is interest?

9. Create and solve a compound interest problem for each.
a) a $10 000 loan
b) a $10 000 investment

10. Carla expects she will need $10 000 in 3 years to buy a car. She has been offered an investment at 10%, compounded semi-annually. How much must she invest today to have enough to buy a car in 3 years?

11. A payment of $1000 is due in 5 years. If it is paid back today, the debt will be discounted at an interest rate of 4%, compounded quarterly. How much is the payment if it is paid today?

ACHIEVEMENT Check | Knowledge/Understanding Thinking/Inquiry/Problem Solving Communication Application

12. a) A $3000 investment earns simple interest at 8% for 5 years. Analyze the growth of this investment. Then, classify the type of growth.
b) How would the growth differ if the interest earned was 8%, compounded annually? Explain.
c) How would the growth differ if the interest earned was 8%, compounded monthly? Explain.

WALNUT COVE   *BY MARK CULLUM*

Reprinted with special permission King Features Syndicate.

THE EFFECTS OF COMPOUNDING

Specific Expectations	Sections
• determine the effect of compound interest on deposits made into savings accounts	4.1, 4.2, 4.3, 4.4
• determine, through investigation, the characteristics of various savings alternatives available from a financial institution	4.1, 4.2, 4.5
• collect relevant information related to the alternatives to be considered in making a decision	4.1, 4.2, 4.5
• solve problems involving the calculation of the interest rate per period (i) and the number of periods (n) in the compound interest formula $A = P(1 + i)^n$, using a spreadsheet	4.3, 4.4
• determine, through investigation, the properties of a variety of investment alternatives, and compare the alternatives from the point of view of risk versus return	4.5

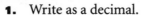et Ready...

1. Write as a decimal.

   a) 6% **b)** 12% **c)** 4.1% **d)** $5\frac{1}{2}\%$

   e) $6\frac{3}{4}\%$ **f)** 5.75% **g)** 6.5% **h)** $3\frac{1}{4}\%$

2. Calculate.

   a) $0.06 \div 12$ **b)** $0.095 \div 2$ **c)** $0.08 \div 4$ **d)** $0.03 \div 12$
   e) $0.10 \div 2$ **f)** $0.09 \div 4$ **g)** $0.085 \div 4$ **h)** $0.09 \div 12$

3. For each investment, determine the values of n and i in $A = P(1 + i)^n$. Recall that n is the number of compounding periods and i is the interest rate per compounding period.

   a) $1000 at 12%, compounded semi-annually, for 4 years
   b) $350 at 12%, compounded quarterly, for 4 years

Recall that interest rates, unless stated otherwise, are annual.

For questions 4 to 9, round to two decimal places, if necessary.

4. Evaluate.

   a) $400(1.07)^6$ **b)** $2300(1.045)^{10}$ **c)** $4360(1.125)^{15}$

5. These keystroke sequences can be used calculate the final amount of $1000 at 12%, compounded quarterly, for 4 years:

   scientific calculator: $1000\,\boxed{\times}\,\boxed{(}\,1\,\boxed{+}\,0.12\,\boxed{\div}\,4\,\boxed{)}\,\boxed{y^x}\,16\,\boxed{=}$

   graphing calculator: $1000\,\boxed{(}\,1\,\boxed{+}\,0.12\,\boxed{\div}\,4\,\boxed{)}\,\boxed{\wedge}\,16\,\boxed{\text{ENTER}}$

   a) Choose and explain one of the sequences.
   b) Use the keystroke sequence as an aid to writing the keystrokes for calculating the final amount of $8500 at 6%, compounded monthly, for 2 years.

6. Copy and complete the description for each time line diagram.

   a) $ **?** at **?** %, compounded ████ **?** ████, for **?** years is $ **?**

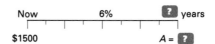

b) $\$$ 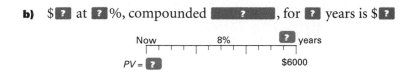 ? at ? %, compounded [?] , for ? years is $\$$?

Now   8%   ? years

$PV=$? $6000

7. a) Sketch a time line diagram for each investment in question 3.
    b) Calculate each final amount using $A = P(1 + i)^{n}$.

8. Calculate the present value using $PV = \dfrac{A}{(1+i)^{n}}$ or $PV = A(1 + i)^{-n}$.
    a) $5000 in 4 years, at 6.5%, compounded annually
    b) $25 000 in 15 years, at 6%, compounded monthly

9. Express each amount of time in years as a decimal.
    a) 6 semi-annual compounding periods is ? years.
    b) 10 quarterly compounding periods is ? years.
    c) 18 monthly compounding periods is ? years.

CASE STUDY

Throughout this chapter, you will continue working with the compound interest formula in order to investigate savings and investment alternatives. In some sections of the chapter, you will solve problems related to the Case Study described below. At the end of the chapter, in the Case Study Wrap-Up on page 161, you will be asked to write a report on the Case Study. Keep five or six pages of your notebook free for work related to the Case Study. Or, you may prefer to keep a Case Study portfolio.

Krysta is a Grade 11 student. She has saved $2400 from her part-time job. She wants to put it toward paying for college in 2 to 3 years. In order to make an informed decision about what to do with her savings, she needs to know about the following:
• the effect of interest rates
• the effect of compounding frequency
• savings alternatives and their advantages and disadvantages
• investment alternatives and their advantages and disadvantages

4.1 | Effect of Interest Rates

Troy has $5000 to save toward buying a used car in 5 years. He wants a savings alternative that is risk-free. He has found a guaranteed investment certificate (GIC) at 6%, compounded annually, at Trust Company A and a GIC at 5%, compounded annually, at Trust Company B. He has chosen the GIC at 5% because he has a savings account at Trust Company B. Will the 1% difference in rates make a big difference to the final amount?

DISCOVER

What Effect Does a 1% Difference Have?

1. Copy and complete the tables to compare two savings alternatives:

Trust Company A 6%, compounded annually		Trust Company B 5%, compounded annually	
Year	Amount ($) $A = P(1 + 0.06)^n$	Year	Amount ($) $A = P(1 + 0.05)^n$
0	$5000(1.06)^0 = 5000.00$	0	$5000(1.05)^0 = 5000.00$
1	$5000(1.06)^1 =$	1	
2		2	
3		3	
4		4	
5		5	

2. **a)** What effect does the 1% difference have?

b) Troy has chosen the GIC with the lower interest rate because he has an account at Trust Company B. Should he change his mind? Why?

c) What factors other than interest rate might affect an investor's decision?

3. Savings accounts and GICs are risk-free. What does "risk-free" mean?

EXAMPLE 1

Different Interest Rates and Final Amount

Jake has saved $2500 and is considering two savings alternatives for 6 years:
- an investment at 10%, compounded annually
- an investment at 8.5%, compounded annually

How much more interest will the investment at 10% earn than the one at 8.5%?

Solution

| **Investment at 10%** | **Investment at 8.5%** |

Draw time line diagrams to organize the information:

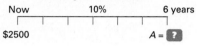

Use the formula, $A = P(1 + i)^n$.
Determine the values of the variables:

$A =$?	$A =$?
$P = 2500$	$P = 2500$
$i = 0.10$ 10% every year is 0.10.	$i = 0.085$ 8.5% every year is 0.085.
$n = 6$ 1 time/year for 6 years	$n = 6$ 1 time/year for 6 years

Use the formula:

$A = P(1 + i)^n$
$A = 2500(1.10)^6$
$A \doteq 4428.90$

$A = P(1 + i)^n$
$A = 2500(1.085)^6$
$A \doteq 4078.67$

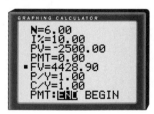

Calculate the interest earned:

$I = A - P$
$I = 4428.90 - 2500.00$
$I = 1928.90$

$I = A - P$
$I = 4078.67 - 2500.00$
$I = 1578.67$

Calculate the difference in interest earned:
$1928.90 - 1578.67 = 350.23$

The investment at 10% will earn $350.23 more interest than the one at 8.5%.

Alternatively, a finance application of a graphing calculator could be used to find the final amounts. (See page 413 in the Technology Appendix).

EXAMPLE 2

Different Interest Rates and Present Value

Susha needs $5000 in 4 years to pay for college. She has the choice of a GIC at 9%, compounded quarterly, or a GIC at 5%, compounded quarterly.

a) Which GIC will require a smaller principal invested today?

b) How much smaller?

Solution

a)
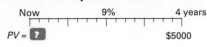

GIC at 9%	GIC at 5%

Draw time line diagrams:

$ [?] at 9%, compounded quarterly, for 4 years is $5000

Now 9% 4 years
$PV = [?]$ $5000

$ [?] at 5%, compounded quarterly, for 4 years is $5000

Now 5% 4 years
$PV = [?]$ $5000

Use the formula, $PV = A(1 + i)^{-n}$.
Determine the values of the variables:

$PV = [?]$ $PV = [?]$

$A = 5000$ $A = 5000$

$i = 0.0225$ 9% every $\frac{1}{4}$ year is $0.09 \div 4$. $i = 0.0125$ 5% every $\frac{1}{4}$ year is $0.05 \div 4$.

$n = 16$ 4 times/year for 4 years $n = 16$ 4 times/year for 4 years

Use the formula:

$PV = A(1 + i)^{-n}$ $PV = A(1 + i)^{-n}$

$PV = 5000(1.0225)^{-16}$ $PV = 5000(1.0125)^{-16}$

$PV \doteq 3502.33$ $PV \doteq 4098.73$

Alternatively, a finance application of a graphing calculator could be used to find the present values, or principals. (See page 413 in the Technology Appendix).

The GIC at 9% requires a lower principal invested today.

b) Calculate the difference between present values:
$4098.73 - 3502.33 = 596.40$

Susha could invest $596.40 less at 9% than at 5% and still have $5000 in 4 years.

EXAMPLE 3

Different Terms, Interest Rates, and Final Amount

a) Which savings alternative results in the greater final amount?
   A: $1600 at 4%, compounded semi-annually, for 10 years
   B: $1600 at 8%, compounded semi-annually, for 5 years
b) What is the difference in the final amounts?

Solution

a)   **Savings Alternative A**   **Savings Alternative B**

Draw time line diagrams:

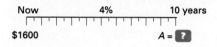

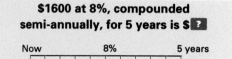

Use the formula, $A = P(1 + i)^n$.
Determine the values of the variables:

$A = \boxed{?}$		$A = \boxed{?}$	
$P = 1600$		$P = 1600$	
$i = 0.02$	4% every $\frac{1}{2}$ year is $0.04 \div 2$.	$i = 0.04$	8% every $\frac{1}{2}$ year is $0.08 \div 2$.
$n = 20$	2 times/year for 10 years	$n = 10$	2 times/year for 5 years

Use the formula:

$A = P(1 + i)^n$ $A = P(1 + i)^n$

$A = 1600(1.02)^{20}$ $A = 1600(1.04)^{10}$

$A \doteq 2377.52$ $A \doteq 2368.39$

$1600 at 4% for 10 years results in a slightly greater final amount than $1600 at 8% for 5 years.

b) Calculate the difference between the final amounts:
   $2377.52 - 2368.39 = 9.13$

$1600 at 4% for 10 years results in a final amount that is $9.13 greater than that of $1600 at 8% for 5 years.

EXAMPLE 4

Compare Savings Alternatives

The Neighbourhood Bank offers two short-term savings alternatives:
- a 60-day GIC, earning 4.1% simple interest, calculated daily and paid at term end
- a savings account, earning 1.5% simple interest, calculated daily and paid monthly

a) Which will earn more interest from February 1 to March 31? Explain.

b) Why might someone choose the savings alternative with the smaller final amount?

Solution

a)

60-Day GIC	Savings Account

Use the annual interest rate to calculate the daily interest rate:

$0.041 \div 365$ is the daily interest rate. $0.015 \div 365$ is the daily interest rate.

Calculate the interest earned using a principal of $10 000:

60-Day GIC	Savings Account
Use the simple interest formula to calculate the interest earned in 60 days:	Use the simple interest formula to calculate the interest for February:
$I = Prt$	$I = Prt$
$I = 10\,000 \times (0.041 \div 365) \times 60$	$I = 10\,000 \times (0.015 \div 365) \times 29$
$I \doteq 67.40$	$I \doteq 11.92$
	Calculate the balance on February 29:
	$A = P + I$
	$A = 10\,000 + 11.92$
	$A = 10\,011.92$
	Calculate the interest for March:
	$I = Prt$
	$I = 10\,011.92 \times (0.015 \div 365) \times 31$
	$I \doteq 12.75$
	Calculate the balance on March 31:
	$A = P + I$
	$A = 10\,011.92 + 12.75$
	$A = 10\,024.67$
	Calculate the interest earned altogether:
	$10\,024.67 - 10\,000 = 24.67$

At the end of 60 days, $67.40 in interest would be earned.   At the end of 60 days, $24.67 in interest would be earned.

The GIC would earn more than twice the interest.

b) Someone might choose the savings account because he or she might need the money before 60 days is up. The GIC might not be cashable.

KEY CONCEPTS

- Interest rate affects the final amount and the present value:
  The greater the interest rate, the greater the final amount.
  The greater the interest rate, the smaller the present value, or principal required.

- Savings alternatives, such as savings accounts and GICs, are risk-free because they are guaranteed. The interest rate is also guaranteed and is often a fixed interest rate.

DISCUSS THE CONCEPTS

1. Discuss, and then, describe the effect of interest rates.

2. One GIC has double the interest rate but half the term length of another GIC. Will they result in the same final amount? Explain. Use an example to illustrate.

3. Why would someone save money in a low-interest savings account instead of in a GIC with a higher interest rate?

PRACTISE

A 1. For each investment,
   i) sketch a time line diagram
   ii) determine the values of n and i in $A = P(1 + i)^n$
   iii) calculate the final amount
   a) $1200 at 6%, compounded semi-annually, for 4 years
   b) $980 at 10%, compounded quarterly, for 5 years
   c) $8564 at 6%, compounded monthly, for 6 years

2. For each investment,
   i) sketch a time line diagram
   ii) determine the values of n and i in $PV = \dfrac{A}{(1+i)^n}$ or $PV = A(1 + i)^{-n}$
   iii) calculate the present value
   a) $3500 in 6 years at 7%, compounded quarterly
   b) $8750 in 10 years at 8%, compounded semi-annually
   c) $16 000 in 2 years at 15%, compounded monthly

3. Different rates How much more will Dana save if she invests $1000 for 5 years at 8%, compounded annually, compared to 5%, compounded annually?

4. Different terms How much more will result if Francis invests $4500 at 10%, compounded semi-annually, for 7 years, compared to $4500 at 10%, compounded semi-annually, for 14 years?

5. Predicting
   a) Which has the greater final amount? Predict, and then, calculate to check.
   A: $2500 at 8%, compounded quarterly, for 6 years
   B: $2500 at 4%, compounded quarterly, for 10 years
   b) How much greater?

6. Predicting
   a) Which requires a smaller principal to grow to $10 000 in the future?
   C: 5%, compounded semi-annually, for 10 years
   D: 10%, compounded semi-annually, for 5 years
   b) How much smaller?

B 7. Inheritance Doreen and her sister Susan each inherited $2000. Doreen plans to save her money in a GIC earning 5.5%, compounded annually, for 4 years. Susan has chosen a GIC earning 6%, compounded annually, for 4 years.
   a) Who will save more?   **b)** How much more?

8. Education fund Steve and Michelle are parents of twins, Anna and Tanner. They plan to invest $5000 for each twin for their education in 18 years. Anna's money will be invested at 7%, compounded semi-annually. Tanner's will be invested at 7.5%, compounded semi-annually. How much more will Tanner have at age 18?

9. Buying a car In 5 years, Wendy plans to buy a car that she estimates will cost $20 000.
   a) How much does she need to invest today
      i) at 5%, compounded quarterly?   **ii)** at 6%, compounded quarterly?
   b) What effect does the 1% difference in interest rates have?

10. Application On June 1, Gage had $5000 in a savings account earning 3% simple interest, calculated daily and paid monthly. How much will be in his account on August 31 in each case?
   a) He makes no withdrawals or deposits.
   b) He makes no withdrawals but deposits $100 at the end of each month.

Did You Know?

Account fees and interest rates for savings accounts vary considerably from institution to institution. Choosing the right account can make a significant difference in the growth of your savings.

11. Communication Create and solve a problem that shows that doubling the compound interest rate of an investment, and then, dividing its term length in half does not result in the same final amount.

12. Inquiry Financial institutions, such as banks and trust companies, offer a variety of savings accounts.

a) Contact an institution or go to *www.school.mcgrawhill.ca/resources/* and follow the links to research information such as the following, for a youth account and a regular savings account:
- the rate and type of interest
- the balance required
- the account fees
- the number of free transactions and cost of additional transactions

b) Why do you think some accounts earn higher interest rates?

c) Is there an advantage to a youth account? Explain.

d) Why do you think banks offer youth accounts?

*C***ASE STUDY**

13. Recall Krysta and her savings of $2400, as described on page 121.

a) What advice would you give her about the effect of interest rates?

b) Until she makes a decision about what to do with her savings, she will keep her money in a savings account earning 5% simple interest, calculated daily and paid at the end of each month. How much interest will she earn if she takes each amount of time to make a decision, starting on May 1?

i) 1 month   **ii)** 2 months   **iii)** 3 months

C 14. College investment Hitesh's grandmother gave him $7000. He plans to invest some of it to help pay for college in 3 years. He estimates he will need $5000.

a) How much will he need to invest today at 6%, compounded quarterly?

b) How much less will he need to invest at 8%, compounded quarterly?

15. Retirement Dora wants to retire with $500 000. If her savings earn 10%, compounded quarterly, she can retire in 21 years. If they earn 7%, compounded quarterly, she can retire in 30 years. Estimate how much she has in savings today.

EXTEND THE CONCEPTS

16. Doubling amounts Describe an investment that has a final amount that is approximately double that of $1000 at 6%, compounded annually, for 5 years, by making each change.

a) Change only the interest rate.

b) Change only the interest rate and term.

c) Change everything but the principal.

4.2 | Effect of Compounding Frequency

Dean has some money that he wants to save in a guaranteed investment certificate (GIC). He called his local trust company to research interest rates. He found three GICs with the same interest rate, but different compounding frequencies. Dean figures that it will not matter which GIC he chooses because the interest rates are the same. Is he right?

DISCOVER

What Effect Does Compounding Frequency Have?

1. This table compares three GICs with the same interest rate but different compounding frequencies.
   a) Describe and compare the compounding frequencies.
   b) Copy and complete the table.

$P at 6%, compounded annually, for 5 years is $A

Now   6%   5 years

P   A

$P at 6%, compounded semi-annually, for 5 years is $A

Now   6%   5 years

P   A

$P at 6%, compounded quarterly, for 5 years is $A

Now   6%   5 years

P   A

	Final Amount After 5 Years		
Principal ($)	GIC A at 6%, compounded annually: $A = P(1 + 0.06)^5$	GIC B at 6%, compounded semi-annually: $A = P(1 + 0.03)^{10}$	GIC C at 6%, compounded quarterly: $A = P(1 + 0.015)^{20}$
100.00	133.82		
1 000.00			
10 000.00			

2. What effect does more frequent compounding have?

3. Which GIC would you choose? Why?

4. a) Estimate the final amount of $10 000 invested at 6%, compounded monthly.
   b) Explain your estimate. Then, calculate to check.

EXAMPLE 1

Compounding Frequencies and Final Amount

Nikko has a choice of saving $1500 for 3 years at 8%, compounded annually, or at 8%, compounded semi-annually. Which should she choose and why?

Solution

Draw time line diagrams to organize the information:

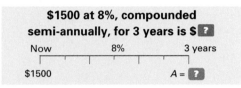

$1500 at 8%, compounded annually, for 3 years is $?

Now	8%	3 years

$1500 $A = ?$

$1500 at 8%, compounded semi-annually, for 3 years is $?

Now	8%	3 years

$1500 $A = ?$

Use the formula, $A = P(1 + i)^n$.
Determine the values of the variables:

$A = ?$ $A = ?$

$P = 1500$ $P = 1500$

$i = 0.08$ 0.08 every 1 year $i = 0.04$ 0.08 every $\frac{1}{2}$ year

$n = 3$ 1 time/year for 3 years $n = 6$ 2 times/year for 3 years

Use the formula:

$A = P(1 + i)^n$ $A = P(1 + i)^n$

$A = 1500(1.08)^3$ $A = 1500(1.04)^6$

$A \doteq 1889.57$ $A \doteq 1897.98$

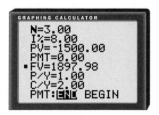

Alternatively, a finance application of a graphing calculator could be used to find the final amounts. (See page 413 in the Technology Appendix).

Nikko should save at 8%, compounded semi-annually, because this results in a greater final amount for the same principal and term.

EXAMPLE 2	**Interest Rates, Compounding Frequencies, and Final Amount**

Sharon has $3000. She can choose a 2-year GIC at 6%, compounded monthly, or a 2-year GIC at 6.5%, compounded semi-annually. Which will earn more interest? How much more?

Solution
Draw time line diagrams:

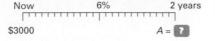

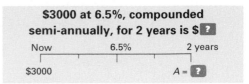

Use the formula, $A = P(1 + i)^n$.
Determine the values of the variables:

$A = $?
$P = 3000$
$i = 0.005$ 0.06 every $\frac{1}{12}$ year
$n = 24$ 12 times/year for 2 years

$A = $?
$P = 3000$
$i = 0.0325$ 0.065% every $\frac{1}{2}$ year
$n = 4$ 2 times/year for 2 years

Use the formula:

$A = P(1 + i)^n$
$A = 3000(1.005)^{24}$
$A \doteq 3381.48$

$A = P(1 + i)^n$
$A = 3000(1.0325)^4$
$A \doteq 3409.43$

Calculate the difference between the final amounts:
$3409.43 - 3381.48 = 27.95$

The GIC at 6.5%, compounded semi-annually, will earn $27.95 more in interest than the GIC at 6%, compounded monthly.

EXAMPLE 3	**Interest Rates, Compounding Frequencies, and Present Value**

Dhari wants to have $7000 in 4 years to buy a car. He has seen ads for two 4-year GICs with the following interest rates and compounding frequencies:
• interest rate of 6%, compounded annually
• interest rate of 5.6%, compounded quarterly
Which will require a smaller principal? How much less?

Solution

Draw time line diagrams:

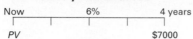

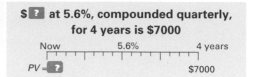

Use the formula, $PV = A(1 + i)^{-n}$.

Determine the values of the variables:

$PV = $ ❓	
$A = 7000$	
$i = 0.06$	0.06 every 1 year
$n = 4$	1 time/year for 4 years

$PV = $ ❓	
$A = 7000$	
$i = 0.014$	0.056 every $\frac{1}{4}$ year
$n = 16$	4 times/year for 4 years

Use the formula:

$$PV = A(1 + i)^{-n}$$
$$PV = 7000(1.06)^{-4}$$
$$PV \doteq 5544.66$$

$$PV = A(1 + i)^{-n}$$
$$PV = 7000(1.014)^{-16}$$
$$PV \doteq 5603.90$$

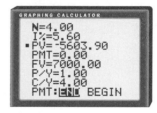

Calculate the difference between the present values:
5603.90 − 5544.66 = 59.24

The GIC at 6%, compounded annually, requires a principal that is $59.24 less than the GIC at 5.6%, compounded quarterly.

Alternatively, a finance application of a graphing calculator could be used to find the principals, or present values. (See page 413 in the Technology Appendix.)

EXAMPLE 4

Compare Savings Alternatives

The Neighbourhood Bank offers two savings alternatives:
- a 180-day GIC earning 4.3% simple interest, calculated daily and paid at term end
- a 1-year term deposit earning 4.35% simple interest

Both investments are only cashable at maturity, or at the end of the term.

a) Which investment will earn more interest in 1 year? Explain.

b) Why might someone choose the savings alternative that earns less interest?

Solution

a)

180-Day GIC for Two 180-Day Terms	1-Year Term Deposit
Use the annual interest rate to calculate the daily interest rate: $0.043 \div 365$	

Use a principal of $10 000 to compare the investments:

180-Day GIC for Two 180-Day Terms	1-Year Term Deposit
Use the simple interest formula to calculate the interest for the first term:	Use the simple interest formula to calculate the interest for the term:
$I = Prt$	$I = Prt$
$I = 10\ 000 \times (0.043 \div 365) \times 180$	$I = 10\ 000 \times 0.0435 \times 1$
$I \doteq 212.05$	$I \doteq 435.00$
Calculate the amount at the end of the first term:	Calculate the amount at the end of the term:
$A = P + I$	$A = P + I$
$A = 10\ 000.00 + 212.05$	$A = 10\ 000.00 + 435.00$
$A = 10\ 212.05$	$A = 10\ 435.00$

Re-invest the final amount for a second term.

Calculate the interest earned in the second term:

$I = Prt$

$I = 10\ 212.05 \times (0.043 \div 365) \times 180$

$I \doteq 216.55$

Calculate the amount at the end of the second term:

$A = P + I$

$A = 10\ 212.05 + 216.55$

$A = 10\ 428.60$

At the end of 360 days, the investment would be worth $10 428.60.	At the end of 365 days, the investment would be worth $10 435.00

The 1-year term deposit will earn more interest than the 180-day GIC invested for two terms.

b) Someone might choose the GIC even though it earns less interest because the money would be available after 180 days, while the term deposit might not be cashable until the end of 1 year.

KEY CONCEPTS

- Compounding frequency affects the final amount and the present value:
  The more frequent the compounding, the greater the final amount.
  The more frequent the compounding, the smaller the present value, or principal required.

- Risk-free savings alternatives, such as savings accounts, GICs, and term deposits, have different features, such as the type of interest earned, interest rate, compounding frequency, term, minimum investment, and cashing restrictions.

DISCUSS THE CONCEPTS

1. Explain why increasing the compounding frequency results in a greater final amount.

2. Make up an example to show that more frequent compounding requires a smaller principal.

3. You have three savings alternatives to choose from. What questions should you ask before choosing?

PRACTISE

A 1. For each investment,
   i) identify the compounding frequency
   ii) sketch a time line diagram
   iii) calculate the final amount or present value
   a) $1000 at 5.7%, compounded annually, for 5 years is $?
   b) $500 at 3%, compounded semi-annually, for 2 years is $?
   c) $? at 8%, compounded quarterly, in 10 years is $10 000
   d) $? at 6%, compounded monthly, in 5 years is $15 000

APPLY THE CONCEPTS

2. **Predicting** Rick has a choice of saving $2000 at 8%, compounded quarterly, or at 8%, compounded semi-annually. Both investments are for 5 years.
   a) Predict which will result in a greater final amount. Explain.
   b) Calculate to check.

3. **Final amount** Shara invested $6000 at 10%, compounded semi-annually, for 15 years. Her friend, Kara, invested at 12%, compounded annually. Which will result in a greater final amount? How much greater?

4. Present value Matt needs $1000 in 2 years. How much less can he invest today at 8%, compounded semi-annually, compared to 8%, compounded annually?

B 5. Savings Martine has $3800 to invest for 7 years. How much more will she have if she invests at 12%, compounded monthly, instead of 12%, compounded semi-annually?

6. Savings How much less will Theresa have in 6 years if she invests $5000 at 8%, compounded semi-annually, instead of at 8%, compounded monthly?

7. Thinking Kali invested $10 000 at 10%, compounded semi-annually, for 10 years. Her friend, Connor, invested the same principal for the same length of time but at 12%, compounded annually.
a) It is difficult to know which will have the greater final amount without calculating. Explain.
b) Make a prediction, and then, calculate to check.

Did You Know?

Sawbuck is slang for a 10-dollar bill. Fin is slang for a 5-dollar bill.

8. Application Farid would like to have $25 000 in 7 years for a down payment on a house. He has a choice of saving at 9%, compounded semi-annually, or at 8.75%, compounded monthly. Which choice will require a smaller principal? How much smaller?

9. Communication In order to see what happens when you increase the compounding frequency of an investment, the principal, interest rate, and term must stay the same. Explain why.

10. Communication Create and solve your own final amount or present value problem that shows the effect of more frequent compounding.

11. Inquiry Financial institutions offer a variety of savings alternatives that are guaranteed and have guaranteed or fixed interest rates, such as GICs and term deposits.
a) Visit a financial institution or go to *www.school.mcgrawhill.ca/resources/* and follow the links to research the following information for several different savings alternatives:
  • the term
  • the minimum balance required
  • the rate and type of interest earned
  • when they are cashable
b) Which alternative is better for savings of less than 1 year? Explain.
c) Which is better for long-term savings? Explain.

12. Recall Krysta and her savings, as described on page 121. She is ready to make a decision about what to do with her savings.

a) What advice could you give her about the effect of compounding frequency?

b) In question 11, you researched different savings alternatives. Which should she choose if she wants to save $2400 for 2 years? 3 years?

c) Explain your choices in part b).

d) Should she consider a combination of savings alternatives? Explain.

ACHIEVEMENT Check | Knowledge/Understanding | Thinking/Inquiry/Problem Solving | Communication | Application

13. Kamal has decided to invest his savings of $5000 for 2 years, starting on January 1, in the following portfolio:
- 20% in a savings account (5% simple interest, calculated daily, paid monthly)
- 50% in a 2-year GIC (6%, compounded annually)
- 30% in a 1-year term deposit (5.5% simple interest, paid at term end)

a) Why do you think he has chosen to save this way?

b) He makes no deposits to, or withdrawals from his savings account and he re-invests the final amount of the term deposit for a second term. How much will he have in his portfolio in 2 years?

c) Suggest a different combination of savings alternatives for Kamal's savings portfolio. Then, use current interest rates for savings accounts, GICs, and term deposits to calculate the value of this portfolio in 2 years.

d) Compare your savings portfolio with Kamal's original portfolio.

   i) Which made more money? Why?

   ii) What changes would you suggest to either portfolio to maximize the value? Explain each change.

EXTEND THE CONCEPTS

C **14.** **Doubling amounts** Describe an investment that has a present value that is approximately double the present value of an investment with a final amount of $5000, invested at 8%, compounded monthly, for 10 years, by making each change.

a) Change only the interest rate and compounding frequency.

b) Change everything but the final amount.

15. Go to *www.school.mcgrawhill.ca/resources/* and follow the links to investigate the role of the Canada Deposit Insurance Corporation (CDIC).

a) Write a brief report telling what you found out.

b) If you have more than $60 000 to invest, what should you consider before deciding where to invest?

4.3 | Find the Interest Rate

Jocelyn has saved $1000 from baby-sitting. She wants to put her savings in a guaranteed investment certificate (GIC) for 1 year. She has the choice of three GICs. Each GIC will result in the same final amount. However, the money compounds quarterly in GIC A, semi-annually in GIC B, and annually in GIC C. How do the interest rates of the three GICs compare?

DISCOVER

Relate Interest Rate and Compounding Frequency

Three GICs have different interest rates and compounding frequencies for the same term:

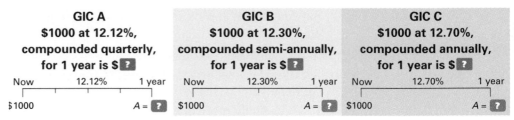

GIC A
$1000 at 12.12%, compounded quarterly, for 1 year is $?

Now   12.12%   1 year

$1000   A = ?

GIC B
$1000 at 12.30%, compounded semi-annually, for 1 year is $?

Now   12.30%   1 year

$1000   A = ?

GIC C
$1000 at 12.70%, compounded annually, for 1 year is $?

Now   12.70%   1 year

$1000   A = ?

1. Describe and compare the compounding frequencies of the three GICs.

2. Copy and complete the table to compare the GICs.

	Principal, P ($)	Interest Rate (%)	Compounding Periods/Year	$A = P(1 + i)^n$	Final Amount, A, rounded to the nearest dollar ($)
GIC A	1000	12.12	4	$A = 1000(1.0303)^4$	1127
GIC B	1000	12.30	2		
GIC C	1000	12.70	1		

3. What do you notice about the values in each column?
   a) Final Amount   **b)** Interest Rate   **c)** Compounding Periods/Year

4. a) What is the relationship between the annual interest rate and the compounding frequency?
   b) A GIC grows from $1000 to $1127 in 1 year with monthly compounding. Will the interest rate be higher than 12.70% or lower than 12.12%? Explain.

Determine Interest Rate

What rate of interest, compounded quarterly, will double a principal of $7000 in 5 years?

Solution

Draw a time line diagram to organize the information:

$7000 at ? %, compounded quarterly, for 5 years is $14 000

Now   ? %   5 years

$7000 $14 000

See page 405 in the Technology Appendix for specific spreadsheet instructions.

Method 1: Use trial and error and a spreadsheet

To prepare the spreadsheet:

Step 1: Enter the column heads in cells A1, B1, C1, D1, and E1, as shown below. Adjust the column widths so the heads will fit across.

Step 2: Format columns A, C, D, and E to **0** decimal places and column B to **4** decimal places.

Step 3: Enter the principal, **7000**, in cell A2.

Step 4: Enter the number of compounding periods, **20**, in cell C2.
(5 years with compounding 4 times a year is 20 compounding periods.)

Step 5: Enter the compound interest formula, $A = P(1 + i)^n$, in cell D2, as the formula **=A2*(1+B2/100)^C2**.

Step 6: Enter the formula **=D2–14000** in cell E2.

	A	B	C	D	E
1	Principal $	Interest Rate % (*i*)	Compounding Periods (*n*)	Final Amount $	Difference $
2	7000		20	7000	-7000
3					
4					
5					
6					
7					
8					
9					
10					

Step 7: Copy cell contents:
- Copy the contents of cell A2 into cells A3 to A10.
- Copy the contents of cell C2 into cells C3 to C10.
- Copy the contents of cell D2 into cells D3 to D10.
- Copy the contents of cell E2 into cells E3 to E10.

To try different interest rates:

Step 8: Enter an estimated interest rate per compounding period in cell B2.
For an annual interest rate of 12%, compounded 4 times a year, enter **3**.
Then, press (ENTER):

	A	B	C	D	E
1	Principal $	Interest Rate % (*i*)	Compounding Periods (*n*)	Final Amount $	Difference $
2	7000	3.0000	20	12643	-1357
3	7000		20	7000	-7000
4	7000		20	7000	-7000
5	7000		20	7000	-7000
6	7000		20	7000	-7000
7	7000		20	7000	-7000
8	7000		20	7000	-7000
9	7000		20	7000	-7000
10	7000		20	7000	-7000

$12 643 is $1357 less than $14 000—an interest rate of 3% per quarter is too low.

Step 9: Try an interest rate of 4% per quarter:

	A	B	C	D	E
1	Principal $	Interest Rate % (*i*)	Compounding Periods (*n*)	Final Amount $	Difference $
2	7000	3.0000	20	12643	-1357
3	7000	4.0000	20	15338	1338
4	7000		20	7000	-7000
5	7000		20	7000	-7000
6	7000		20	7000	-7000
7	7000		20	7000	-7000
8	7000		20	7000	-7000
9	7000		20	7000	-7000
10	7000		20	7000	-7000

$15 338 is $1338 greater than $14 000—an interest rate of 4% per quarter is too high.

Step 10: Try different interest rates until the final amount is $14 000:

	A	B	C	D	E
1	Principal $	Interest Rate % (*i*)	Compounding Periods (*n*)	Final Amount $	Difference $
2	7000	3.0000	20	12643	-1357
3	7000	4.0000	20	15338	1338
4	7000	3.5000	20	13929	-71
5	7000	3.6000	20	14200	200
6	7000	3.5200	20	13982	-18
7	7000	3.5250	20	13996	-4
8	7000	3.5260	20	13999	-1
9	7000	3.5263	20	13999	-1
10	7000	3.5264	20	14000	0

An interest rate of 3.5264% per quarter results in a final amount of $14 000.

To determine the annual interest rate:

Step 11: Change the interest rate per compounding period to an annual rate,
and then, round to two decimal places:
3.5264% × 4 = 14.1056%
3.5264% per quarter is an annual interest rate of 14.11%

A principal of $7000, at an interest rate of 14.11%, compounded quarterly,
will double in value in 5 years.

Method 2: Use a finance application on a graphing calculator

Step 1: Press (MODE) and set the number of decimal places to **2**:

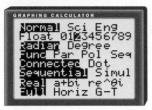

Step 2: Press (APPS) 1 1 to open the **TVM Solver**:

The **TVM Solver** is a finance application that can be used to calculate the Time Value of Money (**TVM**). See page 412 of the Technology Appendix for more details on the **TVM Solver**.

Step 3: Enter the values of the variables as shown below:

What the variables represent:

N (Number of Years)

I% (Annual Interest Rate)

PV (Present Value, or Principal)

PMT (Payment)

FV (Future Value, or Final Amount)

P/Y (Number of Payments/Year)

C/Y (Number of Compounding Periods/Year)

PMT: END BEGIN (Payments at End/Beginning of Payment Interval)

PMT, P/Y, and PMT: END BEGIN are set as follows because there are no regular payments:
PMT=0.00
P/Y=1.00
PMT: END or BEGIN

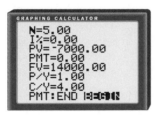

N=**5.00** because the investment is for 5 years.

I%=**0.00** because it is the variable to be solved for.

PV is negative, **−7000.00**, because the principal is money paid out.

FV=**14000.00**, the final amount.

C/Y=**4.00** because compounding is 4 times/year.

Step 4: Cursor to **I%=0.00**, and then, press (ALPHA)(ENTER) to solve for **I%**.

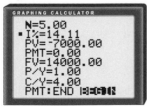

A principal of $7000, at an interest rate of 14.11%, compounded quarterly, will double in value in 5 years.

DISCUSS THE CONCEPTS

1. Suppose you did not have spreadsheet software or a graphing calculator. How could you use a scientific calculator to find the interest rate?

2. If you use a spreadsheet, finding the interest rate of Savings Alternative B requires one more step than for Savings Alternative A:
   A: $6000 at ❓% , compounded annually, grows to $12 000 in 5 years
   B: $6000 at ❓%, compounded semi-annually, grows to $12 000 in 5 years
   a) Describe the extra step.
   b) Why is the extra step necessary?
   c) Which has the higher interest rate? Explain how you know.

PRACTISE

A *Round all interest rates to two decimal places, if necessary.*

1. Copy and complete the table.

	Principal ($)	Final Amount ($)	Term (years)	Compounding	Annual Interest Rate (%)
a)	3 000	5 000	7	annual	
b)	6 500	13 000	10	annual	
c)	1 500	4 650	8	annual	
d)	900	1 200	10	annual	
e)	4 280	6 000	6	semi-annual	
f)	400	750	9	quarterly	
g)	100	200	8	monthly	
h)	4 560	9 120	9.5	semi-annual	

APPLY THE CONCEPTS

2. **Annual compounding** Maureen has $4320 today and needs $6500 in 9 years.
   a) What interest rate, compounded annually, does she need?
   b) If the compounding was monthly, would the interest rate be higher or lower? Explain.

3. **Semi-annual compounding**
   a) What interest rate, compounded semi-annually, is necessary for $5400 to grow to $6500 in 6 years?
   b) If the compounding was annual, would the interest rate be higher or lower? Explain.

B 4. What interest rate, compounded quarterly, is necessary for $1750 to grow to $2500 in 5 years?

5. **Cash gift** Julie's grandmother gave her a birthday gift of $500. What interest rate, compounded monthly, would she need to make $500 grow to $1000 in 10 years?

6. **Double your money** Dave wants his current savings of $250 to double in 8 years. What interest rate, compounded semi-annually, will he need to achieve his goal?

7. **Application** Trish's savings of $3500 grew to $6000 in 8 years.
   a) What interest rate did she earn if the compounding was
      i) annual?   ii) semi-annual?
      iii) quarterly?   iv) monthly?
   b) What do you notice about the four interest rates in part a)? Explain.

8. **Number sense** Trudy does not have a computer or graphing calculator. She is using trial and error and a scientific calculator to determine the interest rate, compounded annually, required for $15 000 to grow to $20 000 in 5 years.
   Here is her work so far:
   Try 4%: $15\,000(1.04)^5 \doteq 18\,249.79$
   too low
   Try 8%: $15\,000(1.08)^5 \doteq 22\,039.93$
   too high
   a) What interest rate should she try next? Why?
   b) Finish her work. List the interest rates you tried in the order you tried them.
   c) What is the interest rate?

9. **Thinking** $10 000 grew to $13 000 in 10 years at 2.64%, compounded semi-annually.
   a) Without calculating, estimate the interest rate required if the interest had been compounded
      i) annually
      ii) quarterly
   b) Explain your estimate in each case in part a).

CASE **STUDY**

10. Recall Krysta and her goal of attending college, as described on page 121. She has $2400 today and wants to have at least $4800 when she goes to college in 2 or 3 years.
    a) What interest rate will she need in order for $2400 to grow to $4800 in 2 years, if it is compounded
       i) monthly?
       ii) quarterly?
       iii) semi-annually?
       iv) annually?
    b) In question 11 on page 136, you researched interest rates for savings alternatives, such as GICs and term deposits. Based on current interest rates, is Krysta's goal realistic? Explain.
    c) Is 3 years a more realistic term? Explain.
    d) What is a more realistic final amount for a 3-year term?

EXTEND THE CONCEPTS

C 11. **Rule of 72** The following method can be used to estimate the interest rate required to double a principal in a given number of years:

$72 \div$ number of years = interest rate

Example:

For $500 to double to $1000 at ?%, compounded quarterly, in 3 years:

$72 \div 3$ years = 24%

Check: $500(1.06)^{12} = \$1006.10$

a) Estimate the interest rate.
   i) $1000 at ?%, compounded annually, for 8 years is $2000
   ii) $1500 at ?%, compounded semi-annually, for 5 years is $3000
   iii) $15 000 at ?%, compounded quarterly, for 4 years is $30 000
b) Use the estimated interest rate to calculate the final amount for each investment in part a). How close were you in each case?
c) Now, find the actual interest rates using a spreadsheet or graphing calculator.

Dan has just graduated from college and has a job. He wants to buy his own home as soon as possible. His grandmother gave him a graduation gift of $15 000 but he needs at least $25 000 for a down payment. If he chooses a guaranteed investment certificate (GIC) earning 6%, compounded semi-annually, what will the term of the GIC have to be?

Recall that you can use trial and error and a spreadsheet, or a graphing calculator to find the interest rate, if you know the principal, compounding frequency, term, and final amount. You can also use these methods to find the term, if you know the principal, interest rate, compounding frequency, and final amount.

EXAMPLE

Determine the Term

How many years will it take $15 000 to grow to $25 000 at 6%, compounded semi-annually?

Solution

Draw a time line diagram to organize the information:

$15 000 at 6%, compounded semi-annually, for [?] years is $25 000

Now   6%   [?] years
semi-annual compounding
$15 000 $25 000

Method 1: Use trial and error and a spreadsheet

To prepare the spreadsheet:

Step 1: Enter the column heads in cells A1, B1, C1, D1, and E1, as shown on page 146. Adjust the column widths so the heads will fit across.

Step 2: Format columns A, D, and E to **0** decimal places, column B to **2** decimal places, and column C to **4** decimal places.

See page 405 in the Technology Appendix for specific spreadsheet instructions.

Step 3: Enter the principal, **15000**, in cell A2.

	A	B	C	D	E
1	Principal $	Interest Rate % (*i*)	Compounding Periods (*n*)	Final Amount $	Difference $
2	15000				
3					

Step 4: Enter the interest rate per compounding period, **3**, in cell B2.
(6%, compounded 2 times a year, is 3%.)

Step 5: Enter the compound interest formula, $A = P(1 + i)^n$, in cell D2, as the formula =**A2*(1+B2/100)^C2**.

Step 6: Enter the formula =**D2–25000** in cell E2.

Step 7: Copy the contents of cell A2 into cells A3 to A10, of cell B2 into cells B3 to B10, of cell D2 into cells D3 to D10, and finally, of cell E2 into cells E3 to E10.

To try different numbers of compounding periods:
Step 8: Enter an estimated number of compounding periods in cell C2. For 8 years with compounding 2 times a year, enter **16**. Then, press [ENTER]:

	A	B	C	D	E
1	Principal $	Interest Rate % (*i*)	Compounding Periods (*n*)	Final Amount $	Difference $
2	15000	3.00	16.0000	24071	-929
3	15000	3.00		15000	-10000
4	15000	3.00		15000	-10000
5	15000	3.00		15000	-10000
6	15000	3.00		15000	-10000
7	15000	3.00		15000	-10000
8	15000	3.00		15000	-10000
9	15000	3.00		15000	-10000
10	15000	3.00		15000	-10000

$24 071 is $929 less than $25 000—16 compounding periods is not long enough.

Step 9: Try different compounding periods until the final amount is $25 000:

	A	B	C	D	E
1	Principal $	Interest Rate % (*i*)	Compounding Periods (*n*)	Final Amount $	Difference $
2	15000	3.00	16.0000	24071	-929
3	15000	3.00	20.0000	27092	2092
4	15000	3.00	17.0000	24793	-207
5	15000	3.00	17.1000	24866	-134
6	15000	3.00	17.2000	24940	-60
7	15000	3.00	17.3000	25014	14
8	15000	3.00	17.2900	25006	6
9	15000	3.00	17.2800	24999	-1
10	15000	3.00	17.2810	25000	0

17.281 compounding periods results in a final amount of $25 000.

To determine the number of years:
Step 10: Round up to the next compounding period, and then, change compounding periods to years:
17.281 compounding periods rounds up to 18 compounding periods.
18 compounding periods at 2/year is 9 years.

$15 000 will grow to $25 000 at 6%, compounded semi-annually, in 9 years.

See pages 141 in the previous section and page 412 in the Technology Appendix for more details about the **TVM Solver**.

Method 2: Use a finance application on a graphing calculator

Open the **TVM Solver** and enter the values of the variables as shown:

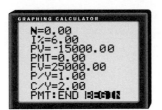

N=0.00 because that is the variable to be solved for.
I%=6.00 because 6% is the annual interest rate.
PV is negative, **−15000.00**, because principal is money that is paid out.
FV=25000.00, the final amount.
C/Y=2.00 because compounding is 2 times/year

Cursor to **N=0.00**, and then, press (ALPHA)(ENTER) to solve for **N**:

Round up to the next compounding period.
For semi-annual compounding, round to the next half year:
8.64 years rounds to 9 years.

$15 000 will grow to $25 000 at 6%, compounded semi-annually, in 9 years.

Now   6%   9 years
$15 000 $25 000

KEY CONCEPTS

- The term, or length of time, of an investment can be found, if you know the principal, interest rate, compounding frequency, and final amount.

- A spreadsheet or a graphing calculator can be used to find the term.

DISCUSS THE CONCEPTS

1. Describe the steps you would follow to find the term required for $50 000 to grow to $75 000 at 8%, compounded semi-annually.

2. Why do you think it is advisable to round up to the next compounding period to find the term?

A **1.** **a)** Round up to the next compounding period. Express in years and months.

   i) 4.35 annual compounding periods

   ii) 6.22 semi-annual compounding periods

   iii) 12.34 quarterly compounding periods

   iv) 15.36 monthly compounding periods

b) Round up to the next compounding period.

   i) 6.25 years, annual compounding

   ii) 3.43 years, semi-annual compounding

   iii) 5.22 years, quarterly compounding

   iv) 6.05 years, monthly compounding

2. Copy and complete the table. Express terms in years and months.

	Principal ($)	Final Amount ($)	Term	Compounding	Interest Rate (%)
a)	3 000	5 000		annual	8
b)	6 500	13 000		annual	7.5
c)	1 550	4 650		annual	6.75
d)	900	12 000		annual	7
e)	4 280	6 000		semi-annual	5
f)	400	750		quarterly	8
g)	100	200		monthly	6
h)	4 560	9 120		semi-annual	9

3. **Annual compounding** What term will allow $5400 to grow to $6500 at $6\frac{1}{2}$%, compounded annually?

4. **Semi-annual compounding** Phillipi has $8320 today. He wants to have $12 500 to pay for college.

   a) How long will he have to save his money at 10.5%, compounded semi-annually?

   b) Copy and complete the time line diagram for Phillipi's savings.

   $** **?** at **?** %, compounded **?**, for **?** years is **$ **?**

   Now   10.5%   **?** years

   semi-annual compounding

   $8320 $12 500

B **5.** **Debt** Sandro needs $8500 as soon as possible to pay off a debt. He invests $4200 today at 6.5% interest, compounded quarterly. How long will it take to grow to $8500?

6. **Savings** Henna's goal is for her savings of $3500 to grow to $6000 at 7.75%, compounded monthly. How long will it take for Henna to achieve her goal?

7. Double your money How long will it take $250 to double in value at 8%, compounded quarterly?

8. Communication At 10%, compounded annually, how long would it take for $3000 to
   a) double in value?
   b) triple in value?
   c) quadruple in value?

9. Down payment Larry plans to buy his first house in 15 years. He estimates that he will need $25 000. He invested $11 550 today at 7%, compounded semi-annually. Will he accomplish his goal? Explain.

10. Application $3500 grew to $6000 at an interest rate of 8%.
   a) What was the term, if the compounding was
      i) annual?   **ii)** semi-annual?   **iii)** quarterly?
   b) What do you notice about your answers for part a)?

11. Number sense Lana does not have a computer or graphing calculator. She has to use trial and error and a scientific calculator to determine the term required for $20 000 to grow to $30 000 at 9%, compounded semi-annually. *Here is her work so far:*
   Try 5 years, or 10 compounding periods: $20\ 000(1.045)^{10} \doteq 31\ 059.39$ *too high*
   Try 4 years, or 8 compounding periods: $20\ 000(1.045)^{8} \doteq 28\ 442.01$ *too low*
   a) What number of compounding periods should she try next? Why?
   b) Finish her work. List the numbers of compounding periods you tried in the order that you tried them.
   c) What is the term?

12. Thinking $1000 grew to $1338 at 6%, compounded annually, in 5 years.
   a) Without calculating, decide whether the following is true or false:
      If the compounding had been semi-annual, it would have taken longer than 5 years.
   b) Explain how you know whether it is true or false.

13. Thinking $20 000 grew to $25 000 in 3.5 years at 7.5%, compounded semi-annually.
   a) Without calculating, estimate the time required if compounding had been
      i) annual   **ii)** quarterly
   b) Explain your estimates in part a).

14. Problem Solving Harpreet invested $4000 at 6%, compounded quarterly, 3 years ago. This investment will mature in 2 years. She has another $2000 to invest today at 5%, compounded annually. Her goal is to have $10 000 in 2 years. Is her goal realistic? Explain.

15. Mitch needs financial advice. He wants his savings of $2500 to double in 10 years or less. What advice would you give Mitch about a realistic interest rate, compounding frequency, and term for his savings?

C **16. Multiple investments** Truphena has $2000. One year from now, she will have an additional $1500. Five years from now, she will have another $4000. Truphena's goal is to have $25 000 within 10 years. Write a letter to Truphena that provides details about what interest rates she will need and the length of time it will take.

EXTEND THE CONCEPTS

17. Multiple answers
a) Copy and complete the following:
   $1000 at **?** %, compounded semi-annually, for **?** years is $5000
b) Find more than one answer.

18. Rule of 72 The following method is often used to estimate the term, in years, required for a principal to double in value at a given annual interest rate:
72 ÷ annual interest rate = number of years
Example:
For $1000 to double to $2000 at 14%, compounded semi-annually, in **?** years:
$72 \div 14 \doteq 5$ years
Check: $1000(1.07)^{10} = \$1967.15$
a) Estimate the term.
   i) $2000 at 10%, compounded annually, for **?** years is $4000
   ii) $500 at 8%, compounded semi-annually, for **?** years is $1000
   iii) $10 000 at 4%, compounded quarterly, for **?** years is $20 000
b) Use the estimated term to calculate the final amount for each investment in part a). How close were you in each case?
c) Now, find the actual terms.

19. Triple your money The Rule of 72 is used to estimate the required term to double your money. Investigate the possibility of a similar rule for tripling your money.

4.5 | Savings and Investment Alternatives

Members of a high school investment club are investing an imaginary $10 000. They have a risk tolerance questionnaire that has been completed by their imaginary client to help them make investment decisions.

EXAMPLE 1

Risk Tolerance Questionnaire

The investment club members have been challenged to create an imaginary $10 000 investment portfolio. Before they can decide how to invest the money, they must find out how much risk their client is willing to take. How can they do this?

Solution

One way to assess how much risk an investor is comfortable with is by asking questions such as the ones in this Risk Tolerance Questionnaire:

Risk Tolerance Questionnaire

1. For how many years are you investing?
   - <3: 4 points
   - 3–10: 8 points ✓
   - >10: 12 points   8

2. What is your purpose?
   - savings: 3 points
   - savings/investment: 7 points ✓
   - investment: 13 points   7

3. How much risk are you comfortable with?
   - no to some risk: 2 points
   - moderate risk: 7 points ✓
   - moderate to high risk: 12 points   7

4. What is your personal financial situation?
   - not secure, in debt or just meeting expenses: –5 points
   - secure, some money to invest: 1 points ✓
   - very secure, extra money to invest: 3 points   1

5. What knowledge do you have about investments?
   - no to basic knowledge: –3 points ✓
   - knowledgeable: 0 points
   - expert: 3 points   –3

Total Points: 20

The club has decided that the portfolio will have
- 20%, or $2000, in savings/low-risk investments
- 70%, or $7000, in moderate-risk investments
- 10%, or $1000, in high-risk investments

Recommendation for Investment Portfolio

<20 points:	100% in savings/low-risk investments
20–30 points:	5% to 20% in savings/low-risk investments 60% to 80% in moderate-risk investments 35% to 0% in higher-risk investments
31–45 points:	0% to 5% in savings/low-risk investments 40% to 50% in moderate-risk investments 60% to 45% in higher-risk investments

EXAMPLE 2

Bonds

The investment club is looking into buying a $2000 bond for the savings/low-risk investment portion of their client's portfolio.

a) What are bonds?

b) What kind of return can the club expect?

c) What is the level of risk?

d) Should the club choose bonds for the savings/low-risk portion of the portfolio?

Solution

a) If you purchase a bond, you are lending money to whoever issues the bond, for instance, the government or a corporation. An example is a $2000 government bond at 6.5%, simple interest, paid out annually, for 10 years. Once bonds are purchased, they can be held until maturity, earning income annually or semi-annually, or they can be sold for a profit or a loss.

b) *Case 1*: $2000 bond at 6.5%, simple interest, paid annually, held to maturity:

$I = Prt$ $\qquad\qquad$ $P = 2000, r = 0.065, t = 1$

$I = 2000(0.065)(1)$ $\quad$ Calculate the simple interest earned each year.

$I = 130$

$130 \times 10 = 1300$ $\qquad$ Calculate the interest earned over 10 years.

If the bond is held until maturity, $130 in interest will be earned each year for 10 years, or $1300 altogether.

Case 2: $2000 government bond sold before maturity:

If the interest rate of next year's government bonds is lower, for instance, 5.5%, a 6.5% bond will be more valuable and could possibly be sold for more than $2130, which is more than it would be worth after 1 year.

c) If the $2000 bond is held to maturity, there is no risk because it is guaranteed. If it is sold before maturity, there is some risk. If the interest rate of next year's bond is higher, for instance, 7.5%, then, the 6.5% bond will be worth less than $2000.

d) The club has decided not to invest in bonds for the following reasons:
- Bonds are usually bought and sold through a broker, which means fees.
- If a bond is held until maturity, the yearly interest would have to be re-invested because their client is not looking for regular income.
- If the bond must be sold, there is risk involved.

EXAMPLE 3

Canada Savings Bonds

The investment club plans to buy $2000 in 10-year compound interest Canada Savings Bonds (C-Bonds) for the savings/low-risk investment part of their client's portfolio.

a) Are C-Bonds a good savings/low-risk investment?

b) What is the rate of return?

c) How much will their investment be worth if it is held
  i) until maturity?
  ii) for 5 years, 3 months, and 26 days?

Solution

a) When you buy C-Bonds, you are lending money to the government. Canada Savings Bonds are a special kind of government bond. They are a good savings alternative because
- they are guaranteed
- they have a guaranteed rate of return
- there are no fees for buying or selling them
- they can be purchased at financial institutions
- they are cashable at any time
- investing in them requires very little investment knowledge

b) The rate of return for the 10-year C-bonds issued in 1996:

Year	1	2	3	4	5	6	7	8	9	10
Interest Rate (%)	3	4	5	6	6.5	6.75	7	7.25	8	8.75

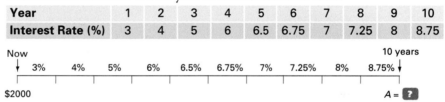

c) **i)** Use a special version of the compound interest formula,
$A = P(1 + i_1)(1 + i_2)(1 + i_3)(1 + i_4)\ldots$, where i_1 is the rate for year 1, i_2 for year 2, and so on.

Calculate the final amount at maturity, after 10 years:
$A = P(1 + i_1)(1 + i_2)(1 + i_3)(1 + i_4)(1 + i_5)(1 + i_6)(1 + i_7)(1 + i_8)(1 + i_9)(1 + i_{10})$
$A = 2000(1.03)(1.04)(1.05)(1.06)(1.065)(1.0675)(1.07)(1.0725)(1.08)(1.0875)$
$A = 3653.82$

If $2000 in C-bonds are kept until maturity, they will be worth $3653.82.

ii) C-Bonds pay compound interest for full years and simple interest for full months.

Calculate the final amount after 5 years:
$$A = P(1 + i_1)(1 + i_2)(1 + i_3)(1 + i_4)(1 + i_5)$$
$$A = 2000(1.03)(1.04)(1.05)(1.06)(1.065)$$
$$A = 2539.48$$

Calculate the simple interest earned in 3 months:

$$I = Prt \qquad\qquad P = 2539.48, \ r = 0.0675, \ t = \frac{3}{12}$$

$$I = (2539.48)(0.0675)\left(\frac{3}{12}\right)$$

$$I = 42.85$$

No interest is paid for the partial month of 26 days, so the value after 5 years, 3 months, and 26 days is $2539.48 + $42.85 = $2582.33.

EXAMPLE 4

Common Stocks

The investment club would like to invest $1000 in the stock market for the high-risk portion of their client's portfolio. They need answers to these questions before making a decision about investing in stocks and which stocks to buy:

a) What are common stocks?   **b)** What is the level of risk?

c) What is the rate of return?   **d)** How "liquid," or cashable, are stocks?

e) Are there any fees?   **f)** What investment knowledge is required?

g) How do you choose a stock?

Solution

a) Common stocks, or shares, represent ownership in a company. If a company has issued a total of 1000 shares, the investor owns $\frac{1}{1000}$ or 0.1% of the company for each share. The value of each share changes according to how well the company is doing and how the stock is trading.

b) Common stocks are risky because they are not guaranteed. Stocks from a large, well-managed, successful company (called "blue-chip" stocks) have relatively low to moderate risk. Stocks from a new, untested company or a company with an unpredictable performance are considered high risk.

c) If the company meets expectations, the rate of return will likely be high. If the company does not meet expectations, the return will likely be low. An investor makes money if stocks are sold at a greater value than the purchase price and loses money if they are sold at a lesser value. There is no guaranteed rate of return.

d) Common stocks can be sold on any business day through a stock exchange, such as the Toronto Stock Exchange (TSE).

e) If shares are bought or sold through a broker, fees are charged.

Electronic Stock Trading

f) Investing in stocks requires investment knowledge. The investor may sell and buy frequently, or hold the stocks for a long time, depending on the market.

g) You choose stocks by considering past and future performance and current price. For example, the following information compares last year's performance of two blue-chip and two new company stocks.

	In Last 52 Weeks			
	High Price/Share	Low Price/Share	Current Share Price	Future Outlook
Blue-Chip Stock A	23.10	21.67	21.90	steady growth
Blue-Chip Stock B	17.30	15.60	17.12	steady growth
New Company Stock A	130.00	10.60	15.50	promising
New Company Stock B	78.56	5.05	67.53	promising

The Club has decided to invest in one blue-chip and one new company stock:
- $800 in Blue-Chip Stock A because it is a relatively low-risk stock, its current price is low, and the future outlook is good.
- $200 in New Company Stock A because the current price is low and the company is expected to do well.

EXAMPLE 5

Mutual Funds

The investment club plans to invest $7000 in mutual funds, for the moderate-risk portion of the portfolio.

a) What should they know about mutual funds?

b) How can they choose mutual funds?

Solution

a) *What is a mutual fund?* A mutual fund is a "pool" of many investors' money. A fund manager decides how to invest the money. The fund manager invests in different investments, making mutual funds less risky than stocks. There are three main types:

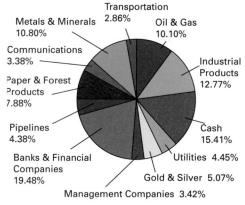

Sample Growth Mutual Fund

- low-risk mutual funds, which are invested in government and corporate bonds and in mortgages
- moderate-risk balanced mutual funds, which are invested in bonds and stocks
- high-risk growth mutual funds, which are invested in stocks (see graph above)

Where can they be purchased? Mutual funds can be purchased through brokers, financial institutions, and directly from the mutual fund manager.

What investment knowledge do you need? People often use a financial planner or a personal banking representative to help them choose, since there are over 3000 mutual funds in Canada. The fund managers handle the management of the funds.

Are there fees? Some funds charge a fee when you buy. Others charge when you sell. Some have no buying or selling fees. All charge a fund management fee.

b) You choose a mutual fund by considering its past performance, or rate of return, and predictions about its future. The following table compares three mutual funds:

Rate of Return Over Last 5 Years								
Savings Mutual Fund A			Balanced Mutual Fund B			Growth Mutual Fund C		
1 year	3 years	5 years	1 year	3 years	5 years	1 year	3 years	5 years
4.7%	4.4%	4.5%	15%	12%	13%	74%	9%	−0.9%
Future Outlook								
stable, no significant change			stable to moderate growth			promising but uncertain		

The club has decided to invest $6000 in Balanced Mutual Fund B and $1000 in Growth Mutual Fund C because overall, the risk will be moderate and the rate of return should be high.

KEY CONCEPTS

- Savings and investment alternatives are described by the answers to questions such as the following:

  What is the level of risk?   *What is the rate of return?*
  How cashable is it?   *Are there any fees?*
  What investment knowledge is required?   *Where can it be purchased?*

- Generally, the higher the potential rate of return, the more risk an investor is willing to take .

DISCUSS THE CONCEPTS

1. What is the difference between saving and investing?

2. Choose one of the savings or investment alternatives described in Examples 2 to 5. Describe it by answering the questions from the Key Concepts.

1. **C-Bonds** If an investor buys $1000 in compound interest Canada Savings Bonds (C-Bonds), how much will the investment be worth (see Example 3 on page 153 for interest rates) if they are
   a) held until maturity?　b) cashed after 7 years, 10 months, and 23 days?

2. **Savings alternatives** A 5-year guaranteed investment certificate (GIC) earns 5%, compounded annually, and is cashable once a year.
   a) Compare the final amounts of $1000 invested in the GIC and in a C-Bond held for 5 years (see Example 3 for interest rates).
   b) Which is the better savings alternative? Explain.

3. **Inquiry** Contact a financial institution or go to *www.school.mcgrawhill.ca/resources/* and follow the links to find out how these types of savings bonds compare to C-Bonds.
   a) regular interest Canada Savings Bonds (R-Bonds)
   b) Canada Premium Bonds (CPB)

4. **Stocks** Why do stock investors include different kinds of stocks in their portfolios, rather than invest in one type of stock?

5. **TSE 300** The graph shows the average stock price of the 300 largest companies on the TSE from 1975 to 2000.

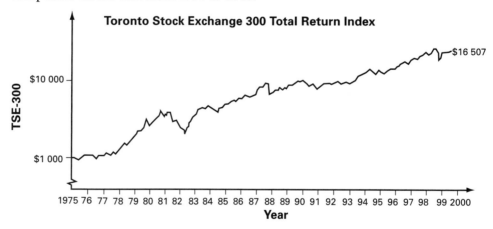

a) According to the graph, if $1000 worth of stocks were purchased in 1975, they could have been sold for $16 507 in 2000. If $1000 in stocks were purchased in 1981 and sold in each of these years, did the investor make money, break even, or lose money?
   i) 1982　　ii) 1983　　iii) 1984　　iv) 1990
b) Why are stocks considered a long-term investment?

6. **Inquiry** Research investment alternatives.

   a) Contact a financial institution or investment broker, visit your library, read the newspaper, or go to *www.school/mcgrawhill.ca/resources/* and follow the links to choose a bond, a mutual fund, and a common stock to investigate.

   b) Describe each investment, and then, answer the questions listed in the Key Concepts.

7. **Application** You are a junior financial planner and have three clients with the following Risk Tolerance scores (see Example 1):

   Client A: 15 points   Client B: 25 points   Client C: 35 points

   What types of savings alternatives and investments would you recommend for each client and why?

8. **Communication** Many investment words also have non-investment meanings. For example, "the *performance* of the mutual fund"; "the actor's *performance*." Choose four words from the list below. Write two sentences for each, one showing its investment meaning and another its other meaning:

tolerance	secure	aggressive	volatile
balance	maturity	bond	diversify
conservative	portfolio	outlook	share

For each situation in questions 9 to 11:

a) Make some general recommendations for savings and investment alternatives. Explain why you recommended each alternative.

b) List any additional information you would need to know before making any specific recommendations.

9. Grant is 22 years old. He finished college a year ago and has saved $5000 in the last year from his job. He plans to continue saving $5000 a year. He plans to buy a $20 000 car in 2 years using part of his savings. What should he do with the $5000 he has in savings now? What should he do with his future savings?

10. Fatima's grandmother has $80 000 in a savings account and receives a monthly pension. She needs additional income because her pension is not enough to meet her expenses. What should she do with the $80 000?

11. Tom is 30 years old and wants to start saving for retirement. He feels he can afford to save $100 a month and still meet his expenses. What should he do with his monthly savings?

Did You Know?

There are many slang investment terms related to animals. For example, bull and bear are used to describe the ups and downs of the stock market, and cats and dogs are speculative investments. Find out what dragons, cash cows, and lemmings are.

12. ABI A simple method for calculating the percent that could be invested in moderate- to high-risk investments is the Age Balance Indicator (ABI). The ABI is equal to 90 subtract the investor's age. For example, a 20-year-old investor should invest no more than 70% (90 – 20) in riskier investments. A 50-year-old should invest no more than 40% (90 – 50).

a) Using this method, the younger you are, the more risk you should take. Is this always true?

b) The ABI does not consider your current financial situation. What other factors are not considered?

13. Minimum investment Another factor that affects investment decisions is the minimum investment. For example, if a minimum of 100 shares must be purchased in a stock at $40 a share, this would be $4000. Find out if there is a minimum investment for the following:

GICs   term deposits   mutual funds   bonds

14. Inflation Many investors feel that safe, low-interest savings and investment alternatives actually lose money because of inflation. Explain what this means.

15. Taxes If money is invested in a registered retirement savings plan (RRSP) or a registered education savings plan (RESP), the money can grow without being taxed.

a) Why do you think the government lets investors make money without taxing them?

b) Find out what restrictions there are on investments in an RRSP.

c) Find out about the government's contribution to RESPs.

d) Explain what deferred tax means. How does it apply to RRSPs and RESPs?

16. Information related to the stock market is found each day in many newspapers.

a) Find out what each item means in this report.

b) Explain why an investor might be interested in each item.

The Markets

TSE 300 +144.03 to 9302.22
S&P/TSE 60 +9.74 to 553.92
CDNX +4.77 to 3219.38
DOW +42.21 to 10 702.19
NASDAQ +57.04 to 2838.34
DOLLAR +0.18¢ (U.S) to 66.60¢
$1 (U.S.) costs $1.5015
GOLD $262.80 (U.S.), $397.50 (Cdn)
OIL –71¢ (U.S.) to $29.06 in New York

CAREER PROFILE

Junior Financial Analyst or Planner

The world of finance is a mystery to many people. It is complicated because of the many choices available. This is why many people turn to financial experts, such as accountants, tax lawyers, and financial planners and analysts. These experts have studied topics such as business trends, the mathematics of finance, and taxation in order to be able to make wise financial decisions.

Are you interested in advising people about managing their money and about saving and investing? If so, a career as a financial analyst or financial planner might interest you.

Several colleges in Ontario offer programs that can lead to a career as an analyst or planner. Some of the courses in the programs are similar to what you will study this year in school. For example:

- Mathematics of Finance
- Financial Analysis
- Taxation for Financial Planners
- Risk Analysis
- Decision Analysis

The programs also have a cooperative education component, which provides students with paid, related work between semesters.

1. Many colleges offer programs with cooperative education.
   a) What makes these programs attractive to students?
   b) Why might an employer prefer to hire a graduate of a cooperative education program?

2. The following courses are also included in the financial analyst and planner programs:
   - Marketing
   - Effective Business Writing
   - Organizational Behaviour
   - Report Writing

   Explain why you think each course is included.

CASE STUDY WRAP-UP

Krysta is a Grade 11 student. She has saved $2400 from her part-time job and wants to put it toward paying for college in 2 to 3 years. She wants to make an informed decision about what to do with her savings.

Throughout this chapter, you have solved problems related to the Case Study. You are now ready to write a report for Krysta. Set up your report by answering the following questions:

1. What effect will interest rates and compounding frequency have on her savings?

2. a) What should she do with her savings until she makes a decision?
   b) How much interest can she expect to earn while she makes up her mind?

3. a) What savings alternative should she choose for 2 years? 3 years?
   b) Should she consider more than one savings alternative?
   c) What interest can she expect to earn in 2 years? 3 years?

4. a) If she wants to double her money, what interest rate and compounding frequency will she need for a 2-year term? a 3-year term?
   b) Is her goal of having $2400 grow to $4800 in 2 to 3 years realistic? Explain.
   c) What is a more realistic final amount?

5. a) Should she consider investing in a low- to moderate-risk investment?
   b) If so, what percent should she invest and what investment(s) should she choose? Explain.

When preparing your report,
• refer to the Case Study questions on pages 129, 137, and 144
• provide complete solutions, including all calculations
• justify, or explain, your answers
• include a list of any materials you used, all your original data, your sources of information, and any formulas, tables, and graphs that you used or created
• use technology, where appropriate

4.1 Effect of Interest Rates, pages 122–129

1. Michelle needs $3500 in 5 years. She can save at 8%, compounded quarterly, or at 7%, compounded quarterly. What principal is required if she chooses to save at each interest rate?

2. Paul deposited $50 on March 1 into a savings account earning 5% simple interest, calculated daily and paid monthly. What is his balance on August 31?

3. Which will result in the greater final amount? How much greater?
- a GIC at 5%, compounded semi-annually, for 2 years
- a GIC at 6%, compounded semi-annually, for 2 years

4.2 Effect of Compounding Frequency, pages 130–137

4. A GIC with a principal of $2000 earns 5%, compounded annually, for 3 years. Another GIC with the same principal and term earns 5%, compounded semi-annually.
   a) Draw a time line diagram for each.
   b) Predict which will result in a greater final amount. Explain.
   c) Calculate to check.

5. Joe wants $5000 in 4 years to buy a big-screen TV. His bank offers a GIC at 6%, compounded semi-annually. A trust company offers a rate of 5%, compounded monthly.
   a) It is difficult to predict which will require a smaller principal. Why?
   b) Which requires a smaller principal? How much smaller?

6. A bank offers a 1-year GIC at 5%, compounded semi-annually, and a 2-year GIC at 6%, compounded annually. Janis could invest $1000 in the 2-year GIC or in the 1-year GIC for two terms.
   a) Which will result in the greater final amount? How much greater?
   b) What are the advantages and disadvantages of each choice?

7. a) Describe several types of savings alternatives.
   b) What are the advantages and disadvantages of each?

4.3 Find the Interest Rate, pages 138–144

8. Darryl will need $5000 in 3 years to pay off a student loan. He has $3800 today.
   a) What rate of interest does he need if compounding is annual? quarterly?
   b) Without calculating, estimate the interest rate for semi-annual compounding. Explain your estimate.

9. $5000 grew to $5962 in 2 years at 9%, compounded semi-annually.
   a) Would the interest rate be lower or higher if the compounding had been annual? monthly?
   b) Explain your answers in part a).
   c) Calculate the interest rates required for annual and monthly compounding.

4.4 Find the Term, pages 145–150

10. Karil needs $7000 to pay a debt as soon as possible. She has $5000 today.
   a) When will she be able to pay off her debt if the $5000 is invested at 6%, compounded annually? compounded quarterly?
   b) Without calculating, estimate the time required for semi-annual compounding. Explain your estimate.

11. For how long must $750 be invested at 7%, compounded quarterly, to result in a final amount of $1000?

12. How long will it take to double a principal of $1000 at 7.2%, compounded semi-annually?

4.5 Savings and Investment Alternatives, pages 151–159

13. a) Describe savings and investment alternatives for each level of risk.
   i) high risk   **ii)** moderate risk
   iii) low risk   **iv)** no risk
   b) Why do people choose high-risk, high-return investments?
   c) Why do people choose low-risk, low-return savings and investment alternatives?

14. Explain why some alternatives are riskier than others.

15. Describe the relationship between risk and return of savings and investment alternatives. Use examples to illustrate.

Practice Test

Achievement Chart Category Connections

Category	Knowledge/Understanding	Thinking/Inquiry/Problem Solving	Communication	Application
Questions	1–11	11	1–6, 10, 11	1, 2, 6, 7–9, 11

1. Susan has $800 and wants to save it for 5 years.
   a) Which interest rate should she choose?
      5%   6%   7%   8%
   b) Which compounding frequency should she choose?
      annual   semi-annual   quarterly   monthly
   c) Explain your choices in parts a) and b).
   d) If she chose 5%, compounded annually, how much less would she end up with than with your choices?

2. Paolo needs $5000 in 3 years for college.
   a) How much must he invest today at 6%, compounded semi-annually?
   b) If the compounding was quarterly, would he need to invest more or less? Explain.

3. Explain how you would show that more frequent compounding results in a greater final amount.

4. What are some of the advantages and disadvantages of savings accounts?

5. a) Where would you find out about savings alternatives?
   b) To compare savings alternatives, what do you need to know?
   c) Describe and compare three different savings alternatives.
   d) Tell why a person would choose each.

6. Fred has $600 to invest. He can choose GIC A at 5.75%, compounded semi-annually, or GIC B, which is compounded monthly. Both result in the same final amount in 4 years.
   a) Predict whether the interest rate of GIC B is higher or lower than that of GIC A. Explain your prediction.
   b) Determine the interest rate for GIC B.

7. Gordo needs $8000 in 4 years to pay off a loan. If he invests $6000 today, what interest rate, compounded quarterly, does he need?

8. Helena has invested $4000 at 6%, compounded semi-annually. How long will it take to double? grow to $10 000?

9. How long must Jenna invest $3000 at 7%, compounded annually, to have $4800 in the future?

10. a) Describe three different types of investments.
    b) List some advantages and disadvantages of each.
    c) Tell why a person might consider each.
    d) Why might an investor combine investments?

ACHIEVEMENT Check   Knowledge/Understanding   Thinking/Inquiry/Problem Solving   Communication   Application

11. Create a savings and investment portfolio for an imaginary client.
    a) Describe your client. Include things such as level of education, income, career, and a description of the family situation.
    b) Complete the Risk Tolerance Questionnaire on page 151.
    c) What percent of the portfolio is invested at each level of risk? Justify your choices.
    d) What specific types of savings and investment alternatives have you included in the portfolio? Explain why you chose each alternative.

DILBERT reprinted by permission of United Feature Syndicate, Inc.

Cumulative Review

Chapters 1–4

1. Jena wants to go to college within 3 years. What do you need to know about her to be able to design an effective financial plan for her?

2. Jena's parents expect her to save $2000 from her job to help pay for college.
   a) Create a current budget for Jena based on the following information.
   Net Income: $110/week
   Expenses: Transportation: $10/week   Entertainment: $50/week
   Clothing: $100/month   Health/Personal: $25 bi-weekly
   b) How long will it take her to save $2000 with her current budget?
   c) What changes would allow her to save $2000 in 2 years? in 1 year?
   d) Create a budget for Jena to follow for 1 year. Display it in a circle graph.

3. **a)** $4000 was invested at 5.25% simple interest and earned $157.50 in interest. What was the term?
   b) If $4000 was invested at 6.25% for the same term, how much more interest would be earned?

4. Ivan borrowed money at 9.5% simple interest for 18 months and paid $712.50 in interest.
   a) How much did he borrow?
   b) If he had paid $825.00 in interest, what would the interest rate have been?

5. Write each expression as a single power, and then, evaluate.
   a) $\dfrac{5^{-3} \times (5^2)^4}{(5^0)^3}$
   b) $\dfrac{2^7 \times (2^{-2})^{-3}}{2^3}$
   c) $\dfrac{7^3 \div 7^{-2}}{7^4 \times 7^{-6}}$
   d) $\dfrac{10^9 \div 10^6}{(10^{-2})^{-3}}$

6. Simplify.
   a) $\dfrac{b^3 \times b^{-7}}{(b^5)^{-3}}$
   b) $\dfrac{8a^2 \times 3a^4}{(12a^1)^3}$
   c) $\dfrac{12x^5 y^4 \div 3x^4 y^3}{4y}$

7. Evaluate. Round to two decimal places, if necessary.
   a) $100^{\frac{1}{2}}$
   b) $1000^{\frac{1}{3}}$
   c) $8^{-\frac{1}{3}}$
   d) $125^{\frac{4}{3}}$
   e) $16^{-\frac{3}{2}}$
   f) $15^{1.7}$
   g) $49^{\frac{1}{2}} + 64^{\frac{1}{3}} + 27^{-\frac{1}{3}} + 81^{\frac{3}{2}}$

8. Solve.

a) $10^x = 100^2$ **b)** $3^{6-x} = 9^7$ **c)** $3^x = \dfrac{1}{27}$ **d)** $5^{2x-12} = \dfrac{1}{25^{2x}}$

9. For each sequence,
i) describe the pattern and determine the next two terms
ii) tell if it is arithmetic or geometric, and how you know
iii) describe the relationship between the term numbers and values
iv) develop a formula for t_n in the sequence, and then, use it to find t_7
a) 13, 18, 23, …   **b)** −4, 12, −36, …   **c)** 312 500, 62 500, 12 500, …

10. A cell splits into 2, then into 4, then 8, and so on. It splits every 3 min.
a) Develop a formula to calculate the number of cells after n splits.
b) How many cells will there be after 1 h?

11. Brenda owes $5000. Payment in full is due in 5 years. The bank will accept payment today at a discounted interest rate of 6%, compounded semi-annually. How much less will she have to pay back if she pays today?

12. Lola invested $15 000 at 7%, compounded semi-annually, for 3 years.
a) How much will her investment be worth? How much of that is interest?
b) What kind of growth is shown by her investment? Explain.
c) If she had invested at 7.64% simple interest, how would the growth differ? Explain.

13. a) Which GIC would you choose? Explain.
• GIC A at 3%, compounded quarterly
• GIC B at 3%, compounded monthly
b) Use a principal of $2500 and a term of 2 years to determine the difference between the final amounts of the two GICs.
c) Use a final amount of $5000 and a term of 5 years to determine the difference between the principals required for the two GICs.

14. a) Is a GIC a savings or an investment alternative? Explain.
b) Why do most GICs have higher interest rates than savings accounts?
c) When might you choose a GIC? a savings account? a combination?

15. Complete each.
a) $5000 at 5%, compounded quarterly, for **?** years is $10 000
b) $5000 at **?** %, compounded quarterly, for 5 years is $10 000

16. Many investors look for investments with the highest rate of return possible but with an acceptable level of risk.
a) Explain what this means.
b) What can an investor do to find the right balance?

CHAPTER

5 SERIES AND ANNUITIES

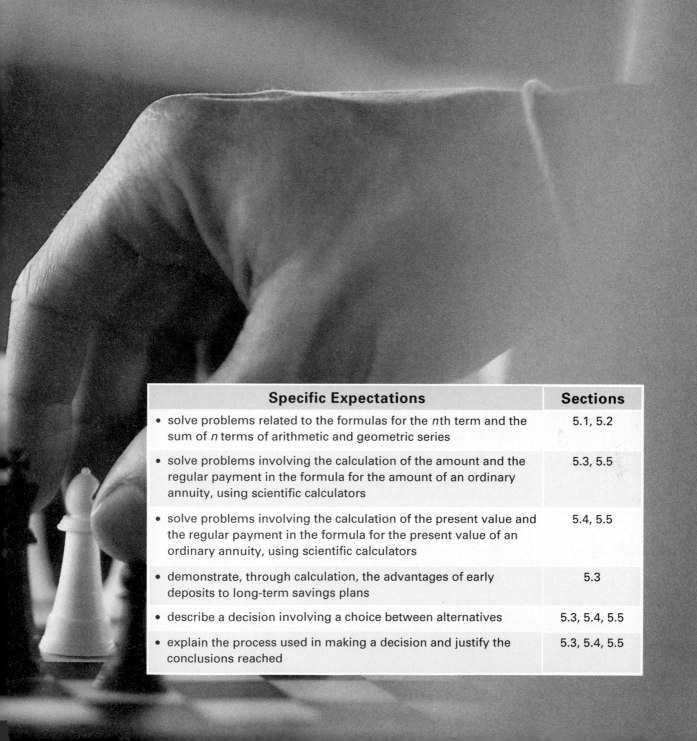

Specific Expectations	Sections
• solve problems related to the formulas for the nth term and the sum of n terms of arithmetic and geometric series	5.1, 5.2
• solve problems involving the calculation of the amount and the regular payment in the formula for the amount of an ordinary annuity, using scientific calculators	5.3, 5.5
• solve problems involving the calculation of the present value and the regular payment in the formula for the present value of an ordinary annuity, using scientific calculators	5.4, 5.5
• demonstrate, through calculation, the advantages of early deposits to long-term savings plans	5.3
• describe a decision involving a choice between alternatives	5.3, 5.4, 5.5
• explain the process used in making a decision and justify the conclusions reached	5.3, 5.4, 5.5

$\mathcal{G}$et Ready . . .

1. Identify each sequence as arithmetic, geometric, or neither. Give a reason for each choice.
   a) $4, 7, 10, 13, \ldots$
   b) $7, 2, -3, -8, \ldots$
   c) $3, 6, 12, 24, \ldots$
   d) $-5, 15, -45, \ldots$
   e) $100, 91, 83, \ldots$
   f) $1, -1, 2, -2, 3, -3, \ldots$

2. State the first term, a, the common ratio, r, and the first five terms for the geometric sequence defined by each formula.
   a) $t_n = (8)(3)^{n-1}$
   b) $t_n = (-5)(-2)^{n-1}$
   c) $t_n = (5120)\left(\dfrac{1}{2}\right)^{n-1}$

3. Factor by finding a common factor.
   a) $5n + 10$
   b) $6n + 3$
   c) $8n + 12$

4. Evaluate each expression. Round to two decimal places, if necessary.
   a) $\dfrac{6}{2}[2(3)+(6-1)(5)]$
   b) $-5[20 + 6(-3)]$
   c) 3^8

   d) 5×2^9
   e) $8(5^7 - 1)$
   f) $\dfrac{-3(5^{-8} - 1)}{5^{-1} - 1}$

   g) $300(1.005)^{12}$
   h) $450(1.03^{10} - 1)$
   i) 1.06^{-8}

   j) $100(1.01)^{-15}$
   k) $25(1 - 1.0025^{-6})$
   l) $\dfrac{50(1.02^9 - 1)}{0.02}$

5. State the number of compounding periods, n, and the interest rate per compounding period, i, for each.
   a) 6%, compounded monthly, for 2 years
   b) 4%, compounded quarterly, for 5 years
   c) 5%, compounded semi-annually, for 3 years
   d) 6.9%, compounded annually, for 6 years

6. Determine the final amount of each investment using $A = P(1 + i)^n$.
   a) $300 at 4%, compounded semi-annually, for 5 years
   b) $1000 at 6%, compounded quarterly, for 3 years
   c) $560 at 4.5%, compounded monthly, for 2 years
   d) $2000 at 5%, compounded annually, for 10 years

7. Determine the present value of each debt using $PV = A(1 + i)^{-n}$ or $PV = \dfrac{A}{(1+i)^n}$.
   a) $1500 due in 3 years, discounted at 7%, compounded annually
   b) $500 due in 4 years, discounted at 2.4%, compounded monthly
   c) $700 due in 8 years, discounted at 6%, compounded quarterly
   d) $2000 due in 6 years, discounted at 5%, compounded semi-annually

*C*ASE STUDY

Throughout this chapter, you will be learning about annuities. Annuities involve regular payments, such as a series of deposits into a savings account, or a series of loan payments. In selected sections, you will solve annuity problems related to the Case Study described below. In the Case Study Wrap-Up on page 211, you will be asked to write a report summarizing what you have learned. To help organize your report, keep 5 or 6 pages of your notebook for any Case Study work, or keep your work in a Case Study Portfolio.

Sarah has recently graduated from community college and has found a job with a good starting salary. Her financial goals include saving enough to buy a used car in 3 years. In addition, she has a $6000 student loan, which she would like to pay off within 10 years.

5.1 Arithmetic Series

Karen works at a grocery store setting up displays. She has been asked to set up a display of boxes at the end of an aisle. There will be 8 layers altogether and each layer is to be 5 boxes deep. The bottom layer will be 20 boxes wide, the next layer will be 18 boxes wide, the next will be 16 boxes wide, and so on. How many boxes will she need for the display?

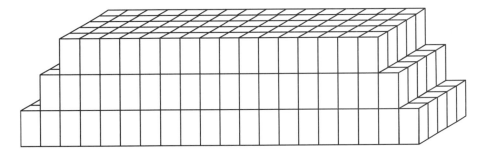

DISCOVER

Determine the Sum of the Terms of a Sequence

1. The numbers of boxes in Karen's grocery store display form a sequence.
   a) Write the sequence.
   b) Is the sequence arithmetic, geometric, or neither? Explain how you know.

2. Copy and complete the table to determine the number of boxes in all 8 layers.

Layer Number	Number of Boxes in the Layer	Sum of the Number of Boxes
1	100	100
2	90	190
3	80	270
4		
5		
6		
7		
8		

3. How many boxes will Karen need for the display?

In the Discover, you solved a problem by determining the sum of the terms of a sequence. The sum of the terms of a sequence is called a **series**. If the terms form an arithmetic sequence, the series is an **arithmetic series**. Below are some examples:

Arithmetic Sequence	Corresponding Arithmetic Series
$t_1, t_2, t_3, t_4, \dots, t_n$	$S_n = t_1 + t_2 + t_3 + t_4 + \dots + t_4$
$\frac{1}{2}, 1, 1\frac{1}{2}$	$S_3 = \frac{1}{2} + 1 + 1\frac{1}{2}$ $= 3$
$3, 0, -3, -6$	$S_4 = 3 + (0) + (-3) + (-6)$ $= -6$
$2, 4, 6, 8, 10$	$S_5 = 2 + 4 + 6 + 8 + 10$ $= 30$

Note that a series such as $3 + 0 - 3 - 6 - \dots$
could also be written as $3 + 0 + (-3) + (-6) + \dots$.

The following formula can be used to determine the sum of the first n terms in any arithmetic series:

$$S_n = \frac{n}{2}[2a + (n-1)d], \text{ where}$$

- S_n is the sum of the first n terms
- a is the first term
- d is the common difference between successive terms

EXAMPLE 1

Cereal Box Display

Karen has been asked to set up a display of boxes. There will be 8 layers of boxes altogether and each layer is to be 5 boxes deep. The bottom layer will be 20 boxes wide, the next layer will be 18 boxes wide, the next will be 16 boxes wide, and so on. How many boxes will she need for the display?

Solution

Determine the terms of the sequence:
$5 \times 20, 5 \times 18, 5 \times 16, 5 \times 14, 5 \times 12, 5 \times 10, 5 \times 8, 5 \times 6$
$100, 90, 80, 70, 60, 50, 40, 30$

Write the series:
$100 + 90 + 80 + 70 + 60 + 50 + 40 + 30$

Determine if the series is arithmetic:
$90 - 100 = -10 \qquad 80 - 90 = -10 \qquad 70 - 80 = -10$
There is a common difference of -10, so, the series is arithmetic.

Use the formula $S_n = \dfrac{n}{2}[2a+(n-1)d]$.

Determine the values of the variables:

$n = 8$ This is the sum of *all* of the terms in the sequence.

$a = 100$ a is the first term.

$d = -10$ d is the common difference.

Use the formula:

$S_n = \dfrac{n}{2}[2a+(n-1)d]$

$S_8 = \dfrac{8}{2}[2(100)+(8-1)(-10)]$ Simplify.

$S_8 = 4[200+7(-10)]$

$S_8 = 520$

Karen will need 520 boxes for the display.

EXAMPLE 2

Develop and Apply a Formula for S_n Given the Arithmetic Series

a) Develop the formula for S_n, the sum of the first n terms in the arithmetic series $3 + 7 + 11 + \ldots$.

b) Determine the sum of the first 25 terms of the arithmetic series, S_{25}.

Solution

a) Use the formula $S_n = \dfrac{n}{2}[2a+(n-1)d]$.

Determine the values of the variables:

$n = $ ❓

$a = 3$ The first term is 3.

$d = 4$ The common difference is 4.

Use the formula:

$S_n = \dfrac{n}{2}[2a+(n-1)d]$

$S_n = \dfrac{n}{2}[2(3)+(n-1)(4)]$ Simplify.

$S_n = \dfrac{n}{2}(6+4n-4)$

$S_n = \dfrac{n}{2}(4n+2)$ $4n + 2 = 2(2n + 1)$

$S_n = \dfrac{n}{2} \times 2(2n+1)$

$S_n = n(2n+1)$ or $2n^2 + n$

The formula for S_n, the sum of the first n terms in the arithmetic series $3 + 7 + 11 + \ldots$, is $S_n = n(2n+1)$ or $2n^2 + n$.

b) Substitute 25 for n in the formula to find the sum of the first 25 terms:

$S_n = n(2n + 1)$
$S_{25} = 25[2(25) + 1]$ Simplify.
$S_{25} = (25)(51)$
$S_{25} = 1275$

The sum of the first 25 terms of the arithmetic series, S_{25}, is 1275.

EXAMPLE 3

Yearly Earnings

Sajid found a part-time job that pays $500 a month, with a $15 raise each month for the first year. How much will Sajid earn in the first year?

Solution

Since Sajid gets a $15 raise each month, the series is arithmetic, with a common difference of 15.

Determine the first four terms in the arithmetic series:
$500 + 515 + 530 + 545 + \dots$

Use the formula $S_n = \dfrac{n}{2}[2a + (n-1)d]$.

Determine the values of the variables:

$n = 12$ There are 12 months/year, so, determine the sum of the first 12 terms.
$a = 500$
$d = 15$

Use the formula:

$S_n = \dfrac{n}{2}[2a + (n-1)d]$

$S_{12} = \dfrac{12}{2}[2(500) + (12-1)(15)]$ Simplify.

$S_{12} = 6[1000 + (11)(15)]$

$S_{12} = 6990$

Scientific Calculator

GRAPHING CALCULATOR
6(1000+11*15)
                6990

Sajid will earn $6990 in his first year.

See pages 407 and 408 in the Technology Appendix for tips on calculating efficiently on a graphing calculator.

KEY CONCEPTS

- A series is the sum of the terms of a sequence.

- An arithmetic series is the sum of the terms of an arithmetic sequence.

- The sum of the first n terms of a sequence is represented by S_n.

- The sum of the first n terms of an arithmetic series can be determined using the formula $S_n = \dfrac{n}{2}[2a + (n-1)d]$, where

  S_n is the sum of the first n terms
  a is the first term
  d is the common difference

DISCUSS THE CONCEPTS

1. a) Create an arithmetic series.
  b) Describe how you created the series.
  c) Explain how you know the series is arithmetic.
  d) Compare your series with a classmate's. How are they the same? different?

2. The following expression could be used to determine the sum of the first 5 terms of an arithmetic series: $\dfrac{5}{2}[2(3) + (5-1)(-5)]$

  a) What do you know about the series by examining the expression?
  b) What are the first 3 terms of the series?

3. Describe the keystrokes you would use on a calculator to evaluate

  $S_{15} = \dfrac{15}{2}[2(3) + (15-1)(-5)]$.

A 1. Determine whether each series is geometric, arithmetic, or neither. For each, explain how you know.

  a) $3 + 8 + 13 + 18$
  b) $9 + 2 - 2 - 10 - \ldots$
  c) $2 + 4 + 6 + 8 + \ldots$
  d) $2 + 4 + 8 + 16 + \ldots$
  e) $1 - 6 - 13 - 20 - \ldots$
  f) $0 + (-5) + (-10) + (-15)$

2. Develop the formula for S_n, the sum of the first n terms in each series. Then, determine the indicated sum.

   a) $1 + 3 + 5 + 7 + \ldots$; $S_{10} = $ ❓

   b) $5 + 8 + 11 + 14 + 17 + 20 + 23$; $S_6 = $ ❓

   c) $10 + 5 + 0 - 5 - \ldots$; $S_{20} = $ ❓

   d) $-3 - 5 - 7 - \ldots$; $S_9 = $ ❓

   e) $4.1 + 5.7 + 7.3$; $S_3 = $ ❓

   f) $100 + 94.5 + 89 + \ldots$; $S_{40} = $ ❓

3. Develop the formula for S_n, the sum of the first n terms of each arithmetic series. Then, determine S_{12}.

   a) first term is -4, common difference is -10

   b) $t_1 = 6$, $d = 2.4$ **c)** $t_1 = 9$, $t_2 = -9$

   d) $t_n = 3n - 1$ **e)** $t_n = 4 - 7n$

APPLY THE CONCEPTS

4. **Triangle pattern** In a supermarket, cans are stacked in layers in a display. There are 100 cans in the bottom layer. Each layer has 4 fewer cans than the layer below. There are 18 layers of cans altogether.

   a) Develop a formula to calculate the number of cans in the first n layers.

   b) How many cans are in the display?

B **5.** **Theatre seating** An architect is designing a theatre that will have 20 seats in the front row, 22 seats in the second row, 24 seats in the third row, and so on. The theatre will have 12 rows.

   a) Develop a formula to calculate the number of seats in the first n rows.

   b) How many seats are in the first 7 rows?

   c) How many seats are in the theatre?

   d) If each seat costs $125 to make and install, how much should be budgeted for the seats?

6. **Application** An 8-week summer job pays $500 a week, with a $5 raise each week. The employer finds that many employees leave before the 8 weeks are over. As an incentive to stay for the whole summer, the employer also offers a starting salary of $350 a week, with a $50 raise each week. Which is the better wage? Explain.

7. **Problem Solving** Sean has been hired at a yearly salary of $40 000 with a $2500 raise at the end of each year. If this yearly salary increase continues, how many years will it take Sean to earn $1 000 000? Explain how you solved this problem.

8. Saving Erin has a part-time job. The first month she managed to save $50. After that, she was able to save $10 more each month. How much will she have saved in total after 2 years?

9. Communication

   a) Design and solve an arithmetic series problem that uses

   $S_n = \dfrac{n}{2}[2a+(n-1)d]$ in its solution.

   b) What could you do to make your problem more challenging? easier to solve?

10. Application To knit the sleeve of a sweater, 70 stitches are cast on for the first row. On every following fourth row, 2 stitches are added. How many stitches are knitted in 48 rows?

11. Natural numbers

   a) Develop a formula for the sum of the first n natural numbers. (Recall that the natural numbers are 1, 2, 3, ….)

   b) What is the sum of the first 100 natural numbers?

   c) Go to *www.school.mcgrawhill.ca/resources/* and follow the links to learn more about Gauss, a famous mathematician. When Gauss was a boy, he tricked his teacher by using a shortcut to find the sum of the first 100 natural numbers. Write a brief report describing what you found out.

EXTEND THE CONCEPTS

12. Problem Solving

   a) Write an arithmetic series for which $S_{10} = 375$.

   b) Explain how you developed your series.

   c) Is more than one series possible? Explain.

13. Communication Two players take turns rolling a pair of dice. Player A rolls and finds the sum of the numbers rolled. Player A then determines his or her points for that turn by multiplying the sum by 5. For instance, if Player A rolls a 6 and a 3, he or she earns 45 points, because $6 + 3 = 9$ and $9 \times 5 = 45$. It is then Player B's turn. Play continues until one player reaches a maximum number of points. Note that each sum can only be used once by each player—if Player A rolls a sum of 9 again, he or she earns no points for that turn.

   a) Explain how you could use the arithmetic series formula to determine the maximum number of points.

   b) What is the maximum number of points?

5.2 Geometric Series

A badminton singles tournament has 128 players signed up. All players will play in round 1, which means 64 matches must be scheduled for this round. Only the winner of each match will move on, so, only 32 matches will have to be scheduled for round 2. How many matches will have to be scheduled altogether?

DISCOVER

Determine the Sum of the Terms of a Sequence

1. The numbers of matches in successive rounds of the badminton tournament form a sequence.
   a) Write the entire sequence.
   b) Is the sequence arithmetic, geometric, or neither? Explain how you know.

2. Copy and complete the table to determine the total number of matches that must be scheduled.

Round	Number of Players	Number of Matches in Round	Sum of Number of Matches
1	128	64	64
2	64	32	96
3			
4			
5			
6			
7			

3. How many matches must be scheduled?

In the Discover, you solved a problem by determining the sum of the terms of a geometric sequence. The sum of the terms of a geometric sequence is called a **geometric series**.

Below are some examples of geometric sequences and series:

Geometric Sequence	Corresponding Geometric Series
$t_1, t_2, t_3, t_4, \ldots, t_n$	$S_n = t_1 + t_2 + t_3 + t_4 + \ldots + t_n$
$\dfrac{1}{2}, \dfrac{1}{4}, \dfrac{1}{8}$	$S_3 = \dfrac{1}{2} + \dfrac{1}{4} + \dfrac{1}{8}$ $= \dfrac{7}{8}$
$3, -6, 12, -24$	$S_4 = 3 - 6 + 12 - 24$ $= -15$
$2, 4, 8, 16, 32$	$S_5 = 2 + 4 + 8 + 16 + 32$ $= 62$

Note that a series such as $3 - 6 + 12 - 24 + \ldots$
could also be written as $\quad 3 + (-6) + 12 + (-24) + \ldots$.

The following formula can be used to determine the sum of the first n terms of any geometric series:
$$S_n = \frac{a(r^n - 1)}{r - 1}, \text{ where}$$

- S_n is the sum of the first n terms
- a is the first term
- r is the common ratio between successive terms

EXAMPLE 1

Determine the Sum of a Geometric Series

A badminton tournament has 128 players signed up to play singles. All players will play in round 1, which means 64 matches must be scheduled for this round. Only the winner of each match will move on, so, 32 matches will have to be scheduled for round 2. How many matches will have to be scheduled altogether?

Solution

Determine the terms of the sequence and write the series:
$64 + 32 + 16 + 8 + 4 + 2 + 1$

Determine if the series is geometric:
$32 \div 64 = 0.5 \quad 16 \div 32 = 0.5 \quad 8 \div 16 = 0.5$
There is a common ratio of 0.5, so, the series is geometric.

Use the formula $S_n = \dfrac{a(r^n - 1)}{r - 1}$.

Determine the values of the variables:

$n = 7$	This is the sum of *all* 7 terms in the sequence.
$a = 64$	a is the first term.
$r = 0.5$	r is the common ratio.

See pages 407 and 408 in the Technology Appendix for tips on calculating efficiently on a graphing calculator.

Use the formula:

$$S_n = \frac{a(r^n - 1)}{r - 1}$$

$$S_7 = \frac{64(0.5^7 - 1)}{0.5 - 1} \qquad \text{Simplify.}$$

$$S_7 = \frac{64(0.5^7 - 1)}{-0.5}$$

$$S_7 = \frac{64}{-0.5}(0.5^7 - 1)$$

$$S_7 = 127$$

Scientific Calculator

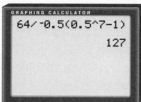

GRAPHING CALCULATOR

64/-0.5(0.5^7-1)

127

Altogether, 127 matches must be scheduled.

EXAMPLE 2

Develop and Apply a Formula for S_n Given the Geometric Series

a) Develop the formula for S_n, the sum of the first n terms in the geometric series $3 + 6 + 12 + 24 + \ldots$.

b) Determine the sum of the first 10 terms of the series, or S_{10}.

Solution

a) The series is geometric. So, use the formula $S_n = \dfrac{a(r^n - 1)}{r - 1}$.

Determine the values of the variables:

$n = \boxed{?}$

$a = 3$ The first term is 3.

$r = 2$ The common ratio is 2 ($6 \div 3 = 2$; $12 \div 6 = 2$).

Use the formula:

$$S_n = \frac{a(r^n - 1)}{r - 1}$$

$$S_n = \frac{3(2^n - 1)}{2 - 1} \qquad \text{Simplify.}$$

$$S_n = 3(2^n - 1)$$

The formula for S_n, the sum of the first n terms of the geometric series $3 + 6 + 12 + 24 + \ldots$, is $S_n = 3(2^n - 1)$.

b) Substitute 10 for n in the formula to find the sum of the first 10 terms, S_{10}:

$$S_n = 3(2^n - 1)$$

$$S_{10} = 3(2^{10} - 1) \qquad \text{Simplify.}$$

$$S_{10} = 3069$$

The sum of the first 10 terms of the series, S_{10}, is 3069.

EXAMPLE 3

Develop and Apply a Formula for S_n Given the Formula for t_n

A geometric sequence is defined by the formula $t_n = 35(5)^{n-1}$.

a) Determine the formula for S_n, the sum of the first n terms in the series.

b) Determine the sum of the first 8 terms, S_8.

Solution

a) Interpret the formula for t_n to determine the values of a and r.

$t_n = ar^{n-1}$

$t_n = 35(5)^{n-1}$

$\quad a = 35$

$\quad r = 5$

Use the formula for S_n:

$S_n = \dfrac{a(r^n - 1)}{r - 1}$

$S_n = \dfrac{35(5^n - 1)}{5 - 1}$ Simplify.

$S_n = \dfrac{35(5^n - 1)}{4}$

$S_n = 8.75(5^n - 1)$

The formula for S_n is $S_n = 8.75(5^n - 1)$.

Alternatively, the sum and sequence functions of a graphing calculator can be used to determine the sum of the first n terms. (See page 410 in the Technology Appendix.)

b) Substitute 8 for n in the formula to determine S_8:

$S_n = 8.75(5^n - 1)$

$S_8 = 8.75(5^8 - 1)$

$S_8 = 3\ 417\ 960$

The sum of the first 8 terms, S_8, is 3 417 960.

KEY CONCEPTS

- A geometric series is the sum of the terms of a geometric sequence.

- The sum of the first n terms of a geometric series can be determined using

  the formula $S_n = \dfrac{a(r^n - 1)}{r - 1}$, where

  S_n is the sum of the first n terms

  a is the first term

  r is the common ratio $(r \neq 1)$

DISCUSS THE CONCEPTS

1. a) Create a geometric series.
   b) Describe how you created the series.
   c) Explain how you know the series is geometric.
   d) Compare your series with a classmate's. How are they the same? different?

2. The following expression could be used to determine the sum of a geometric series: $\dfrac{8(3^{12} - 1)}{3 - 1}$
   a) What do you know about the series by examining the expression?
   b) What are the first 3 terms of the series?

3. Describe the calculator keystrokes you would use to evaluate $S_{12} = \dfrac{8(3^{12} - 1)}{3 - 1}$.

PRACTISE

A 1. Determine whether each series is geometric, arithmetic, or neither. For each, explain how you know.
   a) $3 + 5 + 7 + 9 + \ldots$
   b) $5 + 10 + 20 + 40 + \ldots$
   c) $4 + 2 + 1 + \dfrac{1}{2} + \dfrac{1}{4} + \ldots$
   d) $7 - 3 - 10 - \ldots$
   e) $-3 + 12 - 48 + \ldots$
   f) $20 + 15 + 10 + \ldots$

2. Develop the formula for S_n, the sum of the first n terms in each series. Then, determine the indicated sum.
   a) $3 + 15 + 75 + \ldots$; S_8
   b) $1000 + 500 + 250 + \ldots$; S_{10}
   c) $100 + 100(1.02) + 100(1.02)^2 + \ldots$; S_{10}
   d) $-4 + 16 - 64 + \ldots$; S_9
   e) $10 - 30 + 90 - \ldots$; S_{12}
   f) $15\,625 - 3125 + 625 - \ldots$; S_6

3. Develop the formula for S_n, the sum of the first n terms in each series. Then, determine the value of S_8. Round to two decimal places, if necessary.
   a) $t_n = 4(5)^{n-1}$
   b) $t_n = -320\left(\dfrac{1}{2}\right)^{n-1}$
   c) $t_n = 500(1.05)^{n-1}$

APPLY THE CONCEPTS

4. Tennis tournament There are 256 players entered in a singles tennis tournament. All players will play in the first round. Only the winner of each match will move on to the next round. How many matches will have to be scheduled altogether?

B 5. Family tree Piers began researching his ancestors. He has 2 parents (P), 4 grandparents (GP), 8 great grandparents (GGP), and so on. He wants to reserve a page in his notebook for each ancestor to record any interesting facts that he discovers.

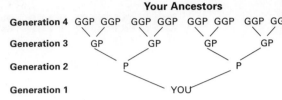

Your Ancestors

Generation 4 GGP GGP GGP GGP GGP GGP GGP GGP

Generation 3 GP GP GP GP

Generation 2 P P

Generation 1 YOU

a) How many pages will he need to record information about
   i) the past 10 generations?   **ii)** the past 15 generations?

b) Explain why there is a great difference between the number of ancestors in the past 10 generations and in the past 15 generations.

6. Application A medical student is conducting an experiment. She treats a virus culture to a dosage of 256 mg of a new drug to see how the virus responds. In the next treatment, she uses $\frac{1}{2}$ the dosage of the drug. In the next treatment, she uses $\frac{1}{2}$ the dosage of the second treatment. This continues for a total of 7 treatments. How many milligrams of the drug will she need to conduct this experiment?

7. Application A runner is training for a competition that is 2 weeks away. She plans to run 2 km today. Each day she plans to increase her distance by 5%. How far will she have run altogether in the 2 weeks leading up to the race?

8. Communication Design and solve a geometric series problem that uses
$S_n = \dfrac{a(r^n - 1)}{r - 1}$ in its solution.

9. Application A computer animation programmer wants to simulate the action of a ball bouncing. To do this, she needs to know how far a real ball would travel under the same conditions. She tosses the ball upward from the floor. It reaches a height of 3 m. The ball drops, hits the floor, and bounces upward and reaches a height that is 60% of its previous height.

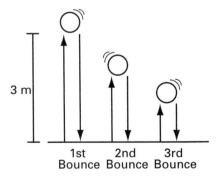

3 m

1st   2nd   3rd
Bounce Bounce Bounce

On each subsequent bounce, the ball reaches 60% of its previous height. How far has the ball travelled over 6 bounces? Round to the nearest metre.

10. Problem Solving A phone tree is sometimes used to spread news quickly to a large number of people. For instance, an organization can use a phone tree to contact its members about an upcoming event. Suppose the first person calls 4 people in stage 1. Then, in stage 2, each of those people calls 2 people. In stage 3, each of those people calls 2 people, and so on. Suppose an organization has 125 000 members. How many stages of calling would be necessary to reach all the members? Explain how you solved the problem.

ACHIEVEMENT Check | Knowledge/Understanding | Thinking/Inquiry/Problem Solving | Communication | Application

11. Suppose your friend had a choice of two prizes:
Prize A: $10 000 on the first day, $20 000 on the second day, $30 000 on the third day, and so on for a month
Prize B: 1¢ on the first day, 2¢ on the second day, 4¢ on the third day, and so on for a month
Write a proposal advising your friend which prize to choose. Justify your advice using mathematical procedures and language.

C **12. Thinking** A legend tells of a proud king who gave a prize to a peasant. The prize was to be 1 grain of rice for the first square on the king's chessboard, 2 grains for the second square, 4 grains for the third square, and so on, doubling the number of grains of rice for each of the chessboard's 64 squares. The peasant told the king that the prize was much too generous, but the king insisted. Very soon, the king realized that he had made a mistake. But he was too proud to admit it.
a) Explain the king's mistake.
b) How many grains of rice did the king have to give the peasant?

13. Powers of 10
a) Develop a formula for the sum of the first n powers of 10:
1, 10, 100, 1000, …
b) What is the sum of the first 10 powers of 10?

EXTEND THE CONCEPTS

14. Application Use what you have learned in this section to simplify the following algebraic expression:
$$y^1 \times y^2 \times y^4 \times y^8 \times \dots \times y^{64}$$

15. Problem Solving
a) Write a geometric series for which $S_{10} = 3069$.
b) Explain how you developed your series.
c) Is more than one series possible? Explain.

Allison is saving money from what she earns at her part-time job. She deposits $100 at the end of each month into a savings account that pays interest at 3%, compounded monthly. Allison would like to know what her savings will be in 1 year.

Regular payments such as Allison's deposits are known as **annuities**. An annuity is a series of equal payments made at equal intervals of time. If the payments are made at the end of each payment interval, the annuity is called an **ordinary annuity**.

DISCOVER

Solve an Annuity Problem Using a Time Line Diagram

Allison deposits $100 at the end of each month into a savings account that earns 3% interest, compounded monthly. What will her savings be at the end of 1 year?

A time line diagram for Allison's savings deposits has been started. Examine it, and then, answer the questions on the next page.

Allison's Savings Deposits

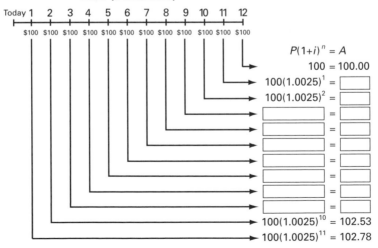

1. Consider Allison's first $100 deposit, or payment.
   a) It will earn interest for only 11 months, not the entire year. Explain why.
   b) It will be worth $102.78 at the end of the year. Explain how this was calculated.

2. Consider Allison's second $100 deposit.
   a) It will earn interest for only 10 months. Explain why.
   b) It will be worth $102.53 at the end of the year. Explain how this was calculated.

3. Consider Allison's last $100 deposit. It will earn no interest and be worth $100 at the end of the year. Explain why.

4. Copy and complete the time line diagram, using the formula $A = P(1 + i)^n$ to calculate the final amount, A, of each deposit, or payment, at the end of the year, where
   - P is the payment: 100
   - i is the interest rate each month: 0.0025
   - n is the number of months the payment earns interest

5. Determine the sum of the final amounts to determine Allison's savings at the end of 1 year.

Did You Know?

The word annuity has the same origin as the word annual, which means yearly. However, annuities are not limited to annual payments. They can be any specified regular payment interval.

In the Discover, you solved an annuity problem by finding the sum of 12 final amounts. The sum of those final amounts is the following geometric series:
$$S_{12} = 100 + 100(1.0025)^1 + 100(1.0025)^2 + \ldots + 100(1.0025)^{10} + 100(1.0025)^{11}$$
where
- the number of terms is 12, which is the number of payments
- the first term is 100, which is the payment
- the common ratio is 1.0025, which is $1 + i$ (i is the interest rate per compounding period)

Annuity problems, such the one in the Discover, involve geometric series. So, they can be solved using the formula for the sum of any geometric series,
$$S_n = \frac{a(r^n - 1)}{r - 1}$$, where, in the case of an annuity,
- S_n is the sum of the final amounts of n payments
- n is the number of payments
- a is the payment
- r is $1 + i$

EXAMPLE 1

Savings Account Future Value

Allison is saving money from what she earns at her part-time job. She deposits $100 at the end of each month into a savings account that pays interest at 3%, compounded monthly. Allison would like to know what her savings will be at the end of 1 year.

Solution

Method 1: Use the formula $S_n = \dfrac{a(r^n - 1)}{r - 1}$

Determine the values of the variables:

$S_{12} = $ ❓　　　This is the sum of the series, or the sum of 12 final amounts.

$n = 12$　　　There are 12 terms, because there are 12 payments.

$a = 100$　　　The first term is 100, because the payments are $100.

$r = 1.0025$　　The common ratio is $1 + i$ or $1 + (0.03 \div 12)$.

Use the formula:

$$S_n = \frac{a(r^n - 1)}{r - 1}$$

$$S_{12} = \frac{100(1.0025^{12} - 1)}{1.0025 - 1} \qquad \text{Simplify.}$$

$$S_{12} \doteq 1216.64$$

Allison's savings at the end of 1 year will be $1216.64.

Method 2: Use the formula $FV = \dfrac{PMT[(1+i)^n - 1]}{i}$

The common ratio of a geometric series involving the future value of an ordinary annuity is $1 + i$, where i is the interest rate per compounding period. Substituting $1 + i$ for r in the geometric series formula results in a formula that can be used to calculate the future value of an annuity:

$$S_n = \frac{a(r^n - 1)}{r - 1} \qquad\qquad r = 1 + i$$

$$S_n = \frac{a[(1+i)^n - 1]}{(1+i) - 1} \qquad\quad \text{Simplify.}$$

$$S_n = \frac{a[(1+i)^n - 1]}{i} \qquad\quad \text{Use } FV \text{ for } S_n \text{ and } PMT \text{ for } a.$$

$$FV = \frac{PMT[(1+i)^n - 1]}{i} \quad \text{where}$$

- FV is the future value of the annuity
- PMT is the payment
- i is the interest rate per compounding period
- n is the number of payments

Use the formula $FV = \dfrac{PMT[(1+i)^n - 1]}{i}$:

Determine the values of the variables:

$FV =$?

$n = 12$ A payment each month for 1 year is 12 payments.

$PMT = 100$ Each payment is $100.

$i = 0.0025$ 3%, compounded monthly, is $0.03 \div 12$.

See pages 407 and 408 in the Technology Appendix for tips on calculating efficiently on a graphing calculator.

Use the formula:

$FV = \dfrac{PMT[(1+i)^n - 1]}{i}$

$FV = \dfrac{100[(1+0.0025)^{12} - 1]}{0.0025}$ Simplify.

$FV \doteq 1216.64$

Scientific Calculator

⊂ 100 ÷ 0.0025 = × (1.0025
y^x 12 − 1) =

Graphing Calculator

100 ÷ 0.0025 (1.0025 ^ 12
− 1) ENTER

Allison's savings after 1 year will be $1216.64.

The formula $FV = \dfrac{PMT[(1+i)^n - 1]}{i}$ is used when working with ordinary annuities because its variables relate directly to annuities.

EXAMPLE 2

Savings Account Future Balance and Interest Earned

Riaz makes deposits of $2000 semi-annually into an account that pays 4% interest, compounded semi-annually.

a) How much money will be in the account after a 5-year term?

b) How much interest will Riaz have earned over the 5-year term?

Solution

Draw a time line diagram to organize the given information:

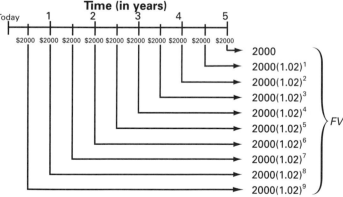

The amount of money in the account after 5 years is the future value of the annuity.

See page 412 in the Technology Appendix for more details about the **TVM Solver**.

a) **Method 1: Use the formula** $FV = \dfrac{PMT[(1+i)^n - 1]}{i}$

Determine the values of the variables:

$FV = $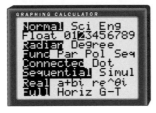

$n = 10$ Semi-annually for 5 years is 10 payments.

$PMT = 2000$ Each payment is \$2000.

$i = 0.02$ 4%, compounded semi-annually, is $0.04 \div 2$ or 0.02.

Use the formula:

$$FV = \frac{PMT[(1+i)^n - 1]}{i}$$

$$FV = \frac{2000[(1+0.02)^{10} - 1]}{0.02} \qquad \text{Simplify.}$$

$$FV \doteq 21\,899.44$$

There will be \$21 899.44 in the account after a 5-year term.

Method 2: Use a finance application of a graphing calculator

The **TVM Solver** is a finance application that can be used to calculate the **Time Value of Money** (**TVM**).

Step 1: Press (MODE) and set the number of decimal places to **2**:

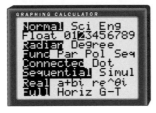

Step 2: Press (APPS) 1 1 to open the **TVM Solver**:

Step 3: Enter the values of the variables as shown.

What the variables represent:

N (Number of Payments)

I% (Annual Interest Rate)

PV (Present Value)

PMT (Payment)

FV (Future Value)

P/Y (Number of Payments/Year)

C/Y (Number of Compounding Periods/Year)

PMT: END BEGIN (Payments at End of Payment Interval)

PMT is negative, **−2000.00**, because money is being paid out.

FV=0.00 because that is the variable to be solved for.

Step 4: Cursor to **FV=0.00**, and then, press ALPHA ENTER to solve for **FV**:

There will be $21 899.44 in the account after a 5-year term.

b) Subtract the total payments from the future value:
$I = FV - (n \times PMT)$
$I = 21\ 899.44 - (10 \times 2000)$ There are 10 payments of $2000 each.
$I = 1899.44$

The interest earned over the 5-year term will be $1899.44.

KEY CONCEPTS

- An annuity is a series of equal payments made at equal intervals of time.

- An annuity for which the interest is compounded is a geometric series.

- The payments of an ordinary annuity are made at the end of each interval.

- The future value of an ordinary annuity is the sum of the final amounts of all the payments.

- The future value of an ordinary annuity can be calculated using the formula
$FV = \dfrac{PMT[(1+i)^n - 1]}{i}$, where FV is the future value
PMT is the payment
i is the interest rate per compounding period
n is the number of payments

DISCUSS THE CONCEPTS

1. Explain how annuities relate to geometric series.

2. The following are annuity payment intervals. How many months long is each?
   a) quarterly   **b)** semi-annual   **c)** monthly   **d)** annual

3. An ordinary annuity has quarterly payments of $100 for a 5-year term. Interest is at 6%, compounded quarterly. Describe how to determine the values of i and n in the formula $FV = \dfrac{PMT[(1+i)^n - 1]}{i}$.

A **1.** For each ordinary annuity,

    i) sketch a time line diagram

    ii) determine the values of *PMT*, *i*, and *n* for the formula $FV = \dfrac{PMT[(1+i)^n - 1]}{i}$

    iii) calculate the future value

	Payment ($)	Payment Interval	Interest Rate (%)	Compounding	Term (years)
a)	300	monthly	6	monthly	1
b)	5000	annual	5.8	annual	10
c)	1500	semi-annual	4.6	semi-annual	4
d)	650	quarterly	4	quarterly	5

2. Determine the future value of each ordinary annuity.

    a) yearly payments of $2000 at 6%, compounded annually, for 8 years

    b) semi-annual payments of $250 at 5%, compounded semi-annually, for 3 years

    c) monthly payments of $1000 at 4.2%, compounded monthly, for 2 years

3. **Saving money** Helen plans to deposit $100 every month into an account that pays interest at 3%, compounded monthly.

    a) How much will she have in her account after 2 years?

    b) How much will be interest?

B **4.** **Buying a house** A newlywed couple is saving for a down payment on a house that they plan to purchase in 4 years. They have budgeted their income so that they can deposit $2500 every 3 months into an investment that earns 5.5%, compounded quarterly.

    a) How much will they have after 4 years?

    b) How much of that will be interest?

5. **Trust fund** A couple invests $1000 in a trust fund each year on their child's birthday. They started the fund on the child's first birthday. The fund pays interest at 6%, compounded annually.

    a) How much will be in the fund on their child's 18th birthday?

    b) How much will be interest?

6. **Application** Mr. Koroloff deposits $5000 into a pension fund every 6 months. The fund pays interest at 6%, compounded semi-annually. He will have the choice of retiring after 25 years or after 30 years. What difference will waiting the extra 5 years make to the future value of his pension?

7. **Communication** Ms. Wong is now 69. When she was 45, she began depositing $5000 each year into an investment earning 5%, compounded annually. Ms. Ellis is also 69 but she began at age 21 depositing $2500 each year into the same type of investment.
   a) How much money did each woman invest?
   b) What is the value of each woman's investment at age 69?
   c) Explain the difference in the investment values.
   d) What advice would you give someone who is planning for retirement? Explain.

8. **Application** Jeremy makes monthly deposits of $100 into an account for 2 years, at 3%, compounded monthly. His friend, Mohsin, makes quarterly deposits of $300 into an account for 2 years, at 3%, compounded quarterly.
   a) How much will each man save?
   b) Both Jeremy and Mohsin will deposit the same amount of money over the 2 years. Explain why their savings will be different.

*C*ASE STUDY

9. Recall Sarah and her financial goals, as described on page 171. She is saving money to buy a used car in 3 years by depositing the same amount into a savings account every month.
   a) What price of car will she be able to afford if she deposits $200 at 3%, compounded monthly?
   b) What price of car will she be able to afford if she increases her deposits to $250 but the interest rate remains the same?
   c) What price of car will she be able to afford if her deposits remain at $200, but she finds an investment that pays 6%, compounded monthly?
   d) Suppose the car ends up costing $12 000. What could Sarah do to save enough money in 3 years?

10. **Communication** List, and then, define any key words that you have learned in this section.

11. **Communication** Design and solve an annuity future value problem.

C 12. **Communication** Describe an annuity whose future value could be calculated using the expression $\dfrac{1000(1.02^5 - 1)}{0.02}$.

EXTEND THE CONCEPTS

13. **Problem Solving** Create a 10-year annuity that has a future value of between $10 000 and $15 000. Include the payment amount, the payment interval, the annual interest rate, and the compounding frequency.

At Durham College, 62% of all students apply to the Ontario Student Assistance Program (OSAP). Of those, 95% actually receive assistance. Six months after graduating, students must begin to make payments to repay their loans.

Stefan finished college 6 months ago and must now begin repaying his student loan. His monthly loan payments will be $200. He has arranged to have the payments withdrawn at the end of each month from an account earning 6% interest, compounded monthly. How much must Stefan deposit in the account today so that the loan payments can be withdrawn for 1 year?

The series of regular loan payments that Stefan will make is an ordinary annuity. The **present value** of an ordinary annuity is the amount of money that must be invested today at a given interest rate, in order to make the regular payments.

DISCOVER

Solve an Annuity Problem Using a Time Line Diagram

Stefan must now begin repaying his student loan. His monthly loan payments of $200 will be withdrawn at the end of each month from an account earning 6% interest, compounded monthly. How much must he deposit in the account today so that the loan payments can be withdrawn for 1 year?

The time line diagram for Stefan's loan payments has been started. Examine it, and then, answer the following questions.

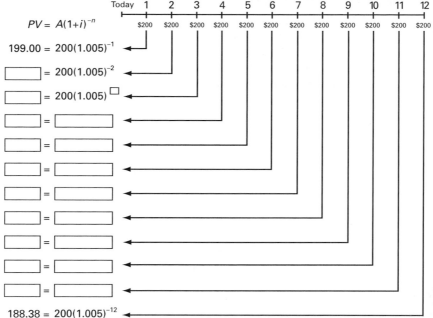

1. Consider the first $200 loan payment. The money that Stefan deposits today will earn interest for 1 month before the payment is withdrawn. In order to make the first $200 loan payment, Stefan has to deposit only $199.00 today. Explain how this was calculated.

2. **a)** How much must Stefan deposit today to make the second $200 payment?
   b) Explain why $188.38 deposited today will be enough to make the 12th and last $200 payment.

3. Copy and complete the time line diagram. Use the following formula to calculate the amount that Stefan must deposit today to make each payment:
   $PV = A(1 + i)^{-n}$, where
   • PV is the present value
   • A is the monthly payment: $200
   • i is the interest rate each month: 0.005
   • n is the number of months the payment earns interest

4. Determine the sum of the present values to determine how much money Stefan must deposit today in order to make all 12 loan payments.

In the Discover, you solved an annuity problem by finding the sum of 12 present values. The sum of those values is the following geometric series:

$$S_{12} = 200(1.005)^{-1} + 200(1.005)^{-2} + 200(1.005)^{-3} + \ldots + 200(1.005)^{-11} + 200(1.005)^{-12}$$

where

- the number of terms is 12, which is the number of payments
- the first term is $200(1.005)^{-1}$, which is the present value of the first payment
- the common ratio is 1.005^{-1}, which is $(1 + i)^{-1}$

Annuity problems, such the one in the Discover, involve geometric series. So, they can be solved using the formula for the sum of any geometric series,

$$S_n = \frac{a(r^n - 1)}{r - 1}$$, where, in the case of an annuity,

- S_n is the sum of the present values of n payments
- n is the number of payments
- a is the present value of the first payment
- r is $(1 + i)^{-1}$

EXAMPLE 1

Student Loan Present Value

Recall Stefan's student loan from page 194. How much must he deposit in his account that earns 6% interest, compounded monthly, so that monthly loan payments of $200 can be withdrawn for 1 year?

Solution

Method 1: Use the formula $S_n = \dfrac{a(r^n - 1)}{r - 1}$

Determine the values of the variables:

$S_{12} = $ 🔲	This is the sum of the series, or the sum of 12 present values.
$n = 12$	There are 12 terms because there are 12 payments.
$a = 200(1.005)^{-1}$	The first term is the present value of the first payment.
$r = 1.005^{-1}$	The common ratio is $(1 + i)^{-1}$, where $i = 0.06 \div 12$ or 0.005.

Use the formula:

$$S_n = \frac{a(r^n - 1)}{r - 1}$$

$$S_{12} = \frac{200(1.005)^{-1}[(1.005^{-1})^{12} - 1]}{1.005^{-1} - 1} \qquad (1.005^{-1})^{12} = 1.005^{-12}$$

$$S_{12} = \frac{200(1.005)^{-1}(1.005^{-12} - 1)}{1.005^{-1} - 1}$$

$$S_{12} \doteq 2323.79$$

Stefan must deposit $2323.79 in the account today, so that the payments can be withdrawn from his account for 1 year.

Method 2: Use the formula $PV = \dfrac{PMT[1-(1+i)^{-n}]}{i}$

The common ratio of a geometric series involving the present value of an ordinary annuity is $(1+i)^{-1}$. Substituting $(1+i)^{-1}$ for r in the geometric series formula results in a formula that can be used to calculate the present value of an annuity:

$$S_n = \frac{a(r^n - 1)}{r - 1} \qquad\qquad r = (1+i)^{-1}$$

$$S_n = \frac{a([(1+i)^{-1}]^n - 1)}{(1+i)^{-1} - 1} \qquad \text{Use } PV \text{ for } S_n \text{ and } PMT \text{ for } a.$$

$$PV = \frac{PMT([(1+i)^{-1}]^n - 1)}{(1+i)^{-1} - 1}$$

This formula can be simplified and expressed as

$$PV = \frac{PMT[1-(1+i)^{-n}]}{i}, \text{ where}$$

- PV is the present value of the annuity
- PMT is the payment
- i is the interest rate per compounding period
- n is the number of payments

Use the formula $PV = \dfrac{PMT[1-(1+i)^{-n}]}{i}$.

Determine the values of the variables:

$PV = $ ❓

$n = 12$	A payment each month for 1 year is 12 payments.
$PMT = 200$	Each payment is $200.
$i = 0.005$	6%, compounded monthly, is $0.06 \div 12$ or 0.005.

See pages 407 and 408 in the Technology Appendix for tips on calculating efficiently on a graphing calculator.

Use the formula:

$$PV = \frac{PMT[1-(1+i)^{-n}]}{i}$$

$$PV = \frac{200[1-(1+0.005)^{-12}]}{0.005}$$

$$PV \doteq 2323.79$$

Scientific Calculator

$\boxed{C}\ 200\ \boxed{\div}\ 0.005\ \boxed{=}\ \boxed{\times}\ \boxed{(}\ 1\ \boxed{-}$
$1.005\ \boxed{y^x}\ 12\ \boxed{(\text{-})}\ \boxed{)}\ \boxed{=}$

Graphing Calculator

$200\ \boxed{\div}\ 0.005\ \boxed{(}\ 1\ \boxed{-}\ 1.005$
$\boxed{\wedge}\ \boxed{(\text{-})}\ 12\ \boxed{)}\ \boxed{\text{ENTER}}$

Stefan must deposit $2323.79 in the account today, so that the payments can be withdrawn from his account for 1 year.

The formula $PV = \dfrac{PMT[1-(1+i)^{-n}]}{i}$ is used when calculating ordinary annuities because its variables relate directly to annuities.

EXAMPLE 2

Sound System Present Value

Alex has purchased a new sound system. The store has offered him a payment plan that consists of $200 payments made at the end of every 3 months, for 2 years. The plan is really a loan that involves interest calculated at 8%, compounded quarterly.

a) What is the actual cost of the system if he pays for it right away?

b) How much will Alex save if he pays right away?

Did You Know?

A store does not have to accept only cash as a method of payment. The store can accept payment by other means such as by cheque or by credit card.

Solution

Draw a time line diagram to organize the given information:

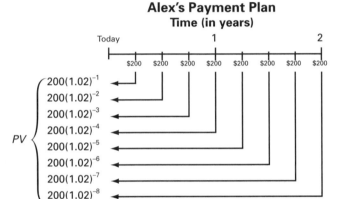

Alex's Payment Plan
Time (in years)

The actual cost of the system is the present value of the annuity.

a) **Method 1: Use the formula** $PV = \dfrac{PMT[1-(1+i)^{-n}]}{i}$

Determine the values of the variables:

$PV =$?

$n = 8$ 4 times a year for 2 years, or 8 payments

$PMT = 200$ Each payment is $200.

$i = 0.02$ 8%, compounded quarterly, is $0.08 \div 4$ or 0.02.

Use the formula:

$$PV = \frac{PMT[1-(1+i)^{-n}]}{i}$$

$$PV = \frac{200[1-(1+0.02)^{-8}]}{0.02}$$

$$PV \doteq 1465.10$$

The actual cost of the system is $1465.10 if Alex pays for it right away.

See page 190 in the previous section and page 412 in the Technology Appendix for more details about the **TVM Solver**.

Method 2: Use a finance application of a graphing calculator

Enter the values of the variables as shown into the **TVM Solver**:

PV=0.00 because it is the variable to be solved for.
PMT is negative, **–200.00**, because money is being paid out.
FV=0.00 because the loan will be paid off when the payments are finished.

Cursor to **PV=0.00**, and then, press ⒜ALPHA ⒠ENTER to solve for **PV**:

The actual cost of the sound system is $1465.10 if Alex pays for it right away.

b) To calculate how much Alex would save by paying right away, subtract the actual cost of the sound system from the total cost of the payment plan:
The payment plan would cost $8 \times \$200 = \$1600$.
The actual cost is $1465.10.
$1600 - 1465.10 = 134.90$

Alex would save $134.90 if he paid right away.

KEY CONCEPTS

- The present value of an ordinary annuity is the amount of money that must be invested today at a given interest rate and compounding frequency in order to provide regular annuity payments over a certain term.

- The present value of an ordinary annuity is the sum of the present values of all the payments.

- The present value of an ordinary annuity can be calculated using the formula
$$PV = \frac{PMT[1-(1+i)^{-n}]}{i}$$, where PV is the present value
   PMT is the payment
   i is the interest rate per compounding period
   n is the number of payments

1. a) Describe two methods for calculating the present value of an annuity.
   b) Which method do you prefer and why?

2. An ordinary annuity consists of $100 payments every 6 months for 4 years, at 3%, compounded semi-annually. What is its present value?
   a) Describe how to create a time line diagram.
   b) How could you use the time line diagram to determine the present value?

PRACTISE

(A) 1. For each ordinary annuity,
   i) sketch a time line diagram
   ii) determine the values of *PMT*, *i*, and *n* for the formula
   $$PV = \frac{PMT[1-(1+i)^{-n}]}{i}$$
   iii) calculate the present value

	Payment ($)	Payment Interval	Interest Rate (%)	Compounding	Term (years)
a)	300	monthly	6	monthly	3
b)	5000	annual	5.8	annual	10
c)	1500	semi-annual	4.6	semi-annual	4
d)	650	quarterly	4	quarterly	5

2. Determine the present value of each ordinary annuity.
   a) yearly payments of $5000 at 7%, compounded annually, for 10 years
   b) quarterly payments of $800 at 3%, compounded quarterly, for 4 years
   c) monthly payments of $300 at 6%, compounded monthly, for 3 years

APPLY THE CONCEPTS

3. Annuity pension Elizabeth has inherited some money. She wants to invest some of it so that she will receive a monthly income of $750 for 10 years, starting 1 month from today. How much must she invest today, at 4.5%, compounded monthly?

(B) 4. Student loan Hugh has 15 monthly payments of $231.73 left on his student loan. Interest on the loan is at 9%, compounded monthly. If the bank will let Hugh pay off his loan today, how much will he have to pay?

5. Application Jenny had $5000 cash for a down payment on a car. She took out a loan at 9%, compounded monthly, to pay for the rest. Her monthly loan payments will be $445.20 for the next 3 years. What is the price of the car?

6. Scholarship fund A service club is creating a fund so that scholarships of $5000 can be paid out to eligible students every year, for 20 years, starting next year. How much does the club need to invest today, at 6.5%, compounded annually?

7. Application Trung was awarded an insurance settlement that consists of an initial payment of $1 000 000. The rest of the settlement has been invested at 7%, compounded semi-annually, so that he will receive payments of $100 000 every 6 months for the next 10 years. What is the value of his settlement?

8. Communication A car insurance 1-year premium can be paid in an annuity of quarterly payments of $300. The quarterly payment option is based on interest at 4%, compounded quarterly. The insurance company also allows its clients to pay in a lump sum equal to the present value of the annuity.
   a) How much is the lump-sum payment?
   b) Would a client always choose the less expensive payment option? Explain.

CASE STUDY

9. Recall Sarah and her goal of buying a car, as described on page 171. A friend wants to sell Sarah his car and is offering her a payment plan of $200 monthly for 3 years. The payment plan is a loan at 9% interest, compounded monthly. Her friend would prefer it if Sarah paid in a lump sum equivalent to the present value of the payment plan.
   a) How much less will she pay for the car if she pays in a lump sum instead of accepting the payment plan?
   b) Why might Sarah prefer the payment plan even though it will cost her more?
   c) Why might it be better for Sarah to save regularly for 3 years, and then, buy a car instead of buying this one now?

10. Communication Design and solve a present value annuity problem.

C **11. Communication** Describe an annuity whose present value could be calculated using the expression $\dfrac{1000(1-1.0025^{-12})}{0.0025}$.

EXTEND THE CONCEPTS

12. Problem Solving Create a 10-year annuity that has a present value of between $10 000 and $15 000. Include the payment amount, the payment interval, the annual interest rate, and the compounding frequency.

Jovan figures that he will need to save $2000 in order to buy a new computer in 2 years. He plans to begin making regular quarterly deposits in 3 months into a savings account that earns 6%, compounded quarterly, for 2 years.

The series of regular deposits, or payments, that Jovan is planning to make is an ordinary annuity. In this case, the annuity's future value, interest rate, and number of payments are known. However, the amount of the regular deposits, or payments, is not known.

DISCOVER

Solve an Annuity Payment Problem Using a Time Line Diagram

Jovan plans to begin making regular quarterly deposits in 3 months, into a savings account that earns 6%, compounded quarterly, for 2 years. What must his regular deposits be in order to achieve his goal of saving $2000 in 2 years?

This time line diagram represents Jovan's savings plan. Examine it, and then, answer the questions on the next page.

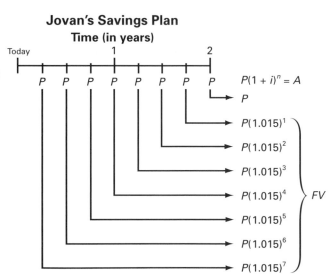

1. **a)** Jovan's deposits will be quarterly. Explain what this means.
   b) His savings plan is an ordinary annuity. Explain what this means.
   c) How many deposits will he make altogether?
   d) The interest rate per compounding period is 0.015, or 1.5%. Explain how this was calculated.

2. **a)** His first deposit will earn interest for 7 compounding periods, not 8. Explain why.
   b) His last deposit will earn no interest. Explain why.

3. The formula $A = P(1 + i)^n$ has been used to write an expression for the final amount of each payment.
   a) What does P represent in each expression?
   b) What does the exponent in each expression represent?

The future value of the annuity is $2000. It is equal to the sum of the final amounts of the 8 deposits:
$$2000 = P + P(1.015)^1 + P(1.015)^2 + \ldots + P(1.015)^6 + P(1.015)^7$$

Solve for P to determine how much each deposit should be:
$$2000 = P + P(1.015)^1 + P(1.015)^2 + \ldots + P(1.015)^6 + P(1.015)^7$$
$$2000 = P(1 + 1.015^1 + 1.015^2 + \ldots + 1.015^6 + 1.015^7)$$
$$2000 \doteq P(8.43)$$
$$\frac{2000}{8.43} = P$$
$$P \doteq 237.25$$

Jovan must make regular quarterly deposits of $237.25 into an account earning 6%, compounded quarterly, in order to achieve his goal of saving $2000 in 2 years.

As you will see in Example 1, the formula for the future value of an ordinary annuity, $FV = \dfrac{PMT[(1+i)^n - 1]}{i}$, can also be used to determine the payment of an annuity, PMT, if you know
• the annuity's future value, FV
• the interest rate per compounding period, i
• the number of payments, n

EXAMPLE 1

Determine Payments From the Future Value of Savings

Recall Jovan's plan to save $2000 in 2 years. What must his regular quarterly deposits be into his savings account that earns 6%, compounded quarterly?

Did You Know?

Piggy banks were named after the orange clay, called "pygg", from which they were originally made.

Solution

Method 1: Use the formula $FV = \dfrac{PMT[(1+i)^n - 1]}{i}$

Determine the values of the variables:

$FV = 2000$

$n = 8$ 4 times/year for 2 years is 8 payments.

$PMT = \boxed{?}$

$i = 0.015$ 6%, compounded quarterly, is $0.06 \div 4$ or 0.015.

Use the formula:

$$FV = \frac{PMT[(1+i)^n - 1]}{i}$$

$$2000 = \frac{PMT(1.015^8 - 1)}{0.015} \qquad \text{Use the cross product rule.}$$

$$(2000)(0.015) = PMT(1.015^8 - 1) \qquad \text{Solve for } PMT.$$

$$\frac{30}{1.015^8 - 1} = PMT$$

$$PMT \doteq 237.17 \qquad \text{Note: The value of \$237.25 in the Discover}$$
is slightly different due to rounding.

Jovan must make regular quarterly deposits of $237.17 to achieve his goal.

See page 190 in this chapter and page 412 in the Technology Appendix for more details about the **TVM Solver**.

Method 2: Use a finance application of a graphing calculator

Enter the values of the variables as shown into the **TVM Solver:**

PV=0.00 because the annuity has no value at the beginning.
PMT=0.00 because it is the variable to be solved for.

Cursor to **PMT=0.00**, and then, press (ALPHA) (ENTER) to solve for **PMT:**

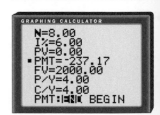

PMT is negative, **–237.17**, because money is paid out.

Jovan must make regular quarterly deposits of $237.17 to achieve his goal.

EXAMPLE 2

Determine Payments From the Present Value of a Loan

A small business has borrowed $10 000 and must begin to repay it today. The payments are to be made at the end of every 6 months over a 5-year term. Interest on the loan is 9%, compounded semi-annually. What will the size of each regular payment be?

Solution

Create a time line diagram to organize the given information:

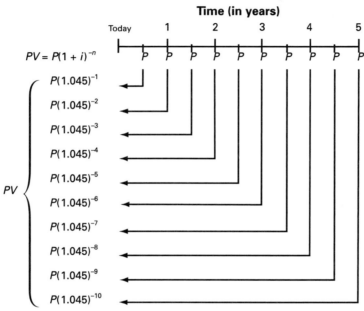

Small Business Loan Payment Plan

- The loan is taken out *before* the repayments begin, so, $10 000 is the present value of the loan.
- The present value formula, $PV = A(1 + i)^{-n}$, can be used to write an expression for the present value of each payment.
- The sum of the present values of the payments is the present value of the loan.

Method 1: Use the formula $PV = \dfrac{PMT[1-(1+i)^{-n}]}{i}$

Determine the values of the variables:

$PV = 10\ 000$

$n = 10$ 2 times/year for 5 years is 10 payments.

$PMT = \boxed{?}$

$i = 0.045$ 9%, compounded semi-annually, is $0.09 \div 2$ or 0.045.

Use the formula:

$$PV = \frac{PMT[1-(1+i)^{-n}]}{i}$$

$$10\ 000 = \frac{PMT(1-1.045^{-10})}{0.045}$$

Use the cross product rule.

$$(10\ 000)(0.045) = PMT(1-1.045^{-10})$$

Solve for PMT.

$$\frac{450}{1-1.045^{-10}} = PMT$$

$$PMT \doteq 1263.79$$

See page 190 in this chapter and page 412 in the Technology Appendix for more details about the **TVM Solver**.

Scientific Calculator

$\boxed{\text{C}}\ 450\ \boxed{\div}\ \boxed{(}\ 1\ \boxed{-}\ 1.045\ \boxed{y^x}\ 10\ \boxed{(-)}\ \boxed{)}\ \boxed{=}$

The regular payments will be $1263.79.

Method 2: Use a finance application of a graphing calculator

Enter the values of the variables as shown into the **TVM Solver**:

PV is negative, **–10 000.00**, because money is paid out.
FV=0.00 because the loan will be paid off when the payments are finished.
PMT=0.00 because it is the variable to be solved for.

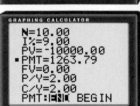

Cursor to **PMT=0.00**, and then, press $\boxed{\text{ALPHA}}\ \boxed{\text{ENTER}}$ to solve for **PMT**:

The regular payments will be $1263.79.

KEY CONCEPTS

- When solving a problem for which you need to determine the payment of an ordinary annuity given its future value, follow these steps.

  Step 1: Use the formula $FV = \frac{PMT[(1+i)^n - 1]}{i}$, where

  FV is the future value
  PMT is the payment
  i is the interest rate per compounding period
  n is the number of payments

  Step 2: Substitute the values of FV, i, and n.

  Step 3: Solve for PMT.

- When solving a problem for which you need to determine the payment of an ordinary annuity given its present value, follow these steps.

  Step 1: Use the formula $PV = \dfrac{PMT[1-(1+i)^{-n}]}{i}$, where

  PV is the present value

  PMT is the payment

  i is the interest rate per compounding period

  n is the number of payments

  Step 2: Substitute the values of PV, i, and n.

  Step 3: Solve for PMT.

DISCUSS THE CONCEPTS

1. Bryn has borrowed $2000. What information does he need in order to determine the amount of his payments?

2. Janis wants to save $5000. What information does she need in order to determine how much she must deposit on a regular basis into a savings account?

3. The known values of an annuity have been substituted into the present value formula: $5000 = \dfrac{PMT[1-(1.002)^{-10}]}{0.002}$

  a) What do you know about the annuity by examining the formula?

  b) Describe how to solve for PMT in order to calculate the payment.

PRACTISE

A 1. For each ordinary annuity,

  i) sketch a time line diagram

  ii) determine the values of FV or PV, i, and n

  iii) calculate the payment

		Payment Interval	Interest Rate (%)	Compounding	Term (years)
a)	PV = $ 1 000	monthly	3	monthly	1
b)	FV = $ 5 000	quarterly	6	quarterly	3
c)	FV = $10 000	semi-annual	7	semi-annual	5
d)	PV = $ 2 500	annual	2.8	annual	2

Did You Know?

When you deposit money into an account you are lending money to the bank. The bank pays you interest for the use of your money. They then lend your money to others at a higher interest rate. That is one of the ways banks make money.

2. Savings Jena wants to save $2000 in 3 years. She plans to begin making regular quarterly deposits in 3 months into an account that earns interest at 4%, compounded quarterly, for 3 years. What must her regular deposits be in order to achieve her goal?

3. Repaying a loan Kendra owes $1000 and plans to begin repaying it. The payments are to be made every month over the next year. Interest on the loan is 6%, compounded monthly. How much will each regular payment be?

B 4. Buying a car Jason wants to save $12 000 to buy a car in 2 years. If his savings account earns interest at 3%, compounded monthly, how much does he need to deposit each month?

5. Retirement Barb's grandmother figures that she will need to have $200 000 at the end of 10 years. The retirement fund that she has chosen earns interest at 6%, compounded semi-annually. How much does she need to invest in the fund every 6 months?

6. Scholarships A scholarship fund pays interest at 5%, compounded annually. If there is $10 000 in the fund now, what scholarship amount could be paid out annually for the next 20 years?

7. A million dollars Corey is 16 years old and dreams of becoming a millionaire by the age of 40. He has found an investment that earns 8%, compounded quarterly. How much does he need to invest every 3 months in order to achieve his dream?

8. Bank account The current balance of Kumar's bank account is $5000. The account earns interest at 4%, compounded semi-annually. How much must he withdraw from his account every 6 months to end up with a zero balance after 4 years?

9. Communication A young couple is in debt. They owe $7412 in student loans, and they have a car loan of $5235 and a credit card balance of $2650. They want to consolidate their loans into a single loan that charges interest at 9%, compounded monthly.
a) What will the monthly payments be if the term of the loan is
i) 5 years? **ii)** 7 years? **iii)** 10 years?
b) It is not always preferable to choose the term with the lowest monthly payment. Explain why.

CASE STUDY

10. Recall Sarah and her student loan of $6000, as described on page 171. Interest on her student loan will be charged at 7.5%, compounded monthly, and the payments are to be made each month.
   a) What will her monthly payments be if the term of the loan is
   i) 5 years?   **ii)** 7 years?   **iii)** 10 years?
   b) Describe a situation for which Sarah might choose to pay off her loan in
   i) 5 years rather than 7 or 10 years
   ii) 10 years rather than 5 or 7 years

11. Application A couple has just purchased $2340 worth of furniture. They pay $1000 down, and the remainder in monthly payments for 1.5 years. Interest is 9%, compounded monthly. How much are the payments?

ACHIEVEMENT Check | Knowledge/Understanding   Thinking/Inquiry/Problem Solving   Communication   Application

12. Canadian financial institutions offer services that require the calculation of the future value, the present value, and payments of annuities.
   a) Identify a service that might use each of the following formulas.
   i) the present value formula   **ii)** the future value formula
   b) Design a problem based on the service and the use of either formula.
   c) Provide a solution for your problem.

 **13. Problem Solving** In order to save $50 000 for the replacement of machinery, a company deposits $10 000 into a fund paying interest at 5%, compounded semi-annually. Equal deposits are then made into the fund every 6 months for 5 years. What is the amount of each deposit?

EXTEND THE CONCEPTS

14. Inquiry An annuity for which the first payment is delayed is called a deferred annuity. A "no payments for 1 year" sale is an example. In these sales, during the year before the first payment is due, the present value of the annuity increases because interest is being charged even though payments are not being made. Investigate deferred payment plans to find out how they work and what they really cost the consumer.

15. Annuity due An annuity for which the payments are made at the beginning of the payment interval is called an annuity due. The future value of an annuity due can be determined by finding the future value as if it were an ordinary annuity, and then, adding on the interest earned on the future value for the last compounding period. Investigate why payments made on a loan that is an annuity due would be less than payments made on an ordinary annuity with the same present value.

CAREER PROFILE

Marketing and Research Assistant

Studying how advertisements affect consumers is a part of marketing. If this sounds appealing, you should consider a career as a marketing and research assistant.

Many careers in marketing require a college diploma. Most colleges offer a diploma program that lasts 2 to 3 years. The entrance requirement is a high school diploma, and some colleges require grade 12 English and Mathematics. Marketing students are introduced to all aspects of marketing—from product research and design to consumer behaviour.

1. **a)** Use a major newspaper or the Internet to find job postings that are related to marketing. Or, go to *www.school.mcgrawhill.ca/resources/* to find links to career web sites. Collect three job postings related to marketing that appeal to you.

   b) Select the job posting that is most suitable to your interests and needs. Prepare a brief summary, using the following headings:
   - Company Name
   - Location
   - Title of Job
   - Salary
   - Job Description
   - Minimum Requirements
   - Why I Chose This Job

2. Some marketing job postings also ask for excellent organizational and communication skills and a positive attitude. Why do you think these are requirements for a job in marketing?

CASE STUDY WRAP-UP

Sarah has recently graduated from community college and has found an interesting job with a good starting salary. Her financial goals include saving enough to buy a used car in 3 years. In addition, she has a $6000 student loan, which she would like to pay off within 10 years.

Throughout this chapter, you have solved problems related to the Case Study using skills that you have learned in the chapter. You are now ready to prepare a report for Sarah, which summarizes what you found out about the following.

a) What price of car can she afford in 3 years if she deposits money regularly into a savings account?

b) Should she accept her friend's offer to buy his car? If so, should she make payments for 3 years or pay in a lump sum?

c) How soon will she be able to pay off her student loan?

When preparing your report,
- refer to the Case Study questions on pages 193, 201, and 209
- provide complete solutions, including all calculations, for each question
- justify, or explain, your answers
- include a list of any materials you used, all your original data, your sources of information, and any formulas, tables, and graphs that you used or created
- use technology, where appropriate

5.1 Arithmetic Series, pages 172–178

1. For each arithmetic series, develop the formula for S_n, the sum of the first n terms. Then, calculate the indicated sum.
   a) $S_n = 3 + 7 + 11 + \ldots$; $S_{12} = $
   b) $S_n = 100 + 80 + 60 + \ldots$; $S_{25} = $
   c) $S_n = -2 - 12 - 22 - \ldots$; $S_{20} = $
   d) $S_n = -100 - 80 - 60 - \ldots$; $S_{10} = $

2. To train for a track meet in 8 weeks, Ken plans to run 3 km/day in his first week of training, 3.5 km/day in the second week, 4 km/day in the third week, and so on until the track meet.
   a) How many kilometres will he run the first week? second week? third week?
   b) Develop a formula to calculate the number of kilometres run in the first n weeks.
   b) How many kilometres will he run in the first 8 weeks of training?

5.2 Geometric Series, pages 179–185

3. For each geometric series, develop the formula for S_n, the sum of the first n terms. Then, calculate the indicated sum.
   a) $S_n = 6 + 12 + 24 + \ldots$; $S_8 = $
   b) $S_n = 625 + 125 + 25 + \ldots$; $S_{10} = $
   c) $S_n = 3 - 6 + 12 - 24 + \ldots$; $S_9 = $
   d) $S_n = 1000 - 100 + 10 - \ldots$; $S_7 = $

4. In stage 1 of a fan-out calling system used by a youth club, the first person calls 3 members. Then, in stage 2, each of those called in stage 1 calls 3 others. In stage 3, each of those called in stage 2 calls 3 others. This continues until everyone on the membership list has been called.
   a) Develop a formula to calculate the number of members called in the first n stages.
   b) How many members are called in 7 stages?

5.3 Future Value of an Ordinary Annuity, pages 186–193

5. For each ordinary annuity,

  i) sketch a time line diagram

  ii) determine the values of PMT, i, and n for the formula $FV = \dfrac{PMT[(1+i)^n - 1]}{i}$

  iii) calculate the future value

	Payment ($)	Payment Interval	Interest Rate (%)	Compounding	Term (years)
a)	200	quarterly	5	quarterly	3
b)	100	monthly	6	monthly	5
c)	2000	semi-annual	3	semi-annual	8

6. Jack is saving to buy a $20 000 car in 3 years. He deposits $550 every month into an account earning interest at 6%, compounded monthly. Will he have enough money to buy the car? Explain.

5.4 Present Value of an Ordinary Annuity, pages 194–201

7. Determine the present value of each ordinary annuity.

  a) monthly payments of $50 for 4 years, at 3%, compounded monthly

  b) quarterly payments of $1200 for 3 years, at 6%, compounded quarterly

8. A charity has budgeted for expenses of $10 000 every 6 months for the next 10 years. A fund is being set up to finance the charity. Interest earned on the fund is 5%, compounded semi-annually. How much money must be in the fund today so that the charity can receive its regular semi-annual income?

9. Sean, a recent college graduate, has monthly loan payments of $200 for 5 years. The interest on the loan is 6%, compounded monthly. If Sean could pay off the loan today, how much would he save?

5.5 Payment of an Ordinary Annuity, pages 202–209

10. The known values for an ordinary annuity have been substituted into the future value formula: $8000 = \dfrac{PMT[(1.03)^{12} - 1]}{0.03}$

  a) What do you know about the annuity from examining the formula?

  b) Describe the steps you would follow to solve for the payment, PMT.

11. Kate's bank account balance is $7400. The account earns interest at 3%, compounded semi-annually. What is the maximum amount she could withdraw every 6 months for 3 years?

12. Henry wants $10 000 for college in 2 years. Interest on his savings is 2.4%, compounded monthly. How much must he deposit monthly?

Practice Test

Achievement Chart Category Connections

Category	Knowledge/Understanding	Thinking/Inquiry/Problem Solving	Communication	Application
Questions	1–10	10	1, 9, 10	2–10

1. For each series,
   i) identify the type as arithmetic or geometric, and give a reason for your choice
   ii) develop the formula for S_n, the sum of the first n terms
   iii) calculate the indicated sum

   a) $S_n = 6 + 9 + 12 + 15 + \dots$; $S_{16} = $ **?**
   b) $S_n = 7 + 14 + 28 + \dots$; $S_{10} = $ **?**
   c) $S_n = 768 + 384 + 192 + \dots$; $S_8 = $ **?**
   d) $S_n = 5 + 1 - 3 - \dots$; $S_{14} = $ **?**

2. Sandi's new part-time job pays her $400 a month, with a $10 raise each month during the first year and a half. What will her total pay be during her first year and a half?

3. A chess tournament has 64 entries. Only the winner of each match remains in the tournament and plays in the next round. How many matches need to be scheduled?

4. An ordinary annuity has monthly payments of $300, for 5 years. Interest is earned at 3%, compounded monthly.
   a) What will the value of the annuity be at the end of its term?
   b) How much interest will have been earned?

5. Paul's grandmother has determined that she needs a monthly income of $2000. How much money does she need to invest today in an ordinary annuity for her to receive a regular income of $2000 a month for 10 years, if the annuity earns 5% interest, compounded monthly?

6. There are 7 semi-annual payments of $325.67 remaining on a loan. If interest on the loan is 8%, compounded semi-annually, what is the present value?

7. Kelly has $23 256 in an account that earns interest at 4%, compounded quarterly. What regular amount could she withdraw from her account at the end of each quarter, over the next 5 years?

8. Jonah is saving $8000 for a new motorcycle in 2 years. How much does he need to deposit at the end of every month into an account that earns interest at 4.5%, compounded monthly?

9. Grace will deposit $2000 into a retirement investment account every 6 months. Interest is 5%, compounded semi-annually.
   a) How much will she save if she begins at age 50 and continues until she retires at 60?
   b) How much will she save if she begins at age 40?
   c) In part b), the term is double that of part a). Will the savings be doubled? Explain why or why not.

ACHIEVEMENT Check | Knowledge/Understanding Thinking/Inquiry/Problem Solving Communication Application

10. Peter is 25 and his goal is to retire at age 55. He has just started to pay $50 a month into a retirement investment that is expected to earn 8%, compounded monthly. He is considering these two options for increasing the future value of his retirement fund:
   Option A: Double his monthly payments every 10 years, that is, at age 35, and then, again at 45
   Option B: Double his monthly payments right away
   Which option should he choose? Justify your advice to Peter using appropriate mathematical calculations and terminology.

Reprinted with special permission King Features Syndicate.

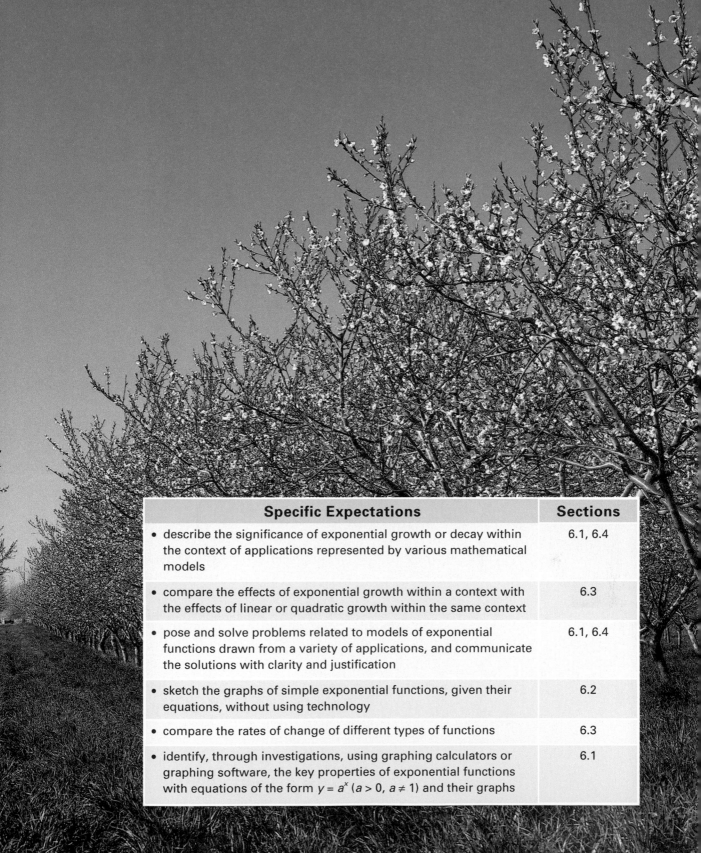

Specific Expectations	Sections
• describe the significance of exponential growth or decay within the context of applications represented by various mathematical models	6.1, 6.4
• compare the effects of exponential growth within a context with the effects of linear or quadratic growth within the same context	6.3
• pose and solve problems related to models of exponential functions drawn from a variety of applications, and communicate the solutions with clarity and justification	6.1, 6.4
• sketch the graphs of simple exponential functions, given their equations, without using technology	6.2
• compare the rates of change of different types of functions	6.3
• identify, through investigations, using graphing calculators or graphing software, the key properties of exponential functions with equations of the form $y = a^x$ ($a > 0$, $a \neq 1$) and their graphs	6.1

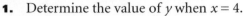

1. Determine the value of y when $x = 4$.
   a) $y = 2x - 1$
   b) $y = 5 - x$
   c) $y = 5 - 3x$
   d) $y = x^2 + 5$
   e) $y = 3x^2$
   f) $y = -2x^2$

2. Determine the value of y when $x = -3$.
   a) $y = x + 2$
   b) $y = 2x - 5$
   c) $y = 6 - x$
   d) $y = x^2$
   e) $y = 4x^2 - 6$
   f) $y = x^2 + 10$

3. Give the slope and the y-intercept of each line.
   a) $y = 2x + 5$
   b) $y = -3x + 4$
   c) $y = -0.2x$
   d) $y = 4$
   e) $2x + y = 6$
   f) $3x - 2y = 6$

4. a) Copy and complete each table of values. Complete the first differences column by subtracting successive y-values. Then, draw the graph of each line.

   i) $y = 2x - 5$

x	y	First Differences
−2	−9	
−1	−7	−7 − (−9) = 2
0	−5	
1		
2		

   ii) $y = -3x + 2$

x	y	First Differences
−2		
−1		
0		
1		
2		

   b) What do the values of the first differences for each equation tell you about the line?

5. Lines with a positive slope are increasing functions. Lines with a negative slope are decreasing functions. Which of the lines in question 3 are increasing functions? Which are decreasing functions?

6. Determine the x-intercept and the y-intercept of each line.
   a) $x + y = 5$
   b) $x - y = -7$
   c) $5x - 3y = 15$

7. Copy and complete each sentence to make it true. Illustrate each with a sketch graph.
   a) Lines rising to the left have a [?] slope.
   b) Lines rising to the right have a [?] slope.
   c) The slope of a horizontal line is [?].
   d) The slope of a vertical line is [?].

8. **a)** What is the equation of the line that is the x-axis?
   b) What is the equation of the line that is the y-axis?

9. Which of the following are quadratic functions? Explain how you can tell.
   a) $2x - 3y = 6$ **b)** $y = 2x^2 - 5$ **c)** $x^2 - y = 10$

10. Without graphing, state the direction of opening and give the coordinates of the vertex of each parabola. State the domain and the range of each.
   a) $y = 0.5x^2$ **b)** $y = -3x^2 + 5$ **c)** $y = -(x + 2)^2 - 1$

Refer to page 410 in the Technology Appendix for details on the standard window.

11. Each parabola has the same shape as $y = x^2$. State the equation of each. The standard window was used for each.

a)
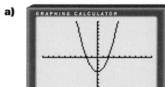

b)
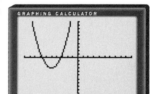

$\mathcal{C}$ASE STUDY

Throughout this chapter, you will be exploring exponential growth. At the end of the chapter, you will apply the concepts to a problem affecting some of Ontario's fruit trees.

Recently, the plum pox virus has threatened plum and peach trees in southern Ontario and other parts of Canada. This virus kills trees or reduces their fruit output. It is spread by aphids, tiny insects that feed on the leaves of stone-fruit trees.

6.1 Exponential Functions

Model an Exponential Function

1. Take a large rectangular sheet of paper and fold it in half. Unfold it and count the number of rectangles formed by the crease. Refold the paper.

2. Fold the paper in half again. Unfold and record the number of rectangles formed by the creases. Refold the paper again.

3. Continue folding in half and recording the number of rectangles until you can no longer fold the paper. Record your answers in a table similar to the one shown.

Number of Folds	Number of Rectangles
0	1
1	2
2	
3	

4. Graph the relation, showing the number of folds on the horizontal axis and the number of rectangles on the vertical axis.

5. If n represents the number of folds and y the number of rectangles, write an equation for the relation.

The relation that you explored in the preceding activity is an exponential function. The general form of the **exponential function** is $y = a^x$, where $a > 0$.

DISCOVER

The Nature of Exponential Functions

1. **a)** Use a graphing calculator to graph the following three functions on the same screen. Then, sketch and label the graphs in your notebook.

   i) $y = 2^x$ **ii)** $y = 3^x$ **iii)** $y = 4^x$

   b) Compare the three graphs. How are they similar? How are they different?

   c) All three graphs have one point in common. What is it?

   d) How does the value of the base of the power affect the shape of the graph?

```
GRAPHING CALCULATOR
WINDOW
  Xmin=-3
  Xmax=3
  Xscl=1
  Ymin=-5
  Ymax=10
  Yscl=1
  Xres=■
```

Refer to pages 410 and 411 in the Technology Appendix for details on graphing.

2. a) Use the same window as in question 1. Graph the following three functions on the same screen. Then, sketch and label the graphs in your notebook.

   i) $y = \left(\dfrac{1}{2}\right)^x$ **ii)** $y = \left(\dfrac{1}{3}\right)^x$ **iii)** $y = \left(\dfrac{1}{4}\right)^x$

  b) Compare the three graphs. How are they similar? How are they different?

  c) All three graphs have one point in common. What is it?

  d) How does the value of the base of the power affect the shape of the graph?

3. a) Predict what the graph of $y = 5^x$ looks like. Make a sketch. As x increases, what happens to the value of y? Check by graphing.

  b) Predict what the graph of $y = \left(\dfrac{1}{5}\right)^x$ looks like. Make a sketch. As x increases, what happens to the value of y? Check by graphing.

4. The general form of the exponential function is $y = a^x$, where $a > 0$. Consider why the restriction $a > 0$ is necessary. Investigate the function $y = (-2)^x$. What happens when you try to graph this relation? Describe what you observe. Look at the table of values. Repeat for another negative value of a.

5. For which value of a, $a > 0$, does the exponential function $y = a^x$ *not* have the basic exponential curve shape? Check by graphing.

EXAMPLE 1

Properties of Exponential Functions

Compare the functions $y = 2^x$ and $y = \left(\dfrac{1}{2}\right)^x$.

a) Give the domain, range, x-intercept, and y-intercept of each.

b) Is each function increasing or decreasing?

Solution

Refer to pages 410 and 411 in the Technology Appendix for details on graphing.

a) Graph both functions on the same screen.

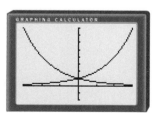

Examine the graphs and check the **TABLE**.

For both, the value of x can be any real number. So, the domain of each function is any real number.

For both, the corresponding y-values are always greater than zero. So, the range of each function is $y > 0$.

Neither graph crosses the x-axis, so neither function has an x-intercept.

Both graphs cross the y-axis at the point $(0, 1)$. So, the y-intercept of each function is 1.

These observations can be summarized, using set notation, as follows.

	Domain	Range	x-intercept	y-intercept
$y = 2^x$	$x \in R$	$y > 0$	none	1
$y = \left(\frac{1}{2}\right)^x$	$x \in R$	$y > 0$	none	1

b) For all possible values of x, as the value of x increases, the value of 2^x increases. So, the function $y = 2^x$ is an increasing function.

For $y = \left(\frac{1}{2}\right)^x$, as the value of x increases, the corresponding value of y decreases. So, $y = \left(\frac{1}{2}\right)^x$ is a decreasing function.

EXAMPLE 2

Model Exponential Decay

Radioactive materials decay over time. The half-life of a radioactive substance is the amount of time required for the amount of radioactive substance to be reduced to half its original quantity. Radium has a half-life of 1600 years.

a) How long will it take for the 16 units of radioactive radium in a sample to decay to 2 units?

b) Use a graph to help you estimate how long it would take to decay to 6 units.

Solution

a) Use a table to analyze the process.

Number of Half-Lives	Amount of Radium
0	16 units
1	8 units
2	4 units
3	2 units

For each half-life, the amount is halved.

It takes three half-lives for 16 units of radium to decay to 2 units. Since each half-life is 1600 years, it will take 3×1600 or 4800 years.

b) The half-life process can be modelled by the exponential function

$y = 16\left(\dfrac{1}{2}\right)^x$, where x is the number of half-lives and y is the amount of

radium. Graph $y = 16(0.5)^x$. Use the (TRACE) function to approximate when $y = 6$.

 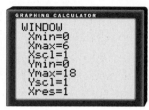 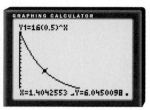

It takes about 1.4 half-lives for 16 units of radium to decay to 6 units. Since each half-life is 1600 years, it will take about 1.4×1600 or 2240 years.

KEY CONCEPTS

- A function of the form $y = a^x$, where $a > 0$ and $a \neq 1$, is an exponential function. Such functions have domain any real number, range greater than zero, y-intercept 1, and no x-intercept.

- For $a > 1$, $y = a^x$ is an increasing function.

- For $0 < a < 1$, $y = a^x$ is a decreasing function.

DISCUSS THE CONCEPTS

1. Describe clearly why $y = 2^x$ is an increasing function, and why the graph soon becomes very steep.

2. Describe clearly why $y = 0.5^x$ is a decreasing function, and why the graph soon becomes very flat.

3. Describe what happens to the exponential function $y = a^x$ when $a = 1$.

PRACTISE

(A) 1. Graph each function. Classify each as increasing or decreasing.

a) $y = 5^x$　　**b)** $y = 10^x$　　**c)** $y = \left(\dfrac{1}{3}\right)^x$　　**d)** $y = (0.2)^x$

2. Graph each function. Classify each as increasing or decreasing.

   a) $y = 1.08^x$ **b)** $y = 0.75^x$ **c)** $y = 1.14^x$

3. Compare the functions $y = 4^x$ and $y = \left(\dfrac{1}{4}\right)^x$.

   a) Give the domain, range, and y-intercept of each.

   b) Which function is increasing? Which is decreasing?

4. Predict which of each pair is increasing more quickly. Graph to check.

   a) $y = 2.5^x, y = 5.2^x$ **b)** $y = 3(1.5)^x, y = 3(1.05)^x$

5. Predict which of each pair is decreasing more quickly. Graph to check.

   a) $y = 0.5^x, y = 0.2^x$ **b)** $y = 120(0.7)^x, y = 120(0.75)^x$

APPLY THE CONCEPTS

6. **Quilt math** A patchwork quilt is made of square patches of material with a similar pattern. The method can be modelled by drawing a large square and then dividing it into smaller squares, as shown.

   a) In your notebook, draw the square after the next division.

   b) Write an exponential function to model the number of squares formed at each step.

   c) Graph the function.

   d) The patchwork quilt is to look like your drawing in part a). The resulting quilt is to be a square with side length 2 m. What should the side length of each patch be?

B 7. A bouncing ball rebounds to half its height on each bounce. The ball was dropped from a height of 500 m. How high would it bounce after it hit the ground for the fifth time?

8. Radiocarbon has a half-life of 5600 years. A piece of excavated wood has one quarter the amount of the radiocarbon that a newly cut piece of the same type of wood has. How old is the excavated wood?

9. Radium has a half-life of 1600 years. A sample contains 160 units of radioactive radium.

   a) How long would it take for the radium to decay to 10 units?

   b) Approximately how long would it take to decay to less than 1 unit?

10. Thinking/Communication Which exponential function represents faster growth, $y = 1.04^x$ or $y = 1.05^x$? Use this information to explain why money should be invested at 5% rather than 4%, if the compounding frequency is the same. How does the same idea apply to borrowing money at 8% or 9%?

11. Communication Mill tailings are a hazardous waste product of uranium mining. The mill tailings contain Thorium-230, which has a half-life of 75 400 years, and Radium-226, which has a half-life of 1600 years. Residents near an old uranium mine are planning a class-action lawsuit against the former owners because of an unusually high rate of lung cancer. The former owners have dismissed the claim, stating that the plant has been closed since 1950, and thus cannot be responsible for any health problems. The site still contains about 750 kg of mill tailings.
Decide whether you support the residents or former owners of the mine. Support your decision with a report discussing the amount of radioactive material that might still be present.

12. Application Dr. Hideyo Noguchi was born in 1876 in Inawashiro, a small fishing village in Japan. Dr. Noguchi successfully overcame a physical disability and childhood poverty to become a doctor. He studied diseases that result from victims' exposure to bacteria. As bacteria multiply in the human body, people get sicker. Antibiotics such as penicillin disrupt the bacterium's ability to divide. Assume that a particular bacterium divides into two every 15 min.

a) Copy the chart into your notebook and complete it for times up to 180 min.

Time (min)	Number of Divisions	Number of Bacteria
0	0	1
15	1	2
30	2	4
45		
60		

b) Graph the data, with Number of Divisions on the horizontal axis and Number of Bacteria on the vertical axis.

c) Write a formula that could be used to find the number of bacteria, y, after n divisions.

d) When there are 1 048 576 bacteria present, how many divisions have occurred? How much time has elapsed?

13. Thinking It takes 45 h for $\frac{7}{8}$ of a highly radioactive sodium isotope to decay. What is the half-life of this isotope?

6.2 | Sketch Graphs of Exponential Functions Without Technology

You need your skills with evaluating powers with integral exponents to graph an exponential function manually.

Recall that $a^0 = 1$ and $a^{-n} = \dfrac{1}{a^n}$. For example, $5^0 = 1$, and $5^{-2} = \dfrac{1}{5^2}$ or $\dfrac{1}{25}$.

DISCOVER

Graph an Exponential Function Manually

1. Copy and complete the table of values for the exponential function $y = 2^x$.

$y = 2^x$

x	y
−4	$\frac{1}{16}$
−3	
−2	
−1	
0	
1	
2	
3	
4	

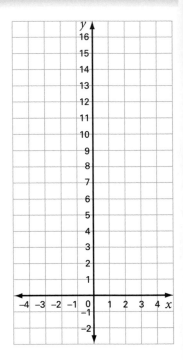

2. Using a sheet of grid paper, label the axes as shown and graph the ordered pairs.
3. What happens to the y-values and the graph as the x-values increase?
4. What is the y-intercept?
5. Is there an x-intercept? Explain why or why not.
6. State the domain and range.

$y = 2^x$ is an example of an exponential function of the form $y = a^x$, with $a > 1$. As the x-values increase, the y-values increase quickly. The graph curves up steeply to the right.
On the left side of the y-axis, the graph gets closer and closer to the x-axis, but does not cross or touch it. There is no x-intercept. The x-axis is called an **asymptote** of the function $y = 2^x$. The equation of the asymptote is $y = 0$.

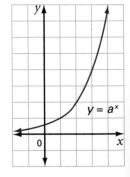

$y = a^x$

EXAMPLE

Graph and Compare Properties

a) On the same set of axes, graph $y=\left(\dfrac{3}{2}\right)^x$ and $y=\left(\dfrac{2}{3}\right)^x$.

b) Give the x-intercept, the y-intercept, the asymptotes, the domain, and the range of each function.

c) Describe the similarities and differences between the two functions. Describe the relationship between the two graphs.

Solution

a) To graph the two functions, find several ordered pairs.

$y=\left(\dfrac{3}{2}\right)^x$

x	y
−2	$\dfrac{4}{9}$
−1	$\dfrac{2}{3}$
0	1
1	$\dfrac{3}{2}$
2	$\dfrac{9}{4}$

$y=\left(\dfrac{2}{3}\right)^x$

x	y
−2	$\dfrac{9}{4}$
−1	$\dfrac{3}{2}$
0	1
1	$\dfrac{2}{3}$
2	$\dfrac{4}{9}$

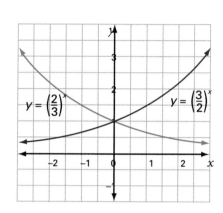

b)

	$y=\left(\dfrac{3}{2}\right)^x$	$y=\left(\dfrac{2}{3}\right)^x$
x-intercept	none	none
y-intercept	1	1
asymptote	x-axis ($y=0$)	x-axis ($y=0$)
domain	all real numbers ($x\in R$)	all real numbers ($x\in R$)
range	all positive real numbers ($y>0$)	all positive real numbers ($y>0$)

c) Both functions have the same y-intercept, domain, range, and asymptote.

The difference between the two is that $y=\left(\dfrac{3}{2}\right)^x$ is an increasing function, but $y=\left(\dfrac{2}{3}\right)^x$ is a decreasing function.

The graphs are reflections of each other in the y-axis.

KEY CONCEPTS

- A table of values can be used to graph an exponential function.

- For exponential functions of the form $y = a^x$, where $a > 0$ and $a \neq 1$:
    There is no x-intercept; the y-intercept is 1.
    There is a horizontal asymptote, the x-axis.
    The equation of the asymptote is $y = 0$.

DISCUSS THE CONCEPTS

1. Explain clearly why the graph of $y = 3^x$ has a y-intercept but no x-intercept. If the domain is all real numbers, why is the range not all real numbers?

2. Describe why the x-axis is an asymptote for the function $y = 3^x$.

3. Explain why the linear function $y = 3x$ does not have an asymptote.

PRACTISE

Ⓐ 1. State the domain and range of each function. If there is an asymptote, give its equation.

a)

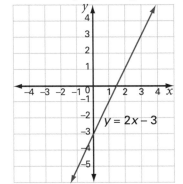
$y = 2x - 3$

b)

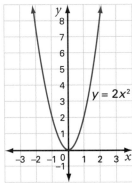
$y = 2x^2$

c)

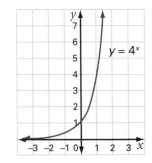
$y = 4^x$

d)

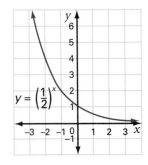
$y = \left(\frac{1}{2}\right)^x$

2. Copy and complete the table of values for each function. Draw the graph of each on grid paper. State the y-intercept, asymptote, domain, and range for each.

a) $y = 3^x$

x	y
−3	
−2	
−1	
0	
1	
2	
3	

b) $y = 5^x$

x	y
−3	
−2	
−1	
0	
1	
2	
3	

c) $y = \left(\frac{1}{2}\right)^x$

x	y
−3	
−2	
−1	
0	
1	
2	
3	

d) $y = \left(\frac{1}{3}\right)^x$

x	y
−3	
−2	
−1	
0	
1	
2	
3	

B **3.** **a)** Make a table of values and graph $y = 5^x$ and $y = \left(\frac{1}{5}\right)^x$ on the same set of axes.

b) State the y-intercept, the domain, the range, and the equation of the asymptote for each.

c) How do the graphs differ? How are they related?

4. **a)** Make a table of values and graph $y = \left(\frac{5}{3}\right)^x$ and $y = \left(\frac{3}{5}\right)^x$ on the same set of axes.

b) State the y-intercept, the domain, the range, and the equation of the asymptote for each.

c) How do the graphs differ? How are they related?

APPLY THE CONCEPTS

5. **Cooling rate** When hot coffee is poured into a mug it cools fairly quickly. The temperature of the coffee was recorded at 2-min intervals after it was poured.

Time (min)	0	2	4	6	8	10	12
Temperature of Coffee (°C)	90	79	69	62	55	49	45

a) Graph the relation, showing time on the horizontal axis and temperature on the vertical axis. Describe the graph.

b) Is the coffee cooling at a constant rate?

c) Use your graph to predict the temperature of the coffee after 20 min.

6. An antique cost $500 and its value is increasing by 20% each year. The value, y, of the antique after x years is given by the function $y = 500(1.20)^x$.

a) What is the domain in this case? Why?

b) Construct a table of values for the value at the end of each of the first 5 years after the antique is bought.

c) Graph the function. Then, state the range and the y-intercept. Is this is an increasing or a decreasing function?

7. **Depreciation** A restaurant owner knows that the furniture in the dining room loses 40% of its value each year. It cost $80 000 to furnish the dining room. The value of the furniture after x years is given by the function $y = 80\,000(0.6)^x$.
   a) What is the domain in this case? Why?
   b) Construct a table of values for the value at the end of each of the first 5 years after the furniture was bought.
   c) Graph the function. Is this is an increasing or a decreasing function?
   d) What is the range of the function? In this context, what might a realistic range be? Explain.

ACHIEVEMENT Check   Knowledge/Understanding   Thinking/Inquiry/Problem Solving   Communication   Application

8. Use tables of values to graph $y = a^x$ for at least three very different values of a. In your notebook, sketch each graph. Label the intercepts and asymptotes. Include a table of values. Record the domain and range. Identify when the function is increasing or decreasing. Write a brief description explaining how to easily identify each of these key features of functions from their graphs.

9. **Organ transplants in Canada** The number of organ transplants in Canada has been increasing. Transplant patients have also been living longer. The table shows the total number of liver and heart transplants performed in Canada from 1990 to 1998.

Year	Liver	Heart
1990	193	161
1991	217	149
1992	218	122
1993	290	172
1994	300	169
1995	319	181
1996	349	169
1997	340	160
1998	338	154

Graph the data. Write a report about the implications of the data for the number of transplants to be done in the future. Include answers to the following in your report.
   a) Which set of data (liver or heart) would you use to make predictions about future numbers of transplants? Justify your selection.
   b) How would you model the data and make predictions about future numbers of transplants?
   c) What factors might affect the reliability of your predictions?

6.3 | Compare Rates of Change

If you were a farmer or an investor, you would be very interested in the rate of growth. One way of comparing growth mathematically is to look at how a change in one variable affects the other variable.

How does the exponential growth defined by $y = 2^x$ compare to the growth of the linear function $y = 2x$ and of the quadratic function $y = x^2$?

DISCOVER

Compare Rates of Change

1. Copy the table into your notebook. Complete it by finding the values of y for each function. Use additional values for x, if you wish.

x	$y = 2x$	$y = x^2$	$y = 2^x$
0			
1			
2			
4			
5			
10			
20			

2. Circle the greatest y-value in each row in your table.
3. Is there any x-value for which all three y-values are the same? If so, which value?
4. Which function seems to represent the slowest growth? Why?
5. Which function seems to represent the fastest growth? Is this true for all the x-values?

In the preceding activity, you probably noticed that you circled some values for $y = x^2$ that were the greatest. But it soon becomes clear that, as x increases, the values for $y = 2^x$ become very great. The y-values for $x = 5$, 10, and 20 clearly show this.

Refer to pages 410 and 411 in the Technology Appendix for details on graphing.

A graph of the three functions also illustrates this. The window is adjusted to show larger y-values.

  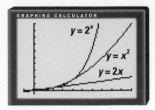

You can see that the line $y = 2x$ is generally below the other two graphs. The graph of $y = 2^x$ is growing faster than the graph of $y = x^2$. Beyond their point of intersection, $(4, 16)$, the graph of $y = 2^x$ is above the graph of $y = x^2$. For $x > 4$, the function $y = 2^x$ has the fastest growth.

An effective way of analyzing the rate of change is to calculate the differences in the y-values for fixed increases in the x-values. Different types of functions have different patterns in their first differences.

For example, consider the linear function $y = 2x$.

Observe that the first differences have a constant value, 2. This constant rate of change is the same as the slope of the line.

$y = 2x$

x	y	First Differences
0	0	
1	2	$2 - 0 = 2$
2	4	$4 - 2 = 2$
3	6	$6 - 4 = 2$
4	8	$8 - 6 = 2$

DISCOVER

Compare First Differences for Different Types of Functions

Use first differences to compare the rates of change of $y = x^2$ and $y = 2^x$.

1. Copy the tables into your notebook. Complete the columns for the y-values and calculate the first differences.

$y = x^2$

x	y	First Differences
0		
1		
2		
3		
4		
5		

$y = 2^x$

x	y	First Differences
0		
1		
2		
3		
4		
5		

2. What does the first differences column indicate about $y = x^2$ and $y = 2^x$? Is there a constant rate of change for either?

3. Describe the sequence formed by the first differences for $y = x^2$. Is the sequence arithmetic or geometric? Explain.

4. Describe the sequence formed by the first differences for $y = 2^x$. Is the sequence arithmetic or geometric? Explain.

EXAMPLE

Compare Linear, Quadratic, and Exponential Growth

Construct tables of values for $x = 1, 2, 3, 4,$ and 5, and compare the first differences for the functions $y = 3x$, $y = 3x^2$, and $y = 3^x$. Describe the rate of change in each.

Solution

$y = 3x$

x	y	First Differences
0	0	
1	3	3
2	6	3
3	9	3
4	12	3
5	15	3

$y = 3x^2$

x	y	First Differences
0	0	
1	3	3
2	12	9
3	27	15
4	48	21
5	75	27

$y = 3^x$

x	y	First Differences
0	1	
1	3	2
2	9	6
3	27	18
4	81	54
5	243	162

For the linear function $y = 3x$, the first differences have a constant value of 3. This constant rate of change, 3, is the slope of the line.

For the quadratic function $y = 3x^2$, the first differences are 3, 9, 15, 21, and 27. The terms increase by 6 each time. They form an arithmetic sequence with first term 3 and common difference 6.

For the exponential function $y = 3^x$, the first differences are 2, 6, 18, 54, and 162. The terms increase by a factor of 3 each time. They form a geometric sequence with first term 2 and common ratio 3.

KEY CONCEPTS

- Linear growth:
    graph is a straight line
    first differences are constant, the rate of change is constant

- Quadratic growth:
    graph is a parabola
    first differences form an arithmetic sequence

- Exponential growth:
    graph is an exponential curve
    first differences form a geometric sequence

1. How can you classify functions as linear, quadratic, or exponential from the equation? Explain clearly.

2. How can you use first differences to classify functions as linear, quadratic, or exponential? Explain clearly, giving examples.

3. How can you classify functions as linear, quadratic, or exponential from the graph? Explain clearly.

PRACTISE **A 1.** Classify each graph as an example of linear, quadratic, or exponential growth.

a)
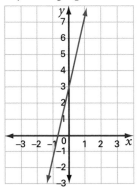

b)
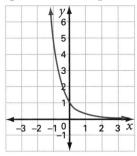

c)
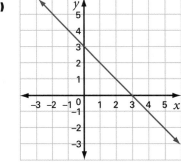

d)
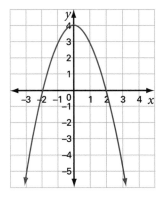

2. Without graphing, classify each of the following as linear, quadratic, or exponential growth.

a) $y = 1.5x^2$ **b)** $y = 1.5^x$ **c)** $y = 1.5x$

3. a) Copy the table into your notebook and complete it for the functions $y = 5x$, $y = 5x^2$, and $y = 5^x$.

x	y = 5x	y = 5x²	y = 5ˣ
0			
1			
2			
3			
4			
5			

If you use a graphing calculator, use the window settings shown.

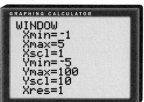

b) Circle the greatest value in each row.

c) On the same set of axes, graph the three functions.

d) Which graph represents the slowest growth? the fastest growth?

4. Copy each table into your notebook. Calculate the first differences column for each. Use the results to describe the type of growth represented by each function.

a) $y = 4x$

x	y
0	
1	
2	
3	
4	
5	

b) $y = 4x^2$

x	y
0	
1	
2	
3	
4	
5	

c) $y = 4^x$

x	y
0	
1	
2	
3	
4	
5	

APPLY THE CONCEPTS

5. Data were collected and recorded for several situations. Classify each type of growth as linear, quadratic, or exponential. Give reasons for your answers.

Did You Know?

A joey is a baby kangaroo.

a)

Week Number	0	1	2	3	4	5
Joey's Mass (g)	10	20	40	80	160	320

b)

Side Length (cm)	1	2	3	4	5	6
Surface Area (cm²)	6	24	54	96	150	216

c)

Day Number	1	2	3	4	5	6
Distance Run (km)	2	4	6	8	10	12

B **6.** Two companies rent backhoes for construction work. Each company uses a formula to determine the rental cost, C, for t hours, as follows:

Rent-All: $C = 500 + 25t$　　　　　　　U-dig: $C = 50 + 5^t$

a) Copy and complete the table of values to determine the cost of renting from each company.

Time, t (h)	Cost to Rent, C ($)	
	Rent-All	U-dig
1		
2		
3		
4		
5		

b) For what number of hours would it be cheaper to rent from Rent-All? from U-dig?

7. **Thinking/Communication** At a carnival, there are two dice games. Each costs $0.05 for a single play and each involves the roll of a single die. The roll number is represented by n and the amount you win, in cents, is w.

In the square game, the formula for the amount you win is $w = n^2$.
For example, if you roll a 3, $w = 3^2$ and you win $0.09.

In the exponent game, the formula for the amount you win is $w = 2^n$.
For example, if you roll a 4, $w = 2^4$ and you win $0.16.

In which game are you likely to win more money? Write a short report to justify your selection.

8. **Problem Solving** Compare the rate of growth represented by the functions

$$y = \frac{1}{2}x,\ y = \frac{1}{2}x^2,\ \text{and } y = \left(\frac{1}{2}\right)^x$$ by making a table of values and graphing each.

a) Which function is always increasing?

b) Which function both increases and decreases? For what x-values is it increasing? decreasing?

c) Which function is always decreasing?

d) State the x- and y-intercepts for each function.

9. Make a table of values and graph each function:

$$y = \frac{1}{4}x, \ y = \frac{1}{4}x^2, \ \text{and} \ y = \left(\frac{1}{4}\right)^x.$$

a) Use the graphs to classify the type of growth for each function.
b) Calculate the first differences for each function.
c) Explain the type of growth represented by each function using the first differences.
d) Compare your answers in part c) with those in part a).

EXTEND THE CONCEPTS

10. The table shows the population of Canada from 1891 to 2001.

Year	1891	1901	1911	1921	1931	1941	1951	1961	1971	1981	1991	2001
Population (in millions)	4.8	5.4	7.2	8.8	10.4	11.5	14.0	18.2	21.6	24.0	27.1	31.1

a) Graph the data.
b) Describe the curve representing the growth of Canada's population.
c) Calculate the first differences column. Does this support your observation in part b)?
d) Determine the percent increase for each 10-year period. Then, calculate the average percent increase for any 10-year period.
e) Use this average percent increase to form an exponential function to describe Canada's population growth.
f) Compare the values determined by the exponential function with the actual values. Explain your method.
g) For what years are the values close? Not close?

11. The world population did not reach 1 billion until 1804. It reached 6 billion in 1999. The table gives the year at which each billion was reached:

Population (billions)	1	2	3	4	5	6
Year	1804	1927	1960	1974	1987	1999

a) Draw a graph using the data in the table.
b) Does the growth appear to be exponential?
c) Determine the first differences. What do they indicate about the type of growth?

There are many situations involving some type of growth or decay that can be modelled by exponential functions. Population growth and price increases can be modelled by increasing exponential functions. Declining populations and depreciation in value can be represented by decreasing exponential functions.

DISCOVER

Distinguish Increase From Decrease Using the Compound Interest Model

Imagine that you invested $1000 in each of two mutual funds.
Fund A earns 2% interest per month, compounding monthly.
Fund B loses 2% in value each month.

1. Copy and complete the table to find the value of each investment for a 5-month period.

Month	0	1	2	3	4	5	n
Fund A	1000	1020					$1000(1.02)^n$
Fund B	1000	980					

2. What formula gives the value of the investment in Fund B after n months?
3. Compare the formulas for the two funds. How can you tell from the formula whether the amount is increasing or decreasing?

EXAMPLE 1

Exponential Growth

The increase in the consumer price index (CPI) for the year 2000 was 3.2%. This means that prices increased an average of 3.2% from the previous year. A pair of designer jeans cost $89.99 in 2000. If the cost of jeans increases at the same rate as the CPI, determine the cost of these jeans each year for the next 3 years. Assume a constant CPI increase for the next 3 years.

Solution

To model the cost of the jeans, use the compound interest formula:
$A = P(1 + i)^n$ with $P = 89.99$ and $i = 3.2\%$ or 0.032
Cost of the jeans in 2000 $= 89.99(1.032)^n$
Cost of the jeans in 2001 $= 89.99(1.032)^1$
$$\doteq 92.87$$
Cost of the jeans in 2002 $= 89.99(1.032)^2$
$$\doteq 95.84$$
Cost of the jeans in 2003 $= 89.99(1.032)^3$
$$\doteq 98.91$$
Assuming that the increase is constant at 3.2% per year, then, the cost of the jeans each year for the next 3 years is $92.87, $95.84, and $98.91.

EXAMPLE 2

Exponential Decay

The price of a new car is $24 599. Its value depreciates by 30% each year. What is the depreciated value of the car after 4 years?

Solution

Use the compound interest formula in modified form. Since the car is losing value each year, use $(1 - i)$ instead of $(1 + i)$.
$A = P(1 - i)^n$ with $P = 24\,599$ and $i = 30\%$ or 0.30
Car value $= 24\,599(1 - 0.30)^n$
$$= 24\,599(0.70)^n$$
To find the value after 4 years, use $n = 4$.
Car value $= 24\,599(0.70)^4$
$$\doteq 5906.22$$
The value of the car after 4 years is $5906.22.

Many problems can be solved by substituting values into the equation for an exponential function. In some situations, you might need to use a graph of the exponential function to solve the problem.

EXAMPLE 3

Predict Population

In 2001, the population of Canada was 31 051 000. The annual growth rate is assumed to be 1%.

a) Predict the population of Canada in 2005, to the nearest thousand.

b) Use a graph of an exponential function to predict in what year the population will be more than 33 000 000.

Solution

a) The exponential function that models the population growth of Canada is
$P = 31\ 051\ 000(1.01)^n$, where P represents the population and n is the number of years since 2001.
In 2005, $n = 2005 - 2001$ or 4.
$P = 31\ 051\ 000(1.01)^4$
$P \doteq 32\ 312\ 000$
The projected population of Canada in 2005 is approximately 32 312 000.

See pages 410 and 411 in the Technology Appendix for details on graphing.

b) Graph
$y = 31\ 051\ 000(1.01)^n$.
Use the (TRACE) function to find the value of x when y becomes greater than 33 000 000.

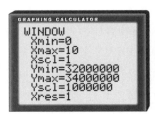 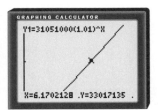

The population exceeds 33 000 000 during the sixth year after 2001.
Using this model, the population will be more than 33 000 000 in 2007.

EXAMPLE 4

Half-Life

The hydrogen isotope tritium is radioactive, with a half-life of 12.5 years. A sample contains 35.2 units of radioactive tritium. What amount would remain after 25 years?

Solution

The amount remaining can be modelled using the exponential function

$A = 35.2\left(\dfrac{1}{2}\right)^n$, where A is the amount of tritium and n is the number of half-lives.

For 25 years, $n = 25 \div 12.5$ or 2.

$A = 35.2\left(\dfrac{1}{2}\right)^n$

$A = 35.2(0.5)^2$

$A = 8.8$

After 25 years, 8.8 units of radioactive tritium would remain in the sample.

KEY CONCEPTS

- Exponential growth or decay can be modelled using an exponential function of the form $y = ka^x$, where k is the initial amount, a is the change factor, and x is the number of changes over a given time.
  For growth, $a > 1$.   For decay or reduction, $0 < a < 1$.

DISCUSS THE CONCEPTS

1. An exponential function is defined as $y = a^x$, where $a > 0$ and $a \neq 1$. For what values of a can this function be used to model exponential growth? exponential decay? Explain.

2. Refer to Example 2 above. How would you change the solution if the annual rate of depreciation was 25%?

3. Refer to Example 4 above. How would you change the solution to determine the amount after 50 years?

PRACTISE

A 1. Write an exponential function to model each investment situation. Determine the final amount for each.

	Initial Amount	Annual Interest Rate	Time	Compounding Period
a)	$100	6%	3 years	semi-annual
b)	$4500	4.5%	5 years	quarterly
c)	$250	5%	20 months	monthly

2. Assume that prices of consumer goods continue to rise at a rate of 3.2% per year. Predict the prices of the items below, each year, for the next 5 years.
   a) 1-year college tuition: $2417   b) mountain bike: $600

APPLY THE CONCEPTS

3. In Canada the population of children in the age group 0–14 years has been declining by 0.7% per year. The population of this age group in 1999 was about 5 917 000. Write an exponential function to model this population decline.

B 4. The population of Ontario in 1999 was about 11 514 000. At that time the annual growth rate was 1.1%.
   a) Write an expression to model the population growth of Ontario.
   b) Use this expression to predict the population of Ontario in 2010, and then, 2020.

5. The average rate of increase or decrease in the population of some birds in Canada is listed.

Bird Type	Rate of Change per Year
Loon	+3.3%
Canada goose	+51.1%
Red-headed woodpecker	−5.3%
Red-winged blackbird	−1.5%
Black-capped chickadee	+2.5%

  a) Write an exponential function to model the growth or decline in the numbers of each bird species.

  b) Use a sample of 1000 of each bird species and predict the number 5 years from now, assuming the given rates of change continue.

  c) Suggest reasons why some bird populations are increasing and others are decreasing.

6. **Application** The value of a computer used in a business can be depreciated at a rate of 30% each year.

  a) Write an expression to model the decrease in value of a computer with initial value $3200.

  b) Determine the value of the computer after 2 years.

  c) The company plans to replace the computer at the end of 5 years. The company offers the old computers to employees to buy for home use. Calculate the depreciated value of the computer at the end of 5 years.

7. Radium-221 has a half-life of 30 s. If a sample contains 96 units of radium-221, how much would remain after each time has elapsed?

  a) 30 s   **b)** 2 min   **c)** 5 min

8. An isotope of sodium, Na-24, has a half-life of 15 h. If a sample contains 3.6 units of Na-24, find the amount remaining after each time has passed.

  a) 30 h   **b)** 60 h   **c)** 5 days

9. **Communication** The population of Newfoundland has been decreasing at an annual rate of 0.8%. The population in 1999 was about 541 000.

  a) Write an exponential function to model the population decrease of Newfoundland.

  b) Use this exponential function to predict the population of Newfoundland in the year 2025.

  c) How reliable do you think this prediction is? Suggest reasons and discuss your ideas with a partner.

10. Problem Solving The population of Yukon in 1999 was 30 633, while the population of Nunavut was 27 039. The population was decreasing in Yukon at a rate of 3.0% per year, and increasing in Nunavut at a rate of 2.3% per year. Assuming these growth rates continue, when would the population of Nunavut be more than that of Yukon?

EXTEND THE CONCEPTS

11. Mr. and Mrs. Rahid have $10 000 to invest. They could invest it for 5 years in a guaranteed investment certificate (GIC) paying 4.5%, compounded monthly. However, economists predict that the interest rate is likely to rise on GICs in the next year, perhaps to as much as 5.5%, compounded monthly.

a) Determine the amount of their investment at the end of 5 years if they invest in the GIC paying 4.5%, compounded monthly.

b) Determine the amount at the end of 5 years if they put the $10 000 into a savings account paying 0.75%, compounded monthly, for 1 year, and then, invest the amount in the account in a GIC for 4 years at 5.5%, compounded monthly.

c) Write a proposal to advise the Rahids of the best way to invest their $10 000. Include reasons to support your proposal.

12. The population of London, Ontario, for 1995 to 1999, is given.

Year	1995	1996	1997	1998	1999
Population (thousands)	408.0	410.4	431.1	415.9	418.7

a) Calculate the average annual growth rate for the years 1995 to 1999.

b) Use this average growth rate to write an expression to model the population growth in London.

c) Use this expression to predict the population of London in 2020.

13. Salary increases What effect does a low salary increase in one year have in the long run? Lyle began to work as a mechanic at BrantLine Cycle making $18 000. He plans to work his way up in the company, to become head mechanic, perhaps even a partner. Lyle can see himself working at BrantLine Cycle for 30 years. Employees have been receiving salary increases of 4% per year for the last few years.

a) Assuming a 4% increase each year, predict Lyle's salary 30 years from now.

b) Unfortunately, this year the employees received only a 1% salary increase. Use this new fact to predict Lyle's salary 30 years from now. Assume that next year and in following years the increase is 4%.

c) What effect will this 1% increase for 1 year have on Lyle's predicted salary after 30 years?

CAREER PROFILE

Environmental Waste Management Technician

Port Hope is a charming town, situated on Lake Ontario, about 70 km east of Toronto. The town is well known for its many antique shops and wonderful bakeries.

Unfortunately, the outer limits of the town are not so nice. Port Hope was once a chemical dumping ground for by-products of uranium ore mines. These by-products are commonly known as radioactive tailings.

Chemical technicians, working for consulting firms or government agencies, frequently conduct tests of soil, water, and air to monitor the amounts of radioactive materials in the area. As an environmental waste management technician, your responsibilities could include carrying out these tests.

The entire waste industry is growing. This is because the increasing population is producing more waste, which needs to be disposed of safely. Large amounts of money are and will continue to be spent in the area of waste management.

Training for a career in this area involves a 2- or 3-year program at a community college. One of the first courses you would take in this type of program is health and safety. College graduates who want to continue their studies can transfer to a university offering a degree program in environmental studies or in environmental engineering, specializing in waste management.

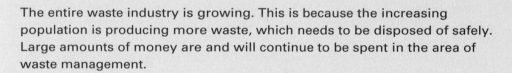

1. Kirkland Lake College, in northern Ontario, offers a 2-year Waste Facility Management Technician program.
   Go to *www.school.mcgrawhill.ca/resources/* and follow the links to learn more about the program.

2. If you would prefer to live at home to reduce your education costs but still want to study in a waste management program, contact your local college to see if it offers a similar program.

CASE STUDY WRAP-UP

Recently, the plum pox virus has threatened plum and peach trees in southern Ontario and other parts of Canada. This virus kills trees or reduces their fruit output. It is spread by aphids, tiny insects that feed on the leaves of stone-fruit trees.

In the first year of detection in southern Ontario, about 40 000 peach and plum trees had to be destroyed. This was about 3% of the total number of trees in southern Ontario.

1. About how many peach and plum trees were in southern Ontario before the virus hit?

2. Suppose that in the next year, 3% of the trees have to be destroyed again. Write an expression to model this situation. Calculate the number of trees that would have to be destroyed.

3. If this pattern continues, after how many years will only half the original number of trees remain?

Review

6.1 Exponential Functions, pages 220–225

1. Graph each function. Classify each as increasing or decreasing. State the y-intercept for each.

   a) $y = 6^x$

   b) $y = 0.6^x$

   c) $y = \left(\dfrac{1}{6}\right)^x$

2. Compare the functions $y = 10^x$ and $y = \left(\dfrac{1}{10}\right)^x$.

   a) Give the domain, range, and y-intercept of each.

   b) Which function is increasing? Which is decreasing?

3. Radiocarbon has a half-life of 5600 years. A piece of excavated wood has $\dfrac{1}{8}$ the amount of radiocarbon that a newly cut piece of the same kind of wood has. How old is the piece of excavated wood?

6.2 Sketch Graphs of Exponential Functions Without Technology, pages 226–230

4. State the domain and the range of each function. If there is an asymptote, give its equation.

   a)

   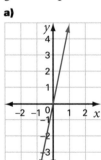

   b)

   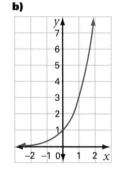

   c)

   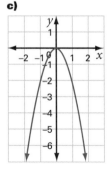

   d)

   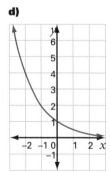

5. Graph $y = 3^x$ and $y = \left(\dfrac{1}{3}\right)^x$ on the same set of axes.

   a) State the domain, the range, the y-intercept, and the equation of the asymptote for each.

   b) How are the two graphs related?

6.3 Compare Rates of Change, pages 231–237

6. Copy the tables into your notebook and complete them.

a) $y = 4x$

x	y	First Differences
0		
1		
2		
3		
4		
5		

b) $y = 4x^2$

x	y	First Differences
0		
1		
2		
3		
4		
5		

c) $y = 4^x$

x	y	First Differences
0		
1		
2		
3		
4		
5		

Describe the pattern in each first differences column. Use the patterns to describe the type of growth represented by each function.

7. **a)** Copy and complete the table of values. Graph the three functions.

x	$y = \frac{1}{4}x$	$y = \frac{1}{4}x^2$	$y = \left(\frac{1}{4}\right)^x$
–8			
–4			
–1			
0			
1			
4			
8			

b) Which function is always increasing? Which is always decreasing?

c) Which function both decreases and increases? For what x-values is it increasing? For what x-values is it decreasing?

d) State the x- and y-intercepts for each function.

6.4 Applications of Exponential Functions, pages 238–243

8. A tractor depreciates at a rate of 30% per year. The purchase price was $32 600.

a) Write an exponential function to model the depreciated value of the tractor.

b) What is the value of the tractor after 4 years?

9. Cedar Grove Elementary School currently has 870 students. The student population is decreasing by 5% per year. If the population drops below 700, the school may be closed.

a) Write an expression to model the population decline.

b) Determine the predicted population 5 years from now.

c) Using a graph, or another method, predict when the population will drop below 700.

d) How reliable is your prediction? What steps might the parent council take to prevent the school from closing?

Practice Test

Achievement Chart Category Connections

Category	Knowledge/Understanding	Thinking/Inquiry/Problem Solving	Communication	Application
Questions	1–9	2, 5, 7, 8, 9	4, 5, 9	2–4, 6–9

1. Classify each function as increasing or decreasing. State the y-intercept, the domain, the range, and the equation of the asymptote.

a) 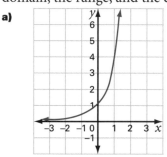   **b)**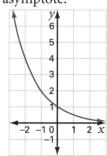

2. A type of bacterium divides into two every 30 min. There are now 5 bacteria in a culture. How many will there be after each time period?

a) 1 h   **b)** $2\frac{1}{2}$ h   **c)** 1 day

3. **a)** Copy and complete the table for $y = 4^x$.

x	y
−2	
−1	
0	
1	
2	

     b) Graph the ordered pairs and label the graph.

     c) State the y-intercept and the equation of the asymptote.

4. Copy and complete the tables of values. Describe the pattern in each first differences column. Explain how the patterns are related to the type of growth represented by each function.

a) $y = 3x$

x	y	First Differences
0		
1		
2		
3		
4		
5		

b) $y = 3x^2$

x	y	First Differences
0		
1		
2		
3		
4		
5		

c) $y = 3^x$

x	y	First Differences
0		
1		
2		
3		
4		
5		

5. a) Which function is increasing more quickly? Explain how you can tell.
$y = 25(1.05)^x$ or $y = 25(1.08)^x$

b) Which function is decreasing more quickly? Explain.
$y = 18(0.6)^x$ or $y = 18(0.06)^x$

6. For each of the graphs shown, state the domain and range. Then state the equation of the asymptote.

a)

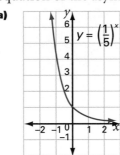

b)

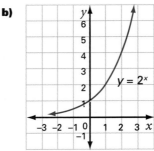

7. Assume that the prices of consumer goods are increasing by 3.2% each year. Write an exponential function to model the increase in prices. Use your model to predict the price of each item 10 years from now.

a) 1 L of milk that cost $1.29 now

b) one dozen golf balls that cost $29.99 now

8. Golden Brae Secondary School has a capacity of 1600 students. The school, which is in a growing area of a city, now has 1150 students. The school population is increasing at a rate of 5% per year.

a) Write an exponential function to model the growth of the school's population.

b) Use the model to predict the population in 2 years.

c) Using a graph, or another method, predict when the school population will be greater than its capacity.

ACHIEVEMENT Check Knowledge/Understanding Thinking/Inquiry/Problem Solving Communication Application

9. Refer to question 12 in 6.4 Applications of Exponential Functions on page 243. Find the corresponding data for your own town or another of your choice. Graph the data and compare them with London's growth predictions. Make up data for two other towns, one that has linear population growth and another that has quadratic growth. Make a composite graph of all these graphs. Describe how you can predict the type of growth from not very much data.

CHAPTER 7 VEHICLE COSTS

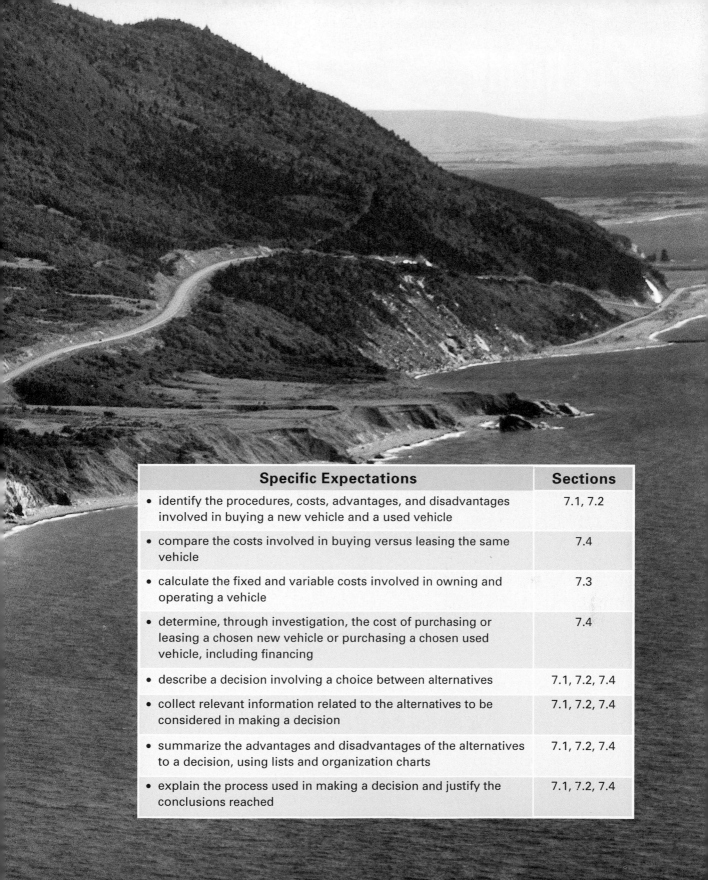

Specific Expectations	Sections
• identify the procedures, costs, advantages, and disadvantages involved in buying a new vehicle and a used vehicle	7.1, 7.2
• compare the costs involved in buying versus leasing the same vehicle	7.4
• calculate the fixed and variable costs involved in owning and operating a vehicle	7.3
• determine, through investigation, the cost of purchasing or leasing a chosen new vehicle or purchasing a chosen used vehicle, including financing	7.4
• describe a decision involving a choice between alternatives	7.1, 7.2, 7.4
• collect relevant information related to the alternatives to be considered in making a decision	7.1, 7.2, 7.4
• summarize the advantages and disadvantages of the alternatives to a decision, using lists and organization charts	7.1, 7.2, 7.4
• explain the process used in making a decision and justify the conclusions reached	7.1, 7.2, 7.4

$\mathcal{G}$et Ready...

1. Evaluate.
   a) $134 \times 6 \div 2$
   b) $768 \times 324 \div 30$
   c) $(1.2 + 2.8)(3.2 + 3.6)$
   d) $\dfrac{27(4)}{6 \times 3}$

2. Calculate. Round to two decimal places, if necessary.
   a) $\dfrac{5.6(3.2)}{3}$
   b) $34.67 + (50.25)(31.02)$
   c) $(18\ 990)(0.08) + \dfrac{1234}{2}$

3. Calculate each value.
   a) 1.5% of 10
   b) 8% of 56
   c) 13% of 362

4. Find each amount.
   a) 15% of $9000
   b) 7% of $8700
   c) 8% of $7900
   d) 10% of $15 000
   e) 15% of $25
   f) 5% of $35 600

5. Evaluate.
   a) $\$10\ 000 + 2 \times \$640$
   b) 15% of $2000 + $2000

6. Find the missing percent in each.
   a) 3 = ?% of 30
   b) 15 = ?% of 75
   c) 245 = ?% of 490
   d) $1800 = ?% of $9000

7. Calculate each value, rounding your answers to two decimal places.
   a) $2400(1.09^5)$
   b) $15\ 600(1 + 0.07)^4$
   c) $568.34(1.045)^{36}$

8. Calculate the cost of each gasoline purchase.
   a) 55 L at 82.3¢/L
   b) 38.5 L at 79.9¢/L
   c) 75 L at 84.5¢/L

9. Calculate the total cost, including 7% GST and 8% PST, both calculated on the sale price of each vehicle.
   a) used car $5400
   b) new motorcycle $8900
   c) new pickup truck $32 500
   d) used van $7500

10. Neil bought a new car for $20 000. He sold the car 1 year later for $15 000. What percent of the original value has the car lost? In other words, what is the rate of depreciation?

11. Vicky's car has a yearly maintenance service, which costs $99.98. When she brings the car in the mechanic finds that it needs its brake pads replaced. The brake pads cost $115.00. How much does Vicky have to pay for this service visit, including taxes at 15%?

12. Find the amount of each car loan.
    a) $6000 at 8%, compounded annually, for 4 years
    b) $9500 at 11%, compounded semi-annually, for 5 years
    c) $8000 at 2.5%, compounded annually, for 3 years

13. The total cost, including all taxes, of Amit's new car is $25 985. He makes a down payment of $5000 and takes a bank loan for the balance. He agrees to repay the loan with equal monthly payments over 4 years. The bank charges 8% interest, compounded monthly.
    a) Determine the principal of his loan.
    b) Determine the amount of the loan.

14. Charlene decides to lease a new car for 3 years at $298 per month. When she signs the leasing agreement, she must make a down payment of $2200, pay other charges of $325, and make the first month's payment. Assume that all required taxes are included in these amounts.
    a) How much must she pay to drive the car away from the dealer's lot?
    b) How much will the car cost her in total for the 3-year lease?

*C*ASE STUDY

Throughout this chapter, you will be following the process of buying a vehicle. At the end of the chapter, you will be asked to prepare a report. Keep two or three pages of your notebook free for exercises that involve the Case Study, and to keep track of the information you are learning that relates to the Case Study.

Theo is an 18-year-old student. He has just obtained his G2 driver's licence. He has saved $5000 from his part-time job and would like to buy his own car. Theo is not sure what kind of car he can buy with this amount of money.

In this chapter, you will learn the mathematical skills Theo needs to help him decide what vehicle best suits his wants, needs, and budget.

7.1 Investigate Buying a New Vehicle

Ah, owning a car... the freedom, the open roads, the wind through your hair...the price of gas, insurance, maintenance...oh-oh, this picture is not so perfect, is it?

There are a lot of advantages to owning a car, one of which is a feeling of independence. There are also many responsibilities. You can learn about these responsibilities in a driver training course.

There are many things to think about before you are ready to buy a vehicle. You should consider the following.
- What kind of vehicle do you want or need?
- What can you afford?
- What purchase option is best for you?
- How will you know if you are paying a fair price for the vehicle?
- Will you know how to bargain or negotiate with a car dealer?

Deciding what you need and/or want, whether in a vehicle or some other product, is the first step in a purchase. Some of the questions you should ask yourself are listed below.

Needs Assessment	
Questions	**Reasons**
1. How much money can I afford to spend?	This will limit the vehicles that are available in your price range.

Questions	Reasons
2. What type of vehicle am I interested in? Do I want a sporty car, a 4-wheel drive, or a sport utility vehicle (SUV)? Do I want an automatic or manual transmission? Have I been properly trained to drive a standard shift vehicle?	Insurance premiums are based on several factors. The age of the owner and the type of vehicle are two key factors. For example, if you drive a sports car, you are statistically more likely to be in a collision. So, your insurance premiums would be higher.
3. Will I be driving anyone else around, such as family members or friends, on a regular basis? If so, how many passengers will I be driving? Will I need a large cargo area? Do I have a large or small garage, carport, or parking space?	These factors will help you determine what size of vehicle you want.
4. Where and how far will I typically be driving? Will I be driving mostly in the city or will I be commuting long distances between towns?	The answers to these questions will tell you how important the vehicle's fuel efficiency and reliability are.
5. How will I be paying for my vehicle?	There are several ways you can pay for a vehicle: • cash, for straight-out ownership • finance, where you make a down payment right away and pay the rest in monthly instalments • lease, where little or no money is paid down and you pay monthly instalments with an option to own the car at the end of the lease
6. Will I buy a new vehicle or a used one?	Newer cars are typically less expensive to maintain. But a good used car is equally, if not more, cost-effective. To avoid making a decision that would lead to expensive repairs, you need to thoroughly research the vehicle before purchasing.

In this section, only new cars will be considered.

DISCOVER

Decisions, Decisions, Decisions!

The needs-assessment list shown above illustrates some of the many questions you should think about when considering buying a new vehicle.

Go through the assessment while thinking about your or your family's situation. Create a list of what you want and/or need in a vehicle. Use the following headings and questions to start organizing your list.

1. *Passengers.* Yes or no? If yes, how many and how often, say, in a typical week?

2. *Commute.* What distances will you be travelling on regular basis?

3. *Use of vehicle.* How will you be using the vehicle? For leisure use or for work?

4. *Size and/or type of vehicle.* What type of vehicle will meet your needs?

EXAMPLE 1

CASE STUDY

Choose the Type of Vehicle

Theo is thinking of buying a car. He has been driving the family car on weekends when he goes out with his friends. His part-time job is close to home, so he usually walks to work. Theo goes to college in a town 25 km away from home. He has been using public transit to get to the college, but will use his car once he gets one. What type of car would meet his needs?

Solution

Consider some basic questions first.

Passengers? Theo will not be using the car to drive his family around since they have a family car. But he will be driving his friends around from time to time.

Commute? Since Theo works close to home, he does not need a car to drive to work. Theo will use the car for commuting to and from school. Since the school is 25 km away, he will be travelling 50 km per day, 5 days per week.

Use of Vehicle? He will use the car for commuting and for leisure use on the weekends.

Size/type of vehicle? Since Theo will be driving quite a lot, he will need a car that is reliable and fuel-efficient. He will not need a large car or one with a lot of cargo space.

What other things should Theo consider in deciding what type of car he should get?

Organize the information.

Price (how much can he afford?)	up to $5000
Transmission	automatic (though there is no information given, it is the most common transmission used in North America)
Commute	25 km each way to school, for a total of 50 km per day
Passengers	not regularly

Discuss with a partner other factors that could be added to the list.

Theo is a student with only a part-time job, but he is driving a large distance each week. So, an energy-efficient small car would probably best meet his needs.

Once you have narrowed down the type of vehicle that suits you, you will need to research the vehicle and the vehicle market. The main classes of vehicles are two-seater, sub-compact, compact, mid-size, full-size, wagon, minivan, pickup truck, special purpose (such as SUVs), and van.

DISCOVER

So, What Can I Buy?

You can do this activity in either of the two ways listed below.

- Go to automobile dealerships' web sites and search for the vehicles that are available in different classes.
  You may use the links at *www.school.mcgrawhill.ca/resources/*.
- Visit dealerships near you. Ask a salesperson if the "sticker" or listed price is the *actual* price paid by the consumer. Include notes on the response in your report.

Make up your own wish list. Choose three vehicles (of different classes) that you would consider owning.

1. Find what options are available for each.
2. Note the base price of each vehicle, the cost of the options you would choose, and what purchasing options are available.
3. Determine how much it would cost to buy each vehicle.

EXAMPLE 2

Costs of a New Vehicle

After a lot of research, Joanna has decided to buy a new sports sedan. This car meets both her needs and budget. The base price is $18 815. She would like the power-group options package, which costs $800, and the Anti-Lock Braking System (ABS), for $779. Joanna prefers a 5-speed manual transmission, which is included in the base price, because it is more fuel-efficient. Since she likes music, she also decides to buy the Premium Sound System with 6-disc CD changer for $500.

a) What is the price of the car with the options that Joanna has selected?
b) Additional vehicle purchasing costs are as follows:
      vehicle title fees and registration: $150
      industry-specific taxes such as air-conditioning tax and fuel conservation
         tax: $75
      dealer pre-delivery, freight, and administrative charges: $920
   How much will the car cost after the additional costs have been added?
c) In addition, taxes must be paid. The GST and PST amount to 15% of the total. How much will Joanna pay in taxes?
d) What is the total cost of the car that Joanna plans to buy?

Solution

a) Add the cost of the options chosen to the base price of the car.
   $800 + $779 + $500 = $2079
   The base price of the car is $18 815. With the options the total is
   $18 815 + $2079 = $20 894.

   The cost of the car, with the options that Joanna has selected, is $20 894.

b) To find the total additional costs, add the costs listed.
$150 + $75 + $920 = $1145

The cost, including additional charges, is $20 894 + $1145 = $22 039.

c) To find the amount of taxes, multiply the cost of the car, with options and additional costs, by 0.15. Taxes are charged on the car cost and related fees.
$22 039.00 × 0.15 = $3305.85
Joanna must pay $3305.85 in taxes.

d) To find the total cost of the car, add the taxes to the pre-taxes cost:
$22 039.00 + $3305.85 = $25 344.85
Note: The total cost, including taxes, can be found in one step by multiplying the cost by 1.15.
$22 039.00 × 1.15 = $25 344.85

The total cost of Joanna's new car is $25 344.85.

EXAMPLE 3

Trade in an Older Vehicle

Amrinder plans to trade in his old car for a new SUV. The cost of the new vehicle, with the options that he has selected, is $29 995. The dealer will give Amrinder $3000 for his trade-in. The additional charges for freight, post-delivery inspection (PDI), registration, and licensing amount to $1200. With taxes at 15%, how much will Amrinder pay for the new SUV?

Solution
Price of SUV including additional charges = $29 995 + $1200
= $31 195

Taxes = $31 195.00 × 0.15
= $4679.25

Total cost of the SUV = Price including additional charges + taxes
= $31 195.00 + $4679.25
= $35 874.25

The price of the SUV will be discounted by the amount of the trade-in.
Price after trade-in = Total cost − trade-in allowance
= $35 874.25 − $3000.00
= $32 874.25

The total amount that Amrinder will have to pay for the new SUV is $32 874.25.

EXAMPLE 4

Car Dealership Discount Sales

Sophia saw an advertisement for a car sale: "DEALER'S CLEARANCE—all demo models on sale!" She went to the dealership to look around. She learned that cars that were used for demonstrations in the showroom or for test-drives had been discounted by 4%. Since she could not choose the options, she read all the specifications on the window stickers carefully. The sticker price of the car she chose was $22 330.

a) What is the price of the car with the discount?

b) The salesperson told Sophia that there was room for negotiation. What do you think this means? Discuss it with a partner.

Solution

a) To find the cost of the car after the discount, calculate the discount. Then, subtract the discount from the list price of the car. The discount is 4% of $22 330.

Discount = $22 330.00 × 0.04
= $893.20

Now, subtract the discount from the list price.

Sale price = $22 330.00 − $893.20
= $21 436.80

The price of the car, with the discount, before taxes, is $21 436.80.

b) The salesperson said there was room for negotiation. This usually means that the price on the sticker, or the manufacturer's suggested retail price, is not necessarily the selling price. These prices are higher than the cost of the dealer's purchase price. That is so the dealer can make a profit. The amount of profit will be determined by how high a price the dealer sells the vehicles for and/or sales volume.

When salespeople are willing to negotiate and accept a lower offer, they are willing to reduce their profit to get a sale now. This is why you need to research the selling price of a vehicle by going to several dealers.

KEY CONCEPTS

- A decision involves making a choice among a number of objects or courses of action based on a set of criteria. Before going to a dealership, prepare a list of the features you want in your vehicle. Know what your specific driving needs are. Have a spending limit in mind. A needs assessment is the first step in buying your new vehicle.

- The costs involved in buying a vehicle include the base price of the vehicle, the options, and applicable taxes. Vehicle registration fees and licensing, freight, and delivery charges are additional costs.

DISCUSS THE CONCEPTS

1. Ted and Despina have one child and a dog. They wish to buy a vehicle. Discuss, with a partner, what things they should consider in deciding what vehicle would best meet their needs.

2. Elysia just received a large bonus at work. She decides to use the money toward the purchase of her dream vehicle, a sports car. In addition to the cost of the car and options, write out a list of other expenses she may have to pay. List some dealer-installed options Elysia might like on her sports car.

APPLY THE CONCEPTS

A 1. A car costs $17 990. How much will it cost, including 15% taxes?

2. Ron wants to buy a new pickup truck for $40 495. How much will the truck cost after the additional charges of $1200?

3. Jahra has had her eye on a new SUV. It is now on sale at a discount of 4.5%. The vehicle costs $24 995. How much will it cost after the discount?

4. Sports cars are usually quite expensive. Imagine that a dealer will give you a discount of 15% off a new sports car priced at $61 000. How much will the car cost after the discount?

B **5.** Martha is buying a new van for $18 995, plus an options package costing $895. The dealer will charge freight and PDI at $860, and registration and licensing at $175. How much will the vehicle cost in total, before taxes?

6. A new vehicle is advertised for a selling price of $22 495, fully optioned.
   a) Write a definition for fully optioned that you think makes sense. Discuss your definition with a partner.
   b) If taxes are 15%, how much will this car cost?

7. **Demo sale** At the end of a model year, most dealers have a "demo sale" to clear out any unsold new vehicles. A new car costs $16 390 and is to be discounted by 5%. How much will the car cost, before taxes?

8. **Communication** Alex and Christina have two children and are expecting another. They live in the city, but travel to their family cottage most weekends during the summer. They will need a new vehicle once the baby has arrived. What kind of vehicle do you think they need? Explain your reasoning.

9. **Courier** Vasil runs his own courier company. His business has grown, so, he can no longer do all his deliveries on his bicycle. He will use his vehicle for deliveries in the city only. What kind of vehicle should he buy?

10. **Inquiry/Communication** If you own a vehicle, at some point you will probably need a new set of tires. Write down all that you would need to think about before buying a set of tires. Which consideration could be the deciding factor?

EXTEND THE CONCEPTS

C **11.** **Zero-percent financing** Zero-percent financing means that you pay the actual cost of a vehicle plus taxes with no interest charges.
   a) On a $27 000 vehicle, over a 48-month term, how much would the monthly payment be? Assume that 15% taxes are charged.
   b) Dealers usually offer this type of financing later in the model year. Find some advertisements that offer zero-percent financing. Create a presentation of the advertisements you find.

12. **Dealership project** Follow the links at *www.school.mcgrawhill.ca/resources/* to go to a car dealer's web site. Select a vehicle that you like. Go to the "build your own car" section and choose the options that you want. In your journal, record the web sites you visited, the model and options you selected, and how much the car will cost. Go to a dealership that specializes in that make/model. Ask a salesperson how much the same car would cost. Write a report about the dealership you went to, the prices you were given, and what the experience was like.

7.2 Compare Buying a New Versus a Used Vehicle

How do you decide whether to buy a new vehicle or a pre-owned (used) vehicle? There are many options to consider. You need to learn about the different vehicle markets. You can buy a new or used vehicle from a dealership, or a used vehicle from a private individual.

New cars lose their value, or depreciate, very quickly. **Depreciation** is the amount by which the value goes down every year. The greatest percent of depreciation of a vehicle happens in the first year. If you were to buy the same vehicle used, you would save a lot of money, which you could invest elsewhere! Review your needs assessment before beginning your search.

DISCOVER

Compare Buying New Versus Used

1. Some advantages and disadvantages of buying a new vehicle are listed.

Advantages	Disadvantages
Has desired options	Expensive
New-car warranty	Warranty may not cover unexpected problems
No previous drivers	Depreciation—greatest in first few years
No wear and tear	Could be a "lemon"—contain manufacturing defects

In your notebook, make a similar list, adding at least two other advantages and disadvantages of buying a new vehicle.

2. This list shows some advantages and disadvantages of buying a used vehicle.

Advantages	Disadvantages
Lower cost	Hidden mechanical problems
Less depreciation	May be poorly maintained
Used-car warranty	No warranty if buying from a private seller after new-car warranty expires

Make a similar list of your own, adding at least two other advantages and disadvantages of buying a used vehicle.

Dealers use the *Black Book* to set the price of a used vehicle. Vehicles are sorted according to make/model and options, and ranked by their condition—extra-clean, clean, average, and rough.

EXAMPLE 1

Depreciation

The sports sedan is considered by consumer advocates to be a good investment, both as a new and as a used car. A new sports sedan sells for $23 756. The table shows the value of this type of vehicle, in clean condition, over a 5-year span.

Age in years	Value
1	$15 700
2	$14 400
3	$13 200
4	$10 900
5	$10 550

a) Express the depreciation in the first year as a percent. Round to the nearest percent.

b) Calculate the percent depreciation from the fourth year to the fifth year.

c) Compare the answers to parts a) and b). What do you notice?

Solution

a) Amount of depreciation during the first year = New price − 1-year-old value
Amount of depreciation = $23 756 − $15 700
$$= \$8056$$

$$\text{Percent depreciation} = \frac{\text{amount of depreciation}}{\text{original price}} \times 100$$

$$= \frac{8056}{23\ 756} \times 100$$

$$\doteq 34$$

The car depreciated approximately 34% in the first year.

b) Amount of depreciation from fourth year to fifth year = $10 900 − $10 550
$$= \$350$$

$$\text{Percent depreciation} = \frac{\text{amount of depreciation}}{\text{original price}} \times 100$$

$$= \frac{350}{10\ 900} \times 100$$

$$\doteq 3$$

The depreciation between the fourth and fifth years is approximately 3%.

c) The depreciation in the first year is more than 10 times the depreciation between the fourth and fifth years. This is value, or money, the new-car owner has lost simply by buying a new vehicle!

DISCOVER

Reading Classified Car Advertisements

As discussed in 7.1 Investigate Buying a New Vehicle, research is the key to making a good buy. When you are looking to buy a used vehicle, you need to understand the abbreviations that are commonly used in vehicle advertisements.

Glossary of Common Terms in Classified Advertisements for Vehicles	
4X4: 4-wheel drive	Loaded/All Pwr Opts: Fully loaded/all power options—air conditioning, power seats, power brakes, power windows, power locks
5 spd: 5-speed transmission (manual gear shifting)	
ABS: anti-lock braking system	mint, excl, A1: condition of the vehicle—mint, excellent, A-1
AC: air conditioning	
Alloy whls: alloy wheels	obo: or best offer—means the seller will consider a price other than that asked for
Auto: automatic transmission (automatic gear shifting)	
CD/cass: CD player/cassette	PB: power brakes
E-test: emissions test	PL: power locks
full pwr: full power	PS: power steering
FWD: front-wheel drive	PW: power windows
Grn/saddle int., lthr: green/saddle interior, leather	pwr sunrf: power sunroof
	tilt: tilt steering wheel

1995 Sedan, Euro. Four door, immaculate 1 owner vehicle, loaded. $5450 cert. 555-7234.

1998 Sporty Sedan, 5 spd, loaded, E-test/cert, 135K $8200. 555-7871

1997 SUV. Red, mint, 65 000 km, 4X4, power windows, brakes, locks. Cruise, ABS, t-tops. $10 500 cert. Paul, 555-0637.

1999 Sedan, 41,000 kms, all original car. $14 675 cert. 555-4995.

2000 Compact. Auto, AM/FM cassette. Red with grey int. 101 000 hwy kms. Good condition. $12 900 firm. 555-6737

Use the advertisements shown, and one of your own chosen from a newspaper or auto-trade magazine, to complete the following questions.

1. Are there any abbreviations in the advertisements that are not found in the Glossary above? Make note of these abbreviations and give a brief description of what you think they mean.

2. List the options for the SUV and for the compact car. What options might the other vehicles have? Explain how you came to your conclusions.

3. Determine what condition each of the vehicles is in. Is each vehicle certified?

4. Why might the advertiser not list the condition of the vehicle? Give reasons for your opinion.

5. Which vehicle would you buy? List your reasons.

6. Which vehicle are you least likely to consider? List your reasons.

When considering making a large purchase, such as a vehicle, try to gather as much information as possible to help you make an informed decision. Consult friends and family members who are experienced with vehicles, consult consumer magazines or books in the public library, or do research on the Internet.

EXAMPLE 2

Research to Help Make a Decision

Lynn has gone to Tri-City Cars in her search for a used car. Lynn does not know much about cars. What strategies might Lynn use to help her make a wise decision?

Solution

Before she went to the car lot, Lynn did some research on the Internet. She found a web site that listed a series of questions she can ask when looking at used vehicles. These questions will help her decide if a car is in good condition or not.

Questions	Reasons
What is the price of the car?	Look for signs the dealer/seller may want to negotiate.
How long has the car been on the lot?	If the car has been on the lot for a long time, the dealer may be eager to get rid of it. This could mean that the car has serious problems.
Are there service records?	These help you determine if the car was well maintained or not.
Has this car ever been in a collision?	This tells you about the condition of the car.
How did the dealer obtain the car?	The car might have been stolen and sold to the dealer.
Is there a warranty?	Some dealers will give used-car warranties.

Consider similar questions when you call about an advertisement in a newspaper or car magazine. Sometimes it helps to prepare a script of your conversation. This will prepare you for how to ask your questions and for what the possible responses might be.

A script might look like this:

Lynn: "Hello, I'm calling about the car you have for sale. I would like to ask some questions."

Seller: "Sure, go ahead."

Lynn: "You haven't listed the price of the car in the ad. How much are you selling it for?

Seller: "$8000, but there's some flexibility on that." *OR* "$8000, but I'll take the best offer." ("flexibility" in the first response and "best offer" in the second response mean that the seller wants to negotiate on the price.)

Lynn: "How long have you had the car?"

Seller: "Only a couple of months."

Lynn: "Do you have all the service records?"

Seller: "Yes, the car has been well maintained." *OR* "No, but don't worry. There's nothing wrong with it." (The second response could signal problems with the car.)

Lynn would then ask the remaining questions in the table.

EXAMPLE 3

CASE STUDY

Choose a Used Vehicle

Theo wants to see what kind of car he can purchase with the $5000 he has. Theo realizes he cannot buy a new car for $5000, without financing. He considers looking at used cars. He searches through the classified advertisements of the local newspaper. Theo is most interested in five advertisements shown.

A: 1995 Sporty Compact. 2 door. V6, auto, air, loaded. A1 shape. $3699, 1 yr. warranty. EZ Auto 555-1769.

B: 1996 Compact. Two door. Hatchback. 77 000 km. Incredible 60 mpg. $4975 obo, Tom 555-6464.

C: 1995 Compact, 2dr blue auto air 4 cyl 73K cert $4000. 555-6444.

D: 1994 Red, 2 door, 179 000 km, economical. $3250 cert. call 555-3531 evgs.

E: 1995 Roadster, $3500 CERT, 2 door, 5 speed, 143 000 km. Excellent condition, 12 mth warranty. A. V. Cars 555-3118

Discuss probable reasons why Theo chose the first two vehicles. What are some possible disadvantages that he should be alert for, or ask about, when he calls the seller?

Solution

Vehicle A: This car is in A-1 condition, with many options (loaded), including air conditioning and automatic transmission. The price is within Theo's range and the dealer includes a warranty. Fuel consumption is not listed—a sporty V6 might use a lot of gas.

Vehicle B: This car is small, with an easily accessed trunk (hatchback). The car has great fuel economy (60 mpg or 4.7 L/100 km). The seller states "or best offer," so, there is room to negotiate the price. This advertisement does not give the condition of the vehicle.

EXAMPLE 4

Extended Warranty

Crystal has decided to buy a 2-year-old pickup truck for her renovation business. She is saving a lot of money by buying used and the truck seems to be in good condition. The dealer has all the service records from the original owner. The dealer provides extended warranties at an additional cost.

The three available extended warranty plans are shown in the table. If the price of the pickup truck is $14 440 and Crystal decides to buy the plan C warranty, how much will she pay for the pickup truck before taxes?

Plan	Cost	Length of Coverage	
		Parts	**Labour**
A	$300	60 days	30 days
B	$450	90 days	90 days
C	$1000	5 years/ 100 000 km	5 years/ 100 000 km

Solution

To find the cost, add the cost of Plan C to the price of the pickup.

Cost = Price of truck + warranty plan C

$\quad\quad$ = $14 440 + $1000

$\quad\quad$ = $15 440

Crystal will pay $15 440 before taxes for the pickup truck with the plan C warranty.

KEY CONCEPTS

- There are many advantages and disadvantages to buying a used or new vehicle. Since a vehicle is a major purchase, you need to be sure you are making a good decision.

- You must assess what your needs and wants are, and then, carefully research what is available to meet them.

DISCUSS THE CONCEPTS

One question you should ask yourself when considering buying a used car is why the current owner is selling it. Discuss, with a partner, some of the reasons why people sell their cars.

1. Why might the original owner sell a 1-year-old car?

2. Why might the original owner sell an 8-year-old car?

3. Why might the second owner of a vehicle resell it after 1 year?

APPLY THE CONCEPTS

A **1.** A 3-year-old car is valued at $9230. The same car, 1 year later, is valued at $8400. By what percent has the value of the car depreciated?

2. A new sports car depreciates 35% in the first year. If the car is worth $86 000 new, how much will it be worth after 1 year?

3. Current model year cars used for demonstration purposes are sold at a discount by most dealers. Theo's parents bought their van for $30 875 at one of these sales. A new van like the one they bought usually sells for $34 350. By what percent was the van discounted?

4. A demo-model sedan is selling for $22 340. Adam compares that price to the price of a new model of $25 270. What percent would he save if he bought the demo model?

5. Depreciation is very important to business owners. For income tax purposes, a vehicle used for the business is a capital cost allowance to the business. The tax preparer can claim 30% of the value of the car in the preceding year. If a car is valued at $23 000, how much can be claimed?

B **6.** A local new car dealership also sells used cars. The dealership offers an extended warranty on its vehicles for $1200 extra. Magda is buying a 1-year-old van for her family. The van sells for $17 995. How much will Magda pay, including taxes at 15%, if she also buys the extended warranty?

7. A used vehicle dealership buys a car for $6200. Before the dealer can resell the car, it needs the following repairs: $175 for brakes, $50 for interior cleaning, and $750 for a new paint job. The dealership charges an additional 12% handling fee on top of the price of the car and repairs.
a) Calculate the total cost of car with all the repairs.
b) How much will the dealership sell the car for?

Did You Know?

A car repair shop must give you a warranty on repair work of 90 days or 5000 km, whichever comes first.

8. Example 2 Continue the script from the solution to Example 2. Discuss the script with a partner. Write additional questions that you can ask when calling private sellers.

9. Example 3 In the solution to Example 3, the first two advertisements are discussed. In your journal or notebook, complete the discussion for the remaining three vehicles advertised. Alternatively, clip some advertisements from your local newspaper and discuss the possible advantages and disadvantages of each of the vehicles.

10. Inquiry Helen is considering buying a used vehicle. She has found two advertisements for the same model vehicle. One is priced $1000 less than the other. Write out at least three questions Helen should ask when she calls the sellers.

11. Communication Compare the two vehicles in the advertisements. Which vehicle would you buy? List your reasons.

> 1999 Sports Sedan, 5 spd manual, cassette, 49 000 km, cert. $12 990. 555-2842.
>
> 1999 Sports Sedan. A1. 87 000 km, 1 owner, air, auto, cassette, power. $13 950 obo. 555-0985.

12. When calling sellers to ask about advertisements listed in the newspaper, you need to ask questions and organize the information you collect. Redo question 11, using a table similar to the one following to organize the information. Add more headings if you feel they are necessary. Since you are not able to call the seller, role-play with a partner.

	Car #1	Car #2
Price		
Transmission		
Options		
Certified?		
Condition		
Collisions*		

*It is important to know if the car has been in any collisions because it could affect the performance and safety of the vehicle.

13. Shawna brings her 1992 European sedan with 250 000 km into Star Vehicle Centre. Shawna wants a price quote to determine the value of her car.
   a) What features will the salesperson consider before giving Shawna a value for her car?
   b) What reference material will the salesperson consult to get a general idea of what the car is worth?

14. Discuss the advantages and disadvantages of selling a car to a used car dealership compared to putting an advertisement in the local newspaper.

ACHIEVEMENT Check   Knowledge/Understanding   Thinking/Inquiry/Problem Solving   Communication   Application

15. Samara is starting college in the fall. She plans to live at home. If she uses public transit to travel the 50 km to school it will take over an hour and require two changes of bus. She thinks that it might be better to buy a car. Make a list of advantages and disadvantages for Samara to compare buying a new or used car with traveling by public transit. State your assumptions about Samara's life style and budget. Write a report to guide her, showing estimated costs and the list of advantages/disadvantages for each method of travel.

EXTEND THE CONCEPTS

C **16. Project** Choose a vehicle and research the current new purchase price. Compare that price to the price of the vehicle in the last model year. Look up the same vehicle in an older model year. You can do a search on the Internet, look at advertisements in a newspaper, or refer to a used car guide at the library. Calculate how much the car has depreciated over the different periods. Record your findings in your notebook or journal.

There are many costs involved in the operation of a vehicle. The operating costs include fixed costs such as licensing and insurance, and variable costs such as fuel and maintenance. **Fixed costs** are expected costs. They do not depend on how the vehicle is

used. Insurance costs are fixed, even though they vary from person to person.

Variable costs are ones that the driver has little control over. Repairs and maintenance are variable costs because the owner does not necessarily know when they will be needed. The frequency and amount of repairs needed can depend on the way the car is driven.

DISCOVER

Cost of Insurance

Several things are considered when determining insurance premiums. This list comes from the Insurance Bureau of Canada (IBC):
- age and type of vehicle
- use of the vehicle, whether for work or leisure
- where most driving will take place—city or highway
- distance typically travelled
- owner's driving record
- previous insurance claims
- other drivers in the household that will be driving the vehicle

The IBC also notes that in some provinces, your age, gender, and marital status may also affect your premium.

1. Discuss the cost of insurance with a friend or family member who owns a vehicle. Determine what types of questions they were asked in order to get insurance. Record these questions in your journal.

EXAMPLE 1

CASE STUDY

Insurance Premiums

Theo has to consider the cost of insurance. He is 18 years old with no previous speeding tickets or motor vehicle accidents. How much will he have to pay in insurance? Insurance tables involve a number of different criteria. Since Theo is male and under 25 years of age, his insurance will be higher. (Statistically, males under 25 years of age are much more likely to have a collision. So, the cost of insurance is more for this group.) Theo is considering buying a compact car. From his research, he has learned that a particular sporty compact sedan is reliable and fuel-efficient. He asks an insurance broker to prepare an insurance quote for him.

Theo's premium is quoted at $4500 per year. The company charges 6% extra for monthly payments. How much will Theo's payments be on a monthly payment plan?

Solution
Add 6% for the monthly payment plan.
Annual total of payments = 1.06 × $4500
$$= \$4770$$

Divide by 12 to find the monthly payment.
Monthly payment = $4770.00 ÷ 12
$$= \$397.50$$

Theo's monthly car insurance payment will be $397.50.

DISCOVER

Cost of Gasoline

Fuel is a variable cost because the amount used depends on the type of car and your driving habits. The cost of a fill-up will vary. Fuel prices go up and down regularly, sometimes on a daily basis. Therefore, the cost of fuel depends also on the day you buy it.

The gas tank in Maria's SUV holds 76 L. The price of gas is usually cheaper on Mondays. One Monday, the cost of gas is 71.1¢/L. Maria finds that it takes 70 L of gas to fill the tank.

1. How much will it cost for Maria to fill up the tank?
2. Discuss possible reasons for the variability in gas prices throughout the week.
3. Make a list of things that influence the price of gas. Give reasons.

EXAMPLE 2

Cost of Fuel

One week gas was selling for 66.9¢/L. Darren put $15 worth of gas into his vehicle. How many litres did he buy? Round to one decimal place.

Solution

The price is 66.9¢/L.

So, $0.669 buys 1 L.

Number of litres bought for $15 $= \dfrac{15}{0.669}$

$\doteq 22.4$

Darren bought approximately 22.4 L of gas.

EXAMPLE 3

Fuel Consumption

Grace is planning a trip to Cape Breton and is budgeting for the costs. The average gas consumption of her small car is 13.3 L/100 km in city driving conditions and 8.5 L/100 km on the highway. On her round trip she estimates she will do about 7600 km of highway driving and about 300 km of city driving.

a) Find the amount of gas she needs for the trip, to the nearest litre.
b) How much should Grace budget for gas costs if she predicts an average cost of $0.80/L? Round your answer to the nearest $10.

Solution

a) For each 100 km of highway driving, her car uses 13.3 L.
   So, for 7600 km, the car will use 76 × 13.3 or 1010.8 L.
   For each 100 km of city driving, her car uses 8.5 L.
   So, for 300 km, the car will use 3 × 8.5 or 25.5 L.
   Total number of litres = 1010.8 + 25.5
   $\qquad\qquad\qquad\qquad\quad = 1036.3$
   The amount of gas she needs is 1036 L, to the nearest litre.

b) Gasoline cost = $0.80 × 1036
   $\qquad\qquad\quad = \$828.80$
   Grace should budget about $830.00 for gas for her trip.

Driver's Licence and Plate Fees

In Ontario, you must renew your driver's licence every 5 years. In order for a vehicle to be on the road, the licence plates must have a current validation sticker. The costs are posted at the Ministry of Transportation web site. You can access this information by following the links at *www.school.mcgrawhill.ca/resources/*.

1. How much does it cost to renew your driver's licence?
2. Does the cost vary for special driver's licences such as motorcycle permits?
3. How much does it cost to renew the validation sticker for car licence plates?
4. Does the cost of licence plates vary by vehicle type?

Drive Clean

Ontario has introduced the Drive Clean program, which is an emissions-testing program that ensures cars pollute the air within acceptable ranges. Every vehicle in Ontario must pass this test every 2 years before the licence plate sticker can be renewed. If there are no problems with the vehicle, the cost is approximately $30. Use the links at *www.school.mcgrawhill.ca/resources/* to access the Drive Clean web site.

1. Why is smog such a problem in Ontario?
2. Which vehicles are required to pass the emissions test?
3. What happens after the test?

The cost of the vehicle emissions test is fixed, but might lead to variable costs if the car does not meet the requirements, as demonstrated in the next example.

EXAMPLE 4

Emissions Test Costs

When his car has the Drive Clean inspection, at a cost of $30, Philip finds out that it needs to have some repairs done. He will have to pay an additional $15 for re-inspection. The cost of the repairs is $62 for parts and $45 for labour. Both PST (8%) and GST (7%) are charged on the parts, but only GST is charged on labour and the re-inspection fee. How much will it cost for Philip to get his car to pass the Drive Clean emissions test?

Solution
Calculate PST and GST on parts.

$0.15 \times \$62.00 = \$9.30$ The PST and GST combined are 15%.

Calculate GST on labour and fees.

$0.07 \times (\$45.00 + \$30.00 + \$15.00) = \$6.30$

Total cost = $62.00 + $45.00 + $30.00 + $15.00 + $9.30 + $6.30
          = $167.60

Philip will have to pay $167.60 in order to get his car to pass the Drive Clean emissions test.

KEY CONCEPTS

- Some of the costs of operating a vehicle are expected, or fixed, costs. Examples are the cost of your driver's licence, licence plates, and insurance. These costs are set and remain the same over time.

- Other vehicle operating expenses change, or vary, from time to time, from vehicle to vehicle, and from driver to driver. Variable costs such as fuel, parking fees, regular vehicle maintenance, and repairs are more difficult to budget for. In particular, repair costs are unpredictable, since they depend on the item that requires fixing.

DISCUSS THE CONCEPTS

1. There are many different costs involved in operating a vehicle. In your notebook, list some expenses and identify whether each will be fixed or variable. For example, you might need gas on a weekly basis, depending on how far you drive. Muffler replacement would occur only when there is a problem, therefore, you would have to pay for that when it happened.

APPLY THE CONCEPTS

A **1.** **Cost of a fill-up** A vehicle's gas tank holds 65 L. How much will it cost to fill up if gas costs 83.3¢/L?

2. **Gas savings** The fuel consumption of a vehicle was 12 L/100 km. The owner had some repairs done to improve the fuel efficiency. It now gets 10.5 L/100 km. How much will the owner save on the cost to drive 100 km, if gas is 69.6¢/L?

Did You Know?

Using an air conditioner in stop-and-go traffic can increase fuel consumption by up to 20%.

3. This year, Philip needs to renew both his driver's licence and plates. The 5-year driving permit costs $50. The renewal sticker for his licence plates costs $74. When he gets to the Ministry of Transportation, he learns he has $135 in unpaid parking tickets. He must pay these before he can renew his licence. How much must he pay? There are no taxes on licence renewals or parking fees.

B 4. Application Pepi thought her brakes were not working properly, so she took her vehicle to Ace Auto Repair for an estimate. The mechanic said the brake rotors and pads needed replacing and the calipers needed to be serviced. Pepi gave the go-ahead to have the brakes repaired. Once the work was complete, she received the bill. Copy and complete the bill. Use a spreadsheet if one is available.

HERMAN®
by Jim Unger

11-4   © 1988 Jim Unger

"I don't know what this is, but you need a new one."

Qty.	Description	Each	Parts	Labour	Total
2	Front Brake Rotors	108.90	217.80		
1	Set Front Brake Pads	72.95	72.95	110.00	
1	Set Rear Brake Pads	72.95	72.95	135.00	
1	Shim Kit Req'd			38.00	
1	Service Sliders Req'd			20.00	
Subtotal					
GST @ 7%					
PST @ 8%					
TOTAL					

5. Tires One year after Jay bought his vehicle, it needed new tires. He did research to find tires that were safe and reliable. He was able to find the tires that would be best for his needs for $105 each. He needed four tires and it would cost an additional $20 per tire for installation and balancing. How much did it cost him to replace his tires, including taxes of 15%?

6. **Metric conversion** Advertisements often give gas consumption in miles per gallon (mpg). In the metric system, gas consumption is expressed as the number of litres needed to drive 100 km. To calculate the equivalent litres per 100 km (L/100 km), use the ratio

$$\frac{\text{number of litres}}{100 \text{ km}} = \frac{282}{\text{number of miles per gallon}}.$$

a) Convert 60 mpg to litres per 100 km.

b) Convert 40 mpg to litres per 100 km.

c) Suggest reasons why Drive Clean uses both metric and imperial units.

7. **Calculating kilometres per litre** Another useful conversion is a variation of the conversion of miles per gallon to kilometres per litre. To calculate the distance travelled on 1 L of gasoline, take the miles per gallon and divide by 2.82. Show that a small car that gets 35 mpg travels approximately 12.4 km/L.

8. **Fuel efficiency** Go to *www.school.mcgrawhill.ca/resources/* and follow the links to the Ministry of Natural Resources' site on fuel efficiency. Use the site to research the most fuel-efficient vehicles.

a) List the most fuel-efficient vehicles under each class and the cost of fuel per year.

b) What did you notice about the most fuel-efficient transmissions?

EXTEND THE CONCEPTS

*C*ASE STUDY

9. **Communication** Theo decides not to buy the sporty compact sedan. What might his insurance cost be for a different type of car? Work with a group and decide on a car that could be suitable for Theo. Use the links at *www.school.mcgrawhill.ca/resources/* to find a broker in your area. Prepare your questions before calling the broker. Call for an insurance quote. (Some web sites will have online quotes available.) Tell the broker you are doing a project for math. Give the broker Theo's age, gender, marital status, and the type of vehicle you are choosing for him. Write down the broker's name, and record the quote. Share and discuss the information you found with the other groups in class.

10. Frank is a married, 40-year-old man with a good driving record. He wants to buy a reliable van for his family. He will be the primary driver and his wife will be the secondary driver. Go to *www.school.mcgrawhill.ca/resources/* and follow the links to find insurance brokers in your area. Get insurance quotes for Frank's van from at least three different brokers. Write a paragraph reporting your findings.

7.4 Buying Versus Leasing

When they buy a car, most people need to consider some form of financing. A vehicle can be bought with a small down payment, and the rest of the amount can be borrowed. The financing is usually from a bank, a trust company, or the car company.

If you are not sure you want to own the vehicle, you can lease and decide later whether you want to buy. This is a good option for people who may have a little cash set away, and would like to drive new vehicles every few years. Once again, there is a cost and you do not actually own the vehicle at the end of the lease.

DISCOVER

Advantages and Disadvantages of Leasing a Vehicle

Some advantages and disadvantages of leasing are listed below.

Advantages	Disadvantages
Driving a new vehicle	Cost of additional mileage over limit
Low down payment	Higher overall cost in long run
Lower monthly payments	Will not own car at end of lease
Can drive a car that you may not be able to afford to buy	Confusing contracts

1. Research some leasing plans in the newspaper or on the Internet. List other advantages and disadvantages of leasing a vehicle.
2. What different types of leasing plans are there? Write a description of them and list two main features of each plan.
3. Create a similar chart to compare the advantages and disadvantages of buying a vehicle rather than leasing it.

Leasing agreements have several parts. There is the monthly payment that you see and hear about in advertisements, but the fine print contains some very important information. In order to lease a vehicle, you must pay a security deposit, freight charges, and the first month's payment, all when you sign the agreement. Often you must also make a down payment.

EXAMPLE 1

Leasing Costs

Dimitri leases a new SUV for $445 a month. In Ontario, both PST and GST are payable on car lease charges. He must put down $4000 and pay a freight charge of $650 plus 15% taxes. He must also give a security deposit of $350. How much does Dimitri have to pay when he signs the leasing agreement?

Solution

First, find the cost of the first month's lease charge, the down payment, and combined freight charge.

Cost = $445 + $4000 + $650

    = $5095

Then, find the cost including the taxes.

Cost with taxes = 1.15 × $5095.00

          = $5859.25

To determine what Dimitri must pay upon signing, add all the amounts due then.

Security deposit + first month's cost = $350 + $5859.25

                        = $6209.25

Dimitri must pay $6209.25 when he signs the leasing agreement.

 The links at *www.school.mcgrawhill.ca/resources/* can be used to access several interactive lease calculators. Some allow you to compare the cost of leasing versus buying the same vehicle with financing. Comparing costs is one major consideration in deciding whether to lease or to buy.

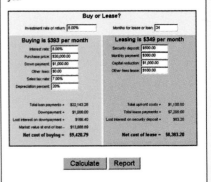

EXAMPLE 2

Finance a New Car

Ellie makes a $3500 down payment on a new car that costs $16 790. She will finance the balance at an interest rate of 1.9%, compounded monthly, over 3 years.

a) What amount will Ellie need to finance?

b) How much will Ellie's monthly payment be?

c) How much more will the car cost Ellie if she chooses the financing?

Solution

a) In order to calculate the amount Ellie needs to finance, the total cost must be calculated, including taxes.

Taxes on the cost are $16 790.00 × 0.15 = $2518.50
Total cost of the car is $16 790.00 + $2518.50 = $19 308.50
Less the down payment $19 308.50 − $3500.00 = $15 808.50

The total cost after the down payment is $15 808.50.

Use the compound interest formula to find the amount to be financed.

$$A = P(1 + i)^n \qquad\qquad P = 15\ 808.50, i = 0.019 \div 12, n = 36$$
$$A = 15\ 808.50(1 + 0.019 \div 12)^{36}$$
$$\doteq 16\ 735.01$$

The amount to be financed is $16 735.01.

b) The amount to be financed is $16 735.01.
If Ellie is making equal monthly payments to accumulate to this amount in 36 months, this is an example of an ordinary annuity.

Use $FV = \dfrac{PMT[(1+i)^n - 1]}{i}$, where FV = 16 735.01, $i = 0.019 \div 12$, and $n = 36$.

$$16\ 735.01 = \frac{PMT[(1 + 0.019 \div 12)^{36} - 1]}{0.019 \div 12}$$

$$16\ 735.01 = PMT(37.015\ 635\ 71)$$

$$PMT = \frac{16\ 735.01}{37.015\ 635\ 71}$$

$$\doteq 452.11$$

Alternatively, use the TVM Solver.

```
GRAPHING CALCULATOR
N=36
I%=1.9
PV=0
•PMT=-452.10651…
FV=16735.01
P/Y=12
C/Y=12
PMT:END  BEGIN
```

Ellie will have to make 36 monthly payments of $452.11 for her new car.

c) From part a), the total cost of the car is $19 308.50.
With financing, Ellie pays 36 × $452.11 + $3500.00 or $19 775.96.

Find the difference.
$19 775.96 − $19 308.50 = $476.46

The car will cost $476.46 more if Ellie uses the financing.

APPLY THE CONCEPTS

B 1. Marina's local car dealership has a special offer on a mid-size sedan. She can lease the car for $199 per month. The down payment is $1700, with freight charge of $650. Upon signing the contract, Marina must pay the down payment, freight, and the first month's payment, plus taxes of 15%. She must also give a security deposit of $300. How much does she have to pay to drive the car off the dealership lot?

2. Calculate how much extra it costs to finance a new vehicle priced at $19 890 at 2.0% interest, compounded monthly, over 5 years. A down payment of $5000 is made. Equal monthly payments are made for 5 years.

3. A buyer trades in an old car for $1150. How much will it cost to finance the balance owing on a used vehicle that costs $13 250, after the deduction for the trade-in, at 3.5% interest, compounded monthly, over 3 years? Equal monthly payments are made for 3 years.

4. Andre buys a used car for $8900 with taxes at 15%. He makes a down payment of $1500 and finances the balance with a 2-year loan at 9%, compounded monthly. How much will his monthly payments be on the car loan?

5. **Monthly payment** A good rule of thumb for financing the purchase of a vehicle is that your monthly payment should not be greater than 20% of your net income. Alana earns a net monthly income of $920. How much can she afford as a monthly payment?

6. **Problem Solving** Frank is considering a car lease that is advertised as having monthly payments of $175. Frank has a net income of $1200 per month. Use the 20% rule given in question 5. Can Frank afford to lease this car? Explain.

7. A car dealership has a special offer on a luxury sedan. Customers can lease the vehicle for $298 per month with a down payment of $2710. They must also pay the freight of $770 and a security deposit of $350. Upon signing the contract, customers must pay the down payment, freight, security deposit, and first month's payment. The customer must also pay 15% taxes on the down payment, freight, and monthly payment. Calculate the total due on signing and the amount of the monthly payments.

8. The new car you are interested in is listed at $18 950. You select the following options: 1.9 L, 90 horsepower, and TDI (Turbo Direct Injection Diesel) engine, at an additional cost of $1850.
   a) What is the cost of the car, before taxes?
   b) With the destination charge of $545 and taxes at 15%, what is the total cost of the car?
   c) You make a down payment of $3000 and finance the balance for 3 years at 0.9%, compounded monthly. Find the amount of each equal monthly payment.
   d) What will the total cost of the car be?

9. Theo is considering purchasing a new sporty compact sedan. He has $5000 for a down payment and will finance the balance with a bank loan at 9%, compounded monthly. The car costs a total of $23 756.
   a) What amount will Theo have to finance?
   b) How much will each monthly payment be if he is financing over 4 years?
   c) How much will Theo pay for his vehicle altogether?

10. **Communication/Application** Discuss with a partner the advantages of using interactive software to explore different leasing or financing scenarios. Explore and compare the costs of driving two different new vehicles by leasing or financing the purchase.

11. **Lease glossary** There are a number of words specific to leasing. Brainstorm with a partner some of the words and what they mean. You might do an Internet search, or go to a local bank or car dealership to look at some leasing agreements. Write a glossary of leasing terms.

CAREER PROFILE

Car Salesperson

The lifespan of today's cars is greater than that of cars made 10 or 20 years ago. Technology, service, and better components contribute to this greater lifespan. Does determining the current value of a used car interest you? Do you enjoy working with people? Having an interest in cars might lead you to career as a car salesperson.

Training in the field of marketing as well as a 2-week course sponsored by the Canadian Automotive Industry will prepare you for a career in car sales. Visit car dealerships and ask salespeople to tell you what they like and dislike about their career.

What hours do they work?

Do they have a dress code?

How much room do they have to negotiate on selling prices?

Do they deal with telephone customers?

Do they receive an hourly rate of pay plus commission, or straight commission?

What times of day and of year are the busiest?

1. Write a short report based on your research, telling why you would, or would not, like to be a car salesperson.

2. Sometimes new cars are given as prizes. Winners can take the prize or they can take the cash value. If the winning car has an advertised value of $32 000, why would the winner only receive $28 000 if he or she took the cash value?

CASE STUDY WRAP-UP

Theo is an 18-year-old student. He has just obtained his G2 driver's licence. He has saved $5000 from his part-time job and would like to buy his own car. Theo is not sure what kind of car he can buy with that amount of money.

Theo's net monthly income is $570. He has decided a small, reliable car with high fuel efficiency would meet his needs the best.

Create a report to answer the following question. Provide support material for your response.

Should Theo buy or lease a new vehicle, or buy a used vehicle?
Give reasons to support your decision.
Points to consider:
- Can Theo afford a new car with $5000? Why or why not?
- Research what types of cars are available for $5000. Select five advertisements/listings that Theo could consider.
- If he decides to purchase a new vehicle and finance the balance after paying $5000, what monthly payments can he afford?
- From your research, what kind of used cars can Theo afford?
- If he decides to lease, what monthly payments can he afford?
- How much can he expect to spend on a monthly basis to operate the vehicle? List some of the unexpected costs he might have to pay.

Ideas for Your Presentation
1. Collect brochures from dealers and present them on poster board, listing costs for options.
2. Collect car sales advertisements from new and used car dealerships, classified listings of cars for sale, ads from car magazines, etc.
3. Create a multimedia presentation describing each of the steps you took in deciding which car would best meet Theo's needs.

Review

7.1 Investigate Buying a New Vehicle, pages 254–261

1. Marie plans to buy her son a new 4X4 SUV as a college graduation present. She has a spending limit of $15 000. A local dealership has a sale on the SUV she would like to buy, offering a 15% discount off the new price of $17 500. Will Marie be able to take advantage of this sale? Explain.

2. Phil has ordered a new sporty compact car listed at $14 500. The basic car is well equipped, so the only option that Phil has ordered is the power package, which gives power windows, steering, and braking. This option costs $350. The dealer charges $500 for freight and PDI, and there are other costs of $150. How much will Phil pay in total, including taxes (PST and GST) of 15%?

7.2 Compare Buying a New Versus a Used Vehicle, pages 262–269

3. A certain model of car depreciates 15% between the fifth and sixth years since it was new. The car is valued at $9990 in the fifth year. How much will it be worth in the sixth year?

4. Knowing what you want and/or need, and how the market works, are two of the best tools you can have when buying a vehicle. Prepare a buyer's guide for someone considering buying a used vehicle, consisting of six dos and six don'ts.

7.3 Fixed and Variable Operating Costs, pages 270–276

5. Amiel has been driving for more than 10 years and has the best safe driving record the insurance company recognizes. He pays $210 per month in insurance on his 6-year-old car. Once a year he renews his licence-plate validation sticker at a cost of $74. This year he has to have an emissions test done on the vehicle. He expects his car to pass the test, so it should only cost $30. How much should Amiel expect to pay in fixed costs for his vehicle this year?

6. MaryAnthe drives 25 km each weekday to work and the same coming home. On the weekends she travels to her family's farm, which is 230 km from her apartment. Her car uses an average of 7.8 L/100 km.
   a) How far does she drive per week? per year?
   b) If the gas price is an average of 71.2¢/L, how much will she spend on gas during the year? Round your answer to the nearest dollar.

7.4 Buying Versus Leasing, pages 277–281

7. Ria is leasing a new vehicle for $185 per month. She must pay the first monthly payment along with a $1500 down payment and delivery/freight charges of $530, plus taxes at 15%. She must also give a security deposit of $250. How much must Ria pay upon signing the agreement?

8. Mohammed is buying a new vehicle priced at $27 650, including all additional costs and taxes. He will be trading in his old vehicle for a discount of $7000 off the purchase price. The balance will be financed over 5 years at 2.1%, compounded monthly. How much will each monthly payment be?

9. Businesses that need many trucks and cars, such as car rental firms, trucking companies, and delivery companies, normally lease instead of buy their vehicles. Research and write a short report explaining their decision to lease.

HERMAN®   by Jim Unger

9-17   © 1986 Jim Unger

"OK, you can stop signaling now."

Practice Test

Achievement Chart Category Connections

Category	Knowledge/Understanding	Thinking/Inquiry/Problem Solving	Communication	Application
Questions	1–5, 8	7, 8	7, 8	6, 8

1. The base price of a new luxury sedan is $51 500. Zack chooses the sport package option at an additional cost of $1900. Other charges added to the price of his car total $1020. How much will the car cost after taxes at 15% have been added?

2. A new van sells for $24 458. One year later the same van is valued at $18 830.
   a) By how much has this van depreciated?
   b) What is the rate of depreciation during the first year, to the nearest percent?

3. Every 6 months Brianne takes her vehicle in for its lubrication service. This service costs $24.95 each visit. Every 12 months, the vehicle requires a maintenance service that costs $99.88. During one such maintenance service, the mechanic finds a problem with the rear brake pads. The cost for replacing the brake pads is $135.00. How much has Brianne spent this year for service on her vehicle, including taxes at 15%?

4. Classify each of the following vehicle costs as either
   A: a fixed cost or B: a variable cost
   a) licence plate validation sticker
   b) oil and gas
   c) car washes
   d) monthly lease payments
   e) parking fees
   f) driver's licence permit fee
   g) insurance premium
   h) engine repairs

5. A popular mid-size vehicle is advertised for lease at $218 per month for 36 months. The fine print states that there is a required down payment of $2250, which includes freight and air tax. A security deposit of $300 is required. Find the total first month's payment, with taxes at 15%, if you assume this leasing agreement.

6. Ben has saved $8000 to spend on a car. He needs a reliable car for getting to work, so, he decides to use his savings as the down-payment on a new car. He takes advantage of the year-end clearance to buy a vehicle for a total of $18 950, including all taxes and delivery charges. The dealership finances the balance at 2%, compounded monthly. Ben agrees to repay the loan in equal monthly payments over 3 years. How much will each monthly payment be?

7. a) Give two reasons why a person might choose to buy a used car rather than a new car.
   b) Give two reasons why a person might choose to lease a new car rather than buy the same new car, even if the monthly payments are greater.

ACHIEVEMENT Check Knowledge/Understanding Thinking/Inquiry/Problem Solving Communication Application

8. Tallie has just finished college and has got her first job as a graphics artist. She lives at home with her parents and her sister Samara. She lives 40 km from her new job, and has decided to buy or lease a small car. She has no other debts, and has $500 for a down payment. Tallie's salary is $30 000 per year and she will pay her parents $100 per month for home expenses.

   Choose a specific car model and investigate the costs of purchasing or leasing a new car, or buying a used model that is 2 or 3 years old. Calculate the monthly vehicle costs. Write a short report with your advice to Tallie. Consider factors such as:
   -assumptions about her salary and lifestyle
   -how much can she afford to pay each month
   -maintenance costs, insurance and other costs [e.g., CAA membership]
   -which method of obtaining a car [new, used, leased] might suit her best
   -loan to be financed and possible sources

CHAPTER

8

CONSUMER SPENDING

Specific Expectations	Sections
• identify the advantages and disadvantages to the purchaser of various types of selling and techniques of selling	8.1
• compare the value of the Canadian dollar with the values of foreign currencies over a period of time and identify possible effects on purchasing and travel decisions	8.3
• determine, through investigation, the features of various credit and debit cards	8.2
• demonstrate, using technology, the effects of delayed payment on a credit card balance, on the basis of current credit card rates and regulations	8.2
• calculate the cost of borrowing to purchase a costly item	8.2
• describe a decision involving a choice between alternatives	8.1, 8.2
• collect relevant information related to the alternatives to be considered in making a decision	8.1, 8.2
• summarize the advantages and disadvantages of the alternatives to a decision, using lists and organization charts	8.1, 8.2
• compare alternatives by rating and ranking information and by applying mathematical calculations and analysis, as appropriate, using technology	8.1, 8.2
• explain the process used in making a decision and justify the conclusions reached	8.1, 8.2

1. Write each percent as a decimal.

a) 24% **b)** 2% **c)** 2.5% **d)** 5.5%

e) 100% **f)** 125% **g)** 3.2% **h)** 0.6%

2. Find each amount.

a) 40% of $200 **b)** 4% of $325 **c)** 1% of $500

d) 105% of $500 **e)** 2.5% of $230 **f)** 15.4% of $2000

3. Calculate the simple interest on each principal.

a) $P = \$500$, $r = 5\%$, $t = 3$ years

b) $P = \$350$, $r = 8\%$, $t = 2.5$ years

c) $P = \$1000$, $r = 3\%$, $t = 8$ months

d) $P = \$568$, $r = 7\%$, $t = 14$ months

e) $P = \$2000$, $r = 4.5\%$, $t = 11$ months

f) $P = \$1200$, $r = 6\%$, $t = 150$ days

g) $P = \$612.17$, $r = 9.5\%$, $t = 260$ days

h) $P = \$10\,000$, $r = 5.64\%$, $t = 281$ days

4. For each price, calculate the increase or decrease, and the final value.

a) $28, increased by 10%

b) $100, increased by 30%

c) $75, decreased by 12%

d) $125, decreased by 5%

e) $200, increased by 8.5%

f) $99, decreased by 15.2%

g) $250, increased by 50%

h) $85.99, decreased by 25%

5. How many days are there from the first date to the second date? Include the first date and the second date.

a) September 3 to September 30

b) January 16 to February 5

c) June 10 to July 21

d) May 29 to July 5

e) December 18 to January 25

f) July 3 to August 14

6. Describe the difference between simple and compound interest.

7. Calculate the final amount for each.
   a) $1000 for 3 years at 6%, compounded annually
   b) $500 for 5 months at 18%, compounded monthly
   c) $750 for 1 year at 8%, compounded quarterly
   d) $5000 for 4 years at 5%, compounded semi-annually

8. Some retailers offer points as rewards for spending money at their store. These points can be used to buy items from the store. Calculate the number of points earned for each situation if $600 is spent.
   a) 1 point for every $20 spent
   b) 1 point for every $50 spent
   c) 100 points for every $100 spent
   d) 10 points for every $25 spent

*C*ASE STUDY

Throughout this chapter, you will be exploring consumer spending. In some sections of the chapter, you will solve problems related to the Case Study described below. At the end of the chapter, you will be asked to write a summary report on the Case Study. Keep five or six pages of your notebook free for work related to the Case Study. Or, you may prefer to keep a Case Study Portfolio.

Shopping today is much different than it was just a few years ago. Now, the Internet provides a whole new way to compare products and their prices. A good plan is to research prices and availability in catalogues, on the Internet, and in retail stores before deciding where to buy.

Select two items that you would like to buy that cost more than $100, such as a television, a CD player, concert tickets, designer clothing, a DVD player, or a computer. You will explore the total cost of buying your items from different sources.

There are many ways you can buy things. Retail stores have been around for centuries, catalogues for about 100 years, and telemarketing for a few decades. The most recent way to buy is on the Internet.

You probably make most of your purchases at a retail store or through a catalogue. However, if you have access to a computer, you can make purchases over the Internet.

How do you know what makes a good retailer? Are there differences in service between types of retailers? How do retailers try to sell you their products or services?

DISCOVER

Advantages and Disadvantages of Buying at a Retail Store

Retail stores include small variety stores, boutiques, large department stores, large specialty stores, and large warehouse stores. There are many different places to shop in cities and larger towns. These include downtown areas, outdoor strip malls, and large indoor shopping centres. There are advantages and disadvantages to each type and location.

Work in groups of two or three. Copy the following table and complete a list of advantages and disadvantages of shopping at a retail store.

Category	Advantages	Disadvantages
Product		
Service		
Delivery		
Payment options		

EXAMPLE 1

Catalogue Sales

Catalogue companies usually publish catalogues every 3 months, one for each season. Most companies are reliable, but some are not. How can you tell whether a catalogue company is reliable?

Solution

A good catalogue merchant will
- publish clear photographs and detailed descriptions of their goods
- provide a full address rather than a post office box
- provide a toll-free telephone number for both sales and service
- clearly outline its return policy
- clearly describe its shipping and handling charges
- be a member of a nationally recognized catalogue merchants' group, such as the Canadian Direct Marketing Association, the National Mail Order Association, or the Canadian Marketing Association

EXAMPLE 2

Shipping and Handling

Many catalogue and Internet retailers charge for shipping (delivery) and handling (preparing your order at the warehouse). Calculate the shipping and handling charge for each sale.

a) 3% shipping and $2 handling on a $120 computer game

b) 5% shipping and handling on a $750 stereo

Solution

a) Shipping and handling charge = shipping rate × cost + handling charge
$$= 0.03 \times 120.00 + 2.00$$
$$= 5.60$$
The shipping and handling charge is $5.60.

b) Shipping and handling charge = shipping and handling rate × cost
$$= 0.05 \times 750.00$$
$$= 37.50$$
The shipping and handling charge is $37.50.

EXAMPLE 3

Installment Buying

Tim is considering buying a computer for $2845.27, including taxes. The store offers a payment plan of 24 monthly payments of $125.

a) How much more does the payment plan cost than paying cash for the stereo right away? In other words, what is the total interest that the store is charging?

b) What annual interest rate is the store charging?

Solution

a) Payment plan cost = number of payments × payment amount

$$= 24 \times 125$$
$$= 3000$$

Interest charges = payment plan cost − cash price

$$= 3000.00 - 2845.27$$
$$= 154.73$$

The total interest charged is $154.73.

b) When regular payments are made over time, the following formula can be used to calculate the annual interest rate being charged:

$$r = \frac{2NI}{P(n+1)}$$

where
- r is the annual interest rate (as a decimal)
- N is the number of payments per year
- I is the total interest charged
- P is the principal
- n is the total number of payments

Use the formula.

$$r = \frac{2NI}{P(n+1)}$$

$$r = \frac{2(12)(154.73)}{(2845.27)(24+1)}$$

$$r \doteq 0.052$$

There are 12 payments per year, the interest charged is $154.73, the principal is $2845.27, and there are 24 payments in total.

You can check using the **TVM Solver**.

Enter

N=24

I%=5.2

PV=2845.27

PMT=0

FV=0

P/Y=12

C/Y=12

PMT:END BEGIN

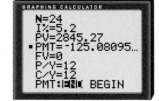

See page 412 in the Technology Appendix for details on the **TVM solver**.

Then, cursor up to **PMT**=0.

Press (ALPHA)(ENTER) for **SOLVE**.

The payment shown is approximately $125, so the result checks.

The interest rate is approximately 5.2% per year.

EXAMPLE 4

Telemarketing

Companies hire telemarketers to sell their goods and services to consumers over the telephone. Describe some of the sales techniques used by telemarketers.

Solution

- The telemarketer usually opens with friendly conversation. "How are you today?" may really mean "How likely are you to buy today?"
- The telemarketer will ask for the target customer by name or, possibly, for the woman or man of the house.
- The telemarketer will read from a script, and probably ask questions designed to determine whether or not you might like their product or service.
- The actual product or service is often not mentioned until after you have answered the questions or the sales pitch is complete.
- If you say no, a good telemarketer will say thank you and hang up. An aggressive telemarketer will keep trying.
- Unless you say no firmly, and then, hang up, the telemarketer will continue to try to convince you to change your mind.

KEY CONCEPTS

- You can buy goods and services from traditional stores, catalogue merchants, telemarketers, and Internet retailers.

- Each type of retailer has advantages, disadvantages, and risks.

- Good retailers will provide good service, secure credit, a fair return policy, and a wide selection of products.

- Most retailers collect both PST and GST. GST is charged on shipping and handling.

- To find the annual interest rate being charged for installment buying, use the formula

$$r = \frac{2NI}{P(n+1)}$$

where r is the annual interest rate (as a decimal)
   N is the number of payments per year
   I is the total interest charged
   P is the principal
   n is the total number of payments

DISCUSS THE CONCEPTS

1. What steps would you take to calculate the shipping and handling charges in each case?
   a) 5% shipping and $2 handling on a $125 pair of running shoes
   b) 7% shipping and handling on a $75 bouquet of flowers

2. Describe a payment plan that could be represented by the following expression:
   $$r = \frac{2(12)(330)}{2070(24+1)}$$

3. Write and act out a script for a telemarketer and a potential customer. The telemarketer is trying to sell a home security system. Compare your script with those of your classmates.

PRACTISE

A

1. Calculate the shipping and handling charges for each sale.

	Item	Price	Retailer	Shipping	Handling
a)	television	$499.00	department store	5% of price	none
b)	CDs	$229.00	catalogue	$5.00	3% of price
c)	clothing	$752.58	Internet	$10.00	4% of price
d)	skates	$375.00	catalogue	6% of price	
e)	concert tickets	$75.00	Internet	2% of price	$15.00

2. Every time a customer pays with a credit card, the retailer must pay a fee of 2% to 3% on the price to the credit card company. At larger retailers, this fee is built into the prices of the products. But in some smaller stores, if a customer uses a credit card, this fee is added to the price. Calculate the credit fee on each item if the rate is 2.5%.
   a) a $2500 computer system
   b) a $650 monitor
   c) a $350 printer
   d) a $529 monitor

Did You Know?

Stores do not have to give refunds, exchanges, or credit notes.

3. Use the formula $r = \frac{2NI}{P(n+1)}$ to determine the annual interest rate in each situation. Round your answers to one decimal place.
   a) Kelvin bought a stereo for 12 monthly payments of $50. The regular price was $500.

b) Tuan bought a camera for 24 monthly payments of $33.50. The regular price was $749.00.

c) Ravi bought a car for $19 500.00. He paid for the car with a $5000.00 down payment and 36 monthly payments of $442.85.

d) Cheryl purchased $2000.00 worth of furniture for her first apartment. She made 26 weekly payments of $79.32.

APPLY THE CONCEPTS **B**

4. **Internet auction sites** A popular way to buy goods and services online is through an Internet auction company. Describe the bidding and sales process for the auction of an autographed National Hockey League jersey. Include the roles of the auction company, the seller, and the buyer.

5. James works long hours and does not have much time for shopping. He needs new running shoes and dress shoes for work. He chooses running shoes that cost $89.99 and dress shoes that cost $95.99 from a catalogue. Shipping is 3% of the cost and handling is $5.00. The same shoes are available at the company's store 40 km away, at a discount of 10%. Parking costs $8.00 and it costs $0.27 per km to drive to the store and back. Which purchase option is better for James? Justify your answer.

6. **Discount cards** Retailers often target groups of consumers by offering discount cards, such as a Student Price Card. Describe how you can take advantage of these cards.

7. **Paying by cheque** At many retailers, consumers must fill in an application and be approved before they can use a cheque to pay for a purchase. Other businesses have different rules. Explain why businesses have these rules.

Work with a group of two or three to complete questions 8 to 13. Research each question and write a detailed report.

8. **Loss leaders** Supermarkets often sell items, called loss leaders, at a loss in order to get shoppers to come to their store and buy other, more profitable, products. Every week in their fliers, supermarkets advertise loss leaders, usually on the front page.

a) Check several supermarket fliers and identify the loss leaders.

b) Explain how shoppers can take advantage of loss leaders.

Did You Know?

A *raincheck* was originally a voucher issued at baseball games that were rained out.

9. Stores often offer "points cards" to their customers to get them to come back. Customers earn points for each purchase made and can spend them in that store, like real money, when they accumulate enough points.

   a) How do you think a points card would affect your shopping habits? Explain.

   b) How can consumers take advantage of points cards? Explain.

   c) Points cards also allow the retailer to track your spending habits. What are the advantages and disadvantages of this? Explain.

10. You can also earn points with some credit cards every time you make a purchase. For example, every time you spend $20 on the Air Miles credit card, you earn one "air mile."

    a) How many air miles could you earn in a year if you spent

       i) $300 per month?

       ii) $600 per month?

       iii) $2000 per month?

    b) How many months would it take to accumulate 3300 air miles to fly from Toronto to Florida for March Break, with an average monthly balance of $400? Is this a realistic goal? Explain.

11. You can also have an Air Miles affinity card, which is separate from the Air Miles credit card. Visit *http://www.school.mcgrawhill.ca/resources/* and follow the links to the Air Miles web site.

    a) Name five companies that accept the Air Miles affinity card. What offer does each company make?

    b) Identify five products or services that can be bought by redeeming air miles. How many air miles does each cost?

    c) What are the advantages of using an Air Miles credit card and an Air Miles affinity card for the same purchase?

    d) Are there any disadvantages of using an Air Miles affinity card? Use examples in your explanation.

Did You Know?

***Affinity* means a close relationship or connection.**

12. Many retailers use telemarketers to reach their customers. Telemarketers telephone people and try to get them to buy their product or service. Visit *http://www.school.mcgrawhill.ca/resources/* and follow the links to research telemarketing.

   a) What risks are involved in buying products or services over the telephone?

   b) What makes a good telemarketing merchant?

   c) Make a list of 10 tips to help consumers identify dishonest telemarketers.

13. Communication/Application Visit *http://www.school.mcgrawhill.ca/resources/* and follow the links to Canadian Internet retail sites selling books, clothing, and computers.

   a) Compare how easy or difficult it was to use each web site.
   - Could you find the products you were interested in?
   - Was it easy to determine the final price, including taxes and shipping and handling?
   - Was the return policy clearly shown?
   - Were customer service options described?

   b) What do you think makes a good Internet retailer? Explain.

   c) Complete a table of advantages and disadvantages of buying products and services from an Internet retailer.

14. Shopping today is much different than it was just a few years ago. Now, the Internet provides a whole new way to compare products and their prices. A good plan is to research prices and availability in catalogues, on the Internet, and in retail stores before deciding where to buy.

   a) Select two items that you would like to buy that cost more than $100, such as a television, a CD player, concert tickets, designer clothing, a DVD player, or a computer.

   b) Research the cost of buying each item from a retail store, from a catalogue, and on the Internet. Use Canadian-based companies.

   c) Calculate and compare the costs (including tax and delivery), ease of ordering, delivery time, variety, credit card security, and availability.

ACHIEVEMENT Check Knowledge/Understanding Thinking/Inquiry/Problem Solving *Communication* Application

15. Look through some retail catalogues for a big-ticket item (expensive) you wish to buy. Complete a table of advantages and disadvantages of buying products from a catalogue. Use your table from Discover Advantages and Disadvantages of Buying at a Retail Store as a guide.

C **16. Multilevel marketing** A multilevel marketing company recruits people to sell their product. These people then recruit more people to sell the product. The company is called a franchiser and the sellers are called franchisees. At each level, the franchisee keeps a part of the profit and gives the rest to the person in the level above. For example, the diagram shows a franchiser and three levels of franchisees.

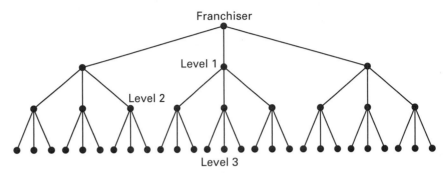

In this example, at level 1, there are 3 or 3^1 franchisees. At level 2, there are 9 or 3^2 franchisees. At level 3, there are 27 or 3^3 franchisees.

A certain multilevel marketing company encourages each franchisee to recruit 5 more franchisees.

a) Determine how many franchisees there would be if there were
  i) 3 levels   **ii)** 4 levels

b) A franchisee in level 3 shares her profit equally with the person immediately above her in each level, including the franchiser. Thus, she shares her profit with 3 other people. How many people does a franchisee in each level share his or her profit with?
  i) level 1   **ii)** level 2   **iii)** level 4

c) How much of a $1 profit does a franchisee in each level get to keep?
  i) level 1   **ii)** level 3   **iii)** level 4

d) If each person on level 4 generated $1 in profit, how much would each franchisee get in each level? Use a diagram to help you.
  i) level 3   **ii)** level 2   **iii)** level 1   **iv)** the franchiser

 17. Visit *http://www.school.mcgrawhill.ca/resources/* and follow the links to research the techniques used by multilevel marketing companies to sell their products. What are some of the risks involved for buyers and franchisees?

Manage Debit and Credit Cards

Many people do not like to carry around large amounts of cash. They like a convenient way to pay for their purchases. Debit and credit cards can be ideal solutions. Each has its own features as well as advantages and disadvantages.

HERMAN®   by Jim Unger

7-7   © 1987 Jim Unger

"When you go to the bank tomorrow, you should find an extra $50,000 in your savings account."

DISCOVER

Features of Debit Cards

1. Visit *http://www.school.mcgrawhill.ca/resources/* and follow the links, or go to a bank or trust company, to research the answers to the following questions:
   a) How do you apply for a debit card?
   b) What criteria must you meet before you apply?
   c) How much must you keep in your account?
   d) Are there any costs to you to use a debit card?
   e) Where can you use the card?
   f) What happens if you try to use the card and do not have enough money in your account?
   g) What are the security features of the card?
   h) What steps should you take if your card is lost or stolen?

2. Compare your answers with those of a classmate who visited a different bank or trust company.
   a) Which features are common between banks?
   b) Which features are different?
   c) Choose the debit card that is best for you and explain why you chose it.

DISCOVER

Features of Credit Cards

1. Visit *http://www.school.mcgrawhill.ca/resources/* and follow the links, or go to a bank or trust company, to research the answers to the following questions:
   a) How do you apply for a credit card?
   b) What annual income do you need before you can get a credit card?
   c) What are the initial and annual fees?
   d) What features, or extras, can you get?

e) What interest rate is charged on unpaid balances?

f) How is the interest calculated on purchases?

g) What happens if you pay the entire balance by the due date?

h) How is interest charged if only part of the balance is paid by the due date?

i) How can you get a cash advance with a credit card?

j) How is interest charged on cash advances?

k) What are the security features of the credit card?

l) What steps should you take if your card is lost or stolen?

2. Compare your answers with those of a classmate who visited a different bank or trust company.

a) Which features are common between banks?

b) Which features are different?

c) Choose the credit card that is best for you and explain why you chose it.

3. Make a list of advantages and disadvantages of using a credit card instead of a debit card.

EXAMPLE 1

Credit Card Bills

Jeela received her credit card bill with the following charges on it.

Previous balance	$578.15	Amount owed on the previous bill
Purchases	725.87	New purchases made this billing period
Cash advances	200.00	Money obtained from a bank machine with your credit card. As soon as you get a cash advance, interest is charged on your entire balance.
Interest	8.45	Interest calculated on the previous unpaid balance, on any cash advance this billing period, and on new purchases if there is an unpaid balance or cash advance
Fees (annual)	50.00	
Debit adjustments		Fees for the use of the card
Other		Corrections (additions) made to the amount owing because of errors or other adjustments
Payments	500.00 CR	Amount paid to the credit card issuer by the card user during the billing period
Credit adjustments		
Other		Corrections (subtractions) made to the amount owing because of errors, returned purchases, or other adjustments
New balance	$1062.47	New amount owing
Amount past due	0.00	Amount owing from previous bills if the minimum payment was not made
Minimum payment	32.00	Smallest amount the user must pay
Credit limit	2000.00	Total amount the user may owe on the credit card at any time
Credit available	937.53	Amount of credit limit available (credit limit minus new balance)
Paid $_____		Amount paid by the user (entered by the user)

a) Why was interest of $8.45 charged on this account? Explain.

b) How is the new balance calculated?

c) What would happen if Jeela paid the entire new balance?

d) If Jeela paid $800.00 of the new balance, describe how interest would be calculated and charged.

Solution

a) Jeela was charged interest because she did not pay the previous balance entirely and she took out a cash advance.

b) The new balance is the sum of all the charges:

New balance = Interest + fees + cash advances + previous balance
$\qquad$ + purchases + debit adjustments − payments
$\qquad$ − credit adjustments
$\qquad$ = 8.45 + 50.00 + 200.00 + 578.15 + 725.87 − 500.00
$\qquad$ = 1062.47

c) You might think that this would erase Jeela's balance and she would no longer be charged interest on her purchases. However, in the time between when the credit card company sent out the bill and when Jeela received it, more interest accumulated. So, even though she paid the entire new balance, she still owes a small amount to the credit card company. She should telephone the credit card company and ask exactly how much she owes that day, and then, go into the bank and pay it. If she mails a cheque, then, more interest will be charged before the credit card company receives the payment. Another way to completely erase the balance is to pay a little bit more than the new balance to cover the extra interest that would accumulate.

d) Interest would be calculated and charged, at a simple interest rate, on *all* purchases and cash advances, dating back to each posting date (date the charge was made). That interest would be paid down first before any new purchases or the previous balance is paid. A new balance, reflecting this interest charge, would then be calculated, and posted on Jeela's bill next month. The interest is then compounded monthly.

When you pay your credit card bill, the money goes to pay charges in the following order:

1. interest from previous bills
2. fees for using the card (usually yearly)
3. cash advances (money taken out of a bank machine)
4. purchases from previous bills for which interest is being charged
5. new purchases for which interest is not yet being charged (if you are not carrying a balance)

EXAMPLE 2

Credit Card Interest

Samar made a $1230 purchase with his credit card on May 12.

a) Calculate the interest charged, at 18% simple interest, on the payment date of June 21, if the credit card bill is not paid off entirely.

b) Calculate the additional interest and total interest due on the following payment date of July 21.

Solution

a) Use the formula $I = Prt$.

$I = Prt$

$I = 1230(0.18)\left(\dfrac{40}{365}\right)$ **40 days from May 12 to June 21**

$I = 24.26$

The interest calculated on June 21 would be $24.26.

b) Use the formula $A = P(1 + i)^n$.

$P = $ purchase + interest

$P = 1230.00 + 24.26$

$P = 1254.26$

$i = 0.18 \div 12$

$i = 0.015$

$A = P(1 + i)^n$

$A = 1254.26(1 + 0.015)^1$

$A = 1273.07$

Interest earned = amount – principal

$I = A - P$

$I = 1273.07 - 1254.26$

$I = 18.81$

Total interest = first month's interest + second month's interest

$$= 24.26 + 18.81$$
$$= 43.07$$

$18.81 in new interest and total interest of $43.07 would be due on July 21.

KEY CONCEPTS

- Debit cards are a replacement for cash. Money is withdrawn directly from the user's bank account, usually with a fee per transaction. If a specific minimum balance is kept in the account, there may be no transaction fee. An annual fee may be charged.

- You need a personal identification number (PIN) to access your bank account using a debit card.

- Credit cards provide free credit to the user until the due date (billing date), if payment is made in full. Otherwise, interest is charged on the entire amount owed. Simple interest is calculated from the posting date until the due date. Then, the interest is compounded monthly until it is paid off entirely. An annual fee may be charged.

- Cash advances on a credit card are charged interest immediately from the posting date. Simple interest is calculated from the posting date until the due date. Then, the interest is compounded monthly until it is paid off entirely. Once you use your card to get a cash advance, interest is charged on your entire balance, including purchases.

- Each debit and credit card has its own features. Some features are included, others involve an extra fee.

DISCUSS THE CONCEPTS

1. Many credit card companies offer credit cards to new college and university students. What are the advantages and disadvantages of these cards? Explain.

2. Which of the following is the best choice for a personal identification number for your debit card? Why?
   a) your birthday
   b) 12345
   c) your phone number
   d) a number meaningful only to you

A **1.** The table shows the credit card purchases made during a 1-month billing period.

i) Determine the number of days from each posting date to the billing date of October 27.

ii) Calculate each interest charge on the billing date of October 27 at 18% per year, simple interest.

iii) Calculate the total interest for the billing period.

iv) Calculate the interest charge on the following billing date, November 27, if no further payments or transactions are made.

	Posting Date	Description	Amount
a)	09/05	Fred's Gas	40.00
b)	09/07	Fairlane Travel	199.50
c)	09/10	Ye Olde Steakhouse	125.00
d)	09/15	K & C Hardware	348.99
e)	09/16	Cash Advance	250.00
f)	09/22	Harbour Dept. Stores	76.24
g)	09/30	Elena's CDs and Books	34.85
h)	10/02	PT Service Station	40.00

2. Jen's October credit card bill is shown.

a) What is her new balance?

b) Jen's credit limit is $5000. How much credit is still available?

c) If Jen paid her new balance entirely, how much interest would she owe on her next statement?

d) If Jen paid only $400 of the new balance, how would the interest be calculated and charged?

Previous balance	$614.15
Purchases	489.32
Cash advances	100.00
Interest	26.18
Fees	
Debit adjustments	
Other	
Payments	300.00 CR
Credit adjustments	45.99 CR

3. Dimitar's January credit card bill is shown.

a) What is his new balance?

b) Dimitar's credit limit is $4000. How much credit is still available?

c) Dimitar could only afford to pay $500 of the new balance after the holiday season. How would the interest be calculated and charged?

Previous balance	$314.77
Purchases	2312.54
Cash advances	500.00
Interest	6.50
Fees	
Debit adjustments	50.00
Other	
Payments	314.77 CR

B **4.** **Credit card interest** Liz bought a stereo for $650 on June 10. She also got a cash advance of $350 on June 18. She paid off only the minimum payment of $32 on the billing date, July 8. She paid off the balance on August 8. How much interest did she pay in total, if interest is charged at an annual rate of 18.5%?

5. **Credit card purchases** Yusuf got a cash advance of $200.00 on January 14, and charged $452.38 for a new coat on January 16 and $129.04 for a restaurant bill on January 26. He made a payment of $300.00 on the billing date, February 5. He paid off the balance on March 5. How much interest did he pay in total, if interest is charged at an annual rate of 20%?

6. **Communication** What are the disadvantages of cash advances on a credit card? Explain.

7. Jason wants to buy a computer for $1999. He can pay cash, use his credit card, take out a bank loan, or make 12 monthly payments of $219 to the store. His credit card charges interest at 18%, compounded monthly. He could arrange a bank loan at an interest rate of 9%, compounded monthly. Jason plans to pay off his debt in 1 year.

a) Use the formula $r = \dfrac{2NI}{P(n+1)}$ from 8.1 Managing Your Retail Dollar, page 295, to calculate the interest rate being charged by the store for the 12 monthly payments.

b) Which option would be the best for Jason? Explain.

8. Niki wants to buy a stereo for $1859. She can pay for it with her credit card, with a bank loan, or with 24 monthly payments of $85. Her credit card charges interest at 16.5%, compounded monthly. She could arrange a bank loan at an interest rate of 8%, compounded monthly. Niki plans to pay off her debt in 2 years.

a) Use the formula $r = \dfrac{2NI}{P(n+1)}$ from 8.1 Managing Your Retail Dollar, page 295, to calculate the interest rate charged by the store.

b) Which option would be the best for Niki? Explain.

9. **Problem Solving** One advantage of using a credit card is the "free" use of money until the due date, if you pay off the balance entirely. To pay for a new TV, Wei used a debit card to withdraw $795 from her bank account. By paying in this way, she no longer receives interest at 3% simple interest from her bank account. If she had paid by credit card, the payment would not have been due for an additional 46 days.

   a) Assume Wei pays off her credit card balance entirely. How much interest did she lose by using her debit card?

   b) Assume that Wei does not pay off her credit card balance entirely. She decides to use the credit card to buy the TV. How much interest would she owe, at 18.4% simple interest?

ACHIEVEMENT Check Knowledge/Understanding Thinking/Inquiry/Problem Solving Communication Application

10. a) Describe situations in which you would use the following. Include reasons for choosing the card in each case.

   i) debit card

   ii) bank credit card

   iii) store credit card

   b) Caitlin wants to buy furniture costing $1859. She can pay for it with her credit card, which charges 18.5%, compounded monthly. Compare the costs of paying off the total in 1 month and in 2 months.

EXTEND THE CONCEPTS

11. Go to *http://www.school.mcgrawhill.ca/resources/* and follow the links to research credit card and bank loan interest rates. Is it better to use a bank loan to pay off all credit charges entirely by the due date, or to let interest on the credit card accumulate? Explain.

12. Most Internet sales are paid for with a credit card. Go to *http://www.school.mcgrawhill.ca/resources/* and follow the links to research the security systems that Internet retail sites have in place for credit card users.

8.3 Foreign Exchange

Many items, such as clothing, electronic goods, and software, can be purchased from foreign-based (mainly U.S.) companies. These can be purchased at retail outlets and through catalogue and Internet retailers. Vacationers also spend a lot of money outside the country. The costs of these purchases and vacations depend on the exchange rate of the Canadian dollar at the time, as well as on import duty on some items.

DISCOVER

Foreign Exchange Rates

1. Go to *http://www.school.mcgrawhill.ca/resources/* and follow the links to research foreign exchange rates. Alternatively, look in the business section of a newspaper.

2. Find a current list of exchange rates for $1 Cdn (Canadian).

3. **a)** What is $1 Cdn worth in U.S. dollars?
   b) How many U.S. dollars would $500 Cdn buy?

4. **a)** What is $1 Cdn worth in Japanese yen?
   b) How many yen would $500 Cdn buy?

5. **a)** What is $1 Cdn worth in Mexican pesos?
   b) How many pesos would $500 Cdn buy?

6. Find a current list of exchange rates for foreign currencies in Canadian dollars.

7. **a)** What is $1 U.S. worth in Canadian dollars?
   b) How much does it cost to buy $500 U.S.?

8. **a)** What is £1 (one British pound) worth in Canadian dollars?
   b) How much would it cost to buy £500?

9. **a)** What is one Indian rupee worth in Canadian dollars?
   b) How much would it cost to buy 500 rupees?

10. Using your list from step 6, calculate the reciprocal of each exchange rate $\left(\dfrac{1}{\text{rate}}\right)$:

a) U.S. dollar　　**b)** German mark　　**c)** South African rand

11. Compare your results in step 10 to the rates in your list from step 2. What do you notice?

EXAMPLE 1

Foreign Money Orders

Deepak sent a money order for 25 000 rupees to his family in India. The exchange rate was 1 rupee = $0.0344 Cdn. The fee for the money order was $3.25 Cdn. What was the total cost of the money order, in Canadian dollars?

Solution

Cost = amount of foreign currency × exchange rate + fee

$$= 25\ 000.00 \times 0.0344 + 3.25$$
$$= 863.25$$

The total cost is $863.25 Cdn.

EXAMPLE 2

Buy Foreign Currency

Michael is planning to drive to Florida for a vacation. He estimates he will need to buy $1300 U.S. from the bank to pay for his hotels, food, gasoline, and entertainment. The price of the U.S. dollar on March 2 was $1.4925 Cdn. The price of the U.S. dollar on March 9 was $1.5267 Cdn. What is the difference in total cost, in Canadian dollars, for the vacation between the two dates?

Solution

Cost = amount of foreign currency × exchange rate

March 2 cost = 1300.00 × 1.4925
　　　　　　= 1940.25

March 9 cost = 1300.00 × 1.5267
　　　　　　= 1984.71

Difference = March 9 cost − March 2 cost
　　　　　= 1984.71 − 1940.25
　　　　　= 44.46

The difference is $44.46 Cdn.

EXAMPLE 3

Visit Canada

When Terry's friend came to Canada from the United States for a vacation, he bought $500.00 Cdn at a rate of $0.6841 U.S. per Canadian dollar.

a) How much did this cost in U.S. dollars?

b) What is the equivalent exchange rate for $1 U.S. in Canadian dollars?

Solution

a) Cost = amount of Canadian currency × exchange rate
$$= 500.00 \times 0.6841$$
$$= 342.05$$
It cost $342.05 U.S. to buy $500 Cdn.

b) Equivalent exchange rate $= \dfrac{1}{\text{given exchange rate}}$
$$= \dfrac{1}{0.6841}$$
$$= 1.4618$$
The equivalent rate is $1.4618 Cdn per U.S. dollar.

EXAMPLE 4

Internet Purchase

Erica bought some clothing from a U.S.-based web site. The cost was $299.99 U.S.

a) Calculate the cost, in Canadian dollars, at an exchange rate of $1 U.S. = $1.495 Cdn.

b) Calculate the import duty at 9.5%.

c) Calculate the PST at 8% and GST at 7%.

d) What is the total cost of Erica's purchase?

Solution

a) Cost = amount of foreign currency × exchange rate
$$= 299.99 \times 1.495$$
$$= 448.49$$
The cost is $448.49 Cdn.

b) Duty = cost (Cdn) × duty rate
$$= 448.49 \times 0.095$$
$$\doteq 42.61$$
The import duty is $42.61.

c) PST = cost (Cdn) × tax rate
$$= 448.49 \times 0.08$$
$$\doteq 35.88$$
The PST is $35.88.

GST = cost (Cdn) × tax rate
$$= 448.49 \times 0.07$$
$$\doteq 31.39$$
The GST is $31.39.

d) Total cost = cost (Cdn) + import duty + PST + GST
$$= 448.49 + 42.61 + 35.88 + 31.39$$
$$= 558.37$$
The total cost is $558.37 Cdn.

KEY CONCEPTS

- When you buy or sell foreign currency, multiply the amount of foreign currency by the exchange rate of that currency in terms of Canadian dollars.

- When you buy or sell Canadian dollars, multiply the amount in Canadian dollars by the exchange rate of the Canadian dollar in terms of the foreign currency.

- The exchange rates between two currencies are reciprocals of each other.

- Small fluctuations in exchange rates can have a large effect on purchases of large amounts of money.

- When you buy most goods from foreign countries, you must pay GST and PST. Some goods also have an import duty, which is a federal tax. Rates vary.

DISCUSS THE CONCEPTS

1. When Gregory purchased U.S. dollars at a bank, the price was $1.4785 per U.S. dollar. The newspaper listed the wholesale price as $1.4675. Why do you think there is a difference?

2. a) Describe the steps you would take to convert £1000 (British pounds) to Canadian dollars if the exchange rate is $2.2164/£1.
b) Describe the steps you would take to convert $800 Canadian into Hong Kong dollars, with an exchange rate of $4.95 H.K./$1 Cdn.

A 1. i) Convert from Canadian dollars to the indicated currency.
ii) Convert each exchange rate to its equivalent rate for the foreign currency.
Round your answers to four decimal places.

	Canadian Dollars	Currency	Exchange Rate (Curr/$Cdn)
a)	100	U.S. dollar	0.6324
b)	250	Jamaican dollar	25.91
c)	1 000	Pakistani rupee	24.07
d)	600	Italian lira	1426.533
e)	2 000	Singaporean dollar	1.0784
f)	200	Venezuelan bolivar	449.4382
g)	500	Swedish krona	6.4475

2. i) Convert to Canadian dollars.
ii) Convert each exchange rate to its equivalent rate for Canadian dollars.
Round your answers to four decimal places.

	Currency	Amount	Exchange Rate ($Cdn/Curr)
a)	U.S. dollar	2 500	1.5237
b)	Mexican peso	15 000	0.1666
c)	Barbadian dollar	800	0.8073
d)	French franc	350	0.1926
e)	Saudi Arabian riyal	500	0.4062
f)	Bermudan dollar	200	1.5294
g)	Brazilian real	750	0.8294

3. Calculate the import duty on each item.

	Item	Value ($Cdn)	Duty Rate
a)	Watch	500	5%
b)	Stereo speakers	800	4.5%
c)	Leather jacket	349	13%
d)	Electric guitar	685	6%

APPLY THE CONCEPTS

4. A 1-week stay at a hotel in Seattle costs $75 U.S. per night. A 1-week stay at a similar hotel in Vancouver costs $94 per night. $1 U.S. costs $1.5124 Cdn.
a) Convert the cost of the Seattle hotel stay to Canadian dollars.
b) Which hotel is more expensive? By how much?

5. The meal package at a hotel in Barbados costs $249 Cdn if it is purchased in Canada. If it is purchased directly from the hotel, the cost is $295 Barbadian. The exchange rate is $1 Barbadian = $0.8073 Cdn.
a) Convert the cost, in Barbadian dollars, to Canadian dollars.
b) Where should the meal package be purchased in order to save money?

B 6. Anna has $800 Cdn and needs to convert it to U.S. dollars. Her bank offers a rate of $0.6523 U.S. per $1 Cdn. The currency exchange booth at the airport offers a rate of $0.6294 U.S. per $1 Cdn. Where would Anna receive more U.S. money? How much more?

7. Ted is planning a vacation to New York. He will buy $800 U.S. from the bank to pay for his hotel room, food, and entertainment. The price of the U.S. dollar was $1.5123 Cdn on July 6. The price of the U.S. dollar on July 13 was $1.4990 Cdn. What is the difference in total cost between the two dates?

8. Angie is planning a trip to Los Angeles. She will buy $1500 U.S. from the bank to pay for her hotel room, food, and entertainment. The price of the U.S. dollar was $1.5017 Cdn on February 16. The price of the U.S. dollar on February 27 was $1.5325 Cdn. What is the difference in total cost between the two dates?

9. Brian is a travel agent. He arranges package deals for seniors to travel to Florida. He checked the business section of his local newspaper for the current exchange rate for U.S. dollars. The rate is now $1.5022 per U.S. dollar. A financial analyst predicts that the rate will decline to $1.485 in 3 months.
   a) Calculate the amount saved by waiting 3 months when purchasing
       i) $5000   **ii)** $10 000
   b) Prepare a short report to show Brian's customers why it is better to wait 3 months before purchasing U.S. dollars.

10. Anila bought a watch from a U.S. outlet mall. The cost was $539 U.S.
   a) Calculate the cost, in Canadian dollars, at an exchange rate of $1 U.S. = $1.4875 Cdn.
   b) Calculate the import duty at 5%.
   c) Calculate the PST at 8% and GST at 7%.
   d) What was the total cost of Anila's purchase, in Canadian dollars?

11. George bought an electronic keyboard from a U.S.-based web site. The price was $1299.99 U.S. Shipping and handling were 5% of the price.
   a) Calculate the price, in Canadian dollars, at an exchange rate of $1 U.S. = $1.4922 Cdn.
   b) Calculate the shipping and handling, in Canadian dollars.
   c) Calculate the import duty at 6% of the price, in Canadian dollars.
   d) Calculate the PST (on the basic price) at 8% and GST (on the price including the shipping and handling) at 7%.
   e) What was the total cost of George's purchase, in Canadian dollars?

12. Travel agents advise people travelling to foreign countries to use traveller's cheques. There is usually an additional fee of 1% of the total value of the cheques. Visit *http://www.school.mcgrawhill.ca/resources/* and follow the links to research the advantages of using traveller's cheques when travelling to foreign countries.

13. Sadie purchased $500 in U.S. traveller's cheques at an exchange rate of $1.4815 Cdn per U.S. dollar plus a 1% fee. What was the total price, in Canadian dollars?

14. Devi needs to send her sister a money order for 6000 Mexican pesos. Her bank offers her an exchange rate of 1 peso = $0.1587 Cdn plus a fee of $3.50 for the money order. What is the total cost, in Canadian dollars?

ACHIEVEMENT Check Knowledge/Understanding Thinking/Inquiry/Problem Solving Communication Application

15. You and a friend are planning a 1-week vacation. Choose your destination and collect currency exchange rates over at least four time frames (weeks or months). For example, the newspaper gave these exchange rates for U.S. dollars:

Week 1	$1 US = $1.6289 Cdn
Week 2	$1 US = $1.5871 Cdn
Week 3	$1 US = $1.6245 Cdn
Week 4	$1 US = $1.5796 Cdn

a) Display your data in two ways, showing exchange rates in each direction.

b) If your vacation is in 3 months, would you advise getting some local currency now or later? Why?

16. Shopping today is much different than it was just a few years ago. Now, the Internet provides a whole new way to compare products and their prices. A good plan is to research prices and availability in catalogues, on the Internet, and in retail stores before deciding where to buy.

a) Select two items that you would like to buy that cost more than $100, such as a television, a CD player, concert tickets, designer clothing, a DVD player, or a computer.

b) Research the cost of buying each item from a foreign-based catalogue and Internet web site.

c) Calculate and compare the costs (including tax and delivery), ease of ordering, delivery time, variety, credit card security, and availability.

CAREER PROFILE

Travel Agent

Are you interested in the geography and culture of different countries? Do you have strong interpersonal skills? Can you speak and understand a language other than English? If so, you should consider a career in travel and tourism.

Two-year diploma programs are offered at colleges throughout Ontario. Areas of study include airline systems, tours, computer reservation systems, and tourism geography. A Travel and Tourism Diploma will allow you to pursue careers at retail travel agencies, wholesale tour companies, airlines, cruise lines, tourist boards, hotels, and corporations with travel departments.

1. Raj works in the travel department of a large international company. He has made a hotel reservation for an employee. If the room rate is $150 U.S. per night and $1 U.S. = $1.5132 Cdn, what is the rate in Canadian dollars?

2. Employees of Raj's company travelling on business are given $45 Cdn per day for meals. An employee is travelling to Hong Kong and will be there 6 days. If $1 Cdn = $5.28 H.K., how many Hong Kong dollars will the employee be able to claim for meals during her trip?

3. Smita is travelling to Costa Rica and wants to take a tour through the rain forests. The hotel where she is staying offers a 1-day rain forest tour for 28 500 colones (Costa Rican currency). If $1 Cdn = 203 colones, how much should she budget for this tour?

4. Several airports have a tax that goes toward their maintenance. The tax varies from airport to airport. How many Canadian dollars should a customer budget for the tax of £50 at Gatwick Airport, just outside London, England? The exchange rate is $1 Cdn = £0.43.

*C*ASE STUDY WRAP-UP

Shopping today is much different than it was just a few years ago. Now, the Internet provides a whole new way to compare products and their prices. A good plan is to research prices and availability in catalogues, on the Internet, and in retail stores before deciding where to buy.

Throughout this chapter, you have researched the best place to purchase certain items. You are now ready to write a summary report. Set up your report by answering the following questions:

1. What is the best place to purchase each item you chose? Take the following into consideration as you make your decision:
   - price (including taxes and delivery, if applicable)
   - availability
   - ease of ordering/purchasing
   - customer service
   - return policy

2. a) Is it better to pay for your purchase with a debit card or a credit card? Explain.
   b) If you are buying from a catalogue or an Internet retailer, how safe is it to use a credit card?

3. What are the advantages and disadvantages of buying from a foreign-based retailer?

   When preparing your report
   - justify, or explain, your reasoning
   - include a list of any materials you used, all your original data, your sources of information, and any formulas, tables, and graphs that you used or created
   - use technology, where appropriate

Review

8.1 Managing Your Retail Dollar, pages 292–300

1. Describe the risks involved in buying merchandise through
   a) an Internet auction house
   b) a telemarketer

2. Use the formula $r = \dfrac{2NI}{P(n+1)}$ to find the annual interest rate charged by a store when Kenji purchases a $459 DVD player for 12 monthly payments of $45.

3. Compare prices, billing options, and delivery for CDs from a retail store, a catalogue, and the Internet.

4. What is the import duty at 13% to be paid on a leather coat valued at $345 Cdn?

5. a) If each franchisee of a multilevel marketing company recruits 10 new franchisees, how many franchisees would there be in 6 levels?
   b) Multilevel marketing companies tend to *saturate* the market with franchisees. What you think this means? Explain.
   c) Would a multilevel marketing company be successful in a small town of 5000 people? Explain.

8.2 Managing Debit and Credit Cards, pages 301–308

6. Outline the order in which your account is credited when you pay your credit card bill.

7. A $325.88 purchase was made with a credit card on March 7. Calculate the interest due, at 18.2% simple interest, on the payment date of April 15.

8. Anna's October credit card bill is shown.

a) What is her new balance?

b) Her credit limit is $3500. How much credit is still available?

c) If Anna paid her new balance entirely, how much interest would she owe on her next statement?

d) If Anna paid only $500 of the new balance, how would the interest be calculated and charged?

Previous balance	$498.13
Purchases	567.43
Cash advances	200.00
Interest	10.45
Fees	35.00
Debit adjustments	
Other	
Payments	200.00 CR
Credit adjustments	

9. What are some advantages and disadvantages of using a debit card for purchases? Are there any risks involved? Explain.

8.3 Foreign Exchange, pages 309–315

10. Convert each amount to Canadian dollars.

a) $600 U.S. at an exchange rate of $1 U.S. = $1.4923 Cdn

b) 1000 European euros at an exchange rate of 1 euro = $1.3133 Cdn

11. Convert each amount.

a) $500 Cdn to Philippine pesos at an exchange rate of $1 Cdn = 32.237 pesos

b) $800 Cdn to Japanese yen at an exchange rate of $1 Cdn = 70.1755 yen

12. One Vermont hotel's rates are $78 U.S. per night. Another hotel has rates of $85 U.S. and accepts Canadian dollars at U.S. dollar values (at par). At an exchange rate of $1.5238 Cdn per U.S. dollar, how much would you save by staying at the second hotel?

13. Ted bought some clothing from a U.S.-based catalogue. The cost was $478.77 U.S, including shipping and handling of $10.

a) Calculate the cost, in Canadian dollars, at an exchange rate of $1 U.S. = $1.5231 Cdn.

b) Calculate the import duty at 9.5%.

c) Calculate the PST (on the basic price) at 8% and GST (on the price including shipping and handling) at 7%.

d) What is the total cost of Ted's purchase?

Practice Test

Achievement Chart Category Connections

Category	Knowledge/Understanding	Thinking/Inquiry/Problem Solving	Communication	Application
Questions	1–12	5, 8, 12	5, 8, 10–12	10, 12

1. Use the formula $r = \dfrac{2NI}{P(n+1)}$ to calculate the interest rate charged by the store when Casey paid for a $699 TV set with 24 monthly payments of $36.

2. Calculate the shipping and handling charge at 2.5% for the delivery of a $125 pair of concert tickets.

3. How much interest would be charged on a due date of October 20, for a credit card purchase of $295.47 made on September 12, at a simple interest rate of 17.5%?

4. a) Determine the equivalent value, in Canadian dollars, of $200 U.S., at an exchange rate of $1 U.S. = $1.5124 Cdn.
   b) Determine the equivalent value, in Greek drachma, of $700 Cdn, at an exchange rate of $1 Cdn = 258.665 drachma.

5. Describe how retailers use discount cards as a sales technique.

6. Compare the advantages and disadvantages of purchasing concert tickets over the telephone, through the Internet, and at a sales kiosk. Consider price, service, and accessibility.

7. Neetu's April credit card bill is shown.
   a) What is her new balance?
   b) Her credit limit is $5000. How much credit is still available?
   c) Neetu could only afford to pay $300 of the new balance. How would the interest be calculated and charged?

Previous balance	$826.78
Purchases	512.84
Cash advances	100.00
Interest	5.50
Fees	
Debit adjustments	
Other	
Payments	600.00 CR

8. For a vacation to England, the Ellises purchased £500 (British pounds) at an exchange rate of $2.298 per British pound. A week earlier, the exchange rate was $2.255 per British pound. How much extra, in Canadian dollars, did the Ellises spend by waiting the extra week?

9. John bought $245.84 U.S. worth of books from a U.S. catalogue. The catalogue merchant charges $10.00 for shipping plus a 2% handling fee and requires payment with a money order. There is no import duty or PST on books, but GST will be charged at 7% of the total cost, including shipping and handling. John's bank offers an exchange rate of $1 U.S. = $1.502 Cdn and will charge him $4.00 for the money order.
   a) What is each individual cost, in Canadian dollars? Use a spreadsheet if you wish.
   b) What is the total cost, in Canadian dollars, of John's book order?

10. A travel agency advises Monique to wait until the end of the month to purchase U.S. dollars for a trip to Florida. The exchange rate now is $1.5294 Cdn = $1 U.S. The travel agency predicts the rate will drop to $1.4832 by the end of the month.
   a) If Monique takes the agency's advice, how much will she save on a purchase of $1000 U.S.?
   b) List 3 ways Monique could research the current exchange rate for U.S. dollars.

11. **Import prices** The exchange rate on the Saudi Arabian riyal recently increased to $0.4238 Cdn per riyal from $0.4047 Cdn per riyal. What effect will this have on Canadian imports from Saudi Arabia?

ACHIEVEMENT Check Knowledge/Understanding Thinking/Inquiry/Problem Solving Communication Application

12. Choose a high-priced item you would like to have in the future.
   a) Identify at least three sources for your item and set up a chart or table to compare price, quality, and service options.
   b) Write a brief report describing the advantages and disadvantages of each source.
   c) Compare the total costs of loans from at least two different banks or trust companies and two or three credit cards from banks and stores.
   d) Choose one method of acquiring your item and justify your choice.

Cumulative Review

Chapters 5–8

1. Identify each series as arithmetic or geometric. Then, find the indicated sum.

   a) $1 + 5 + 9 + 13 + \ldots ; S_{12}$

   b) $1 + 3 + 9 + 27 + \ldots ; S_7$

   c) $2 - 4 + 8 - 16 + \ldots ; S_6$

   d) $5 + 10 + 15 + 20 + \ldots ; S_8$

   e) $(-16) + (-12) + (-8) + \ldots ; S_{10}$

   f) $10 + 7 + 4 + 1 + \ldots ; S_{15}$

2. A mechanic earned $26 000 one year and had raises of $950 per year for the next 5 years. What was the mechanic's total income over the 6-year period?

3. Marni is saving to buy a condominium. She invests $600 every month in an account earning interest at 6%, compounded monthly.

   a) How much will she save in 4 years?

   b) How much interest will her investment earn over the 4 years?

4. Anton has monthly student loan payments of $275 over the next 5 years. The interest rate is 8.5%, compounded monthly.

   a) What is the present value of his loan?

   b) If Anton could pay off the loan today, how much would he save?

5. Graph each function. Classify each as increasing or decreasing. Give the domain, range, and y-intercept of each.

   a) $y = 5^x$

   b) $y = 0.5^x$

   c) $y = \left(\dfrac{1}{5}\right)^x$

6. The value of computer equipment depreciates at a rate of 30% per year. Wayne paid $3500 for his new computer system.

   a) Write an exponential function to model the depreciated value of Wayne's computer system.

   b) What is the value of his system after 3 years?

7. The population of a new school is increasing by 8% each year. The school has 650 students now. The school is built for a maximum of 1000 students.

   a) Write an expression to model the population growth.

   b) Determine the predicted population 3 years from now.

   c) Using a graph, or another method, predict when the number of students will be greater than 1000.

   d) What factors might cause the predicted number to be incorrect?

8. Davyd drives a total of 60 km each weekday. He estimates that he drives about 100 km each weekend. His car averages 8.9 L/100 km.
   a) How far does he drive each week?
   b) If the gas price is an average of 80.9¢/L, what are his weekly fuel costs? Round your answer to the nearest dollar.

9. **Car choice** Rena has saved $6000 and wants to buy a car. She is considering three options.
   A: A used car for $5000, plus 15% taxes.
   B: A new car for a total of $18 970, plus 15% taxes. She would make a down payment of $5500 and finance the balance over 4 years at 2%, compounded monthly.
   C: A new car lease for $229 per month. She would pay the first month's payment, a down payment of $2000, and delivery/freight charges of $500, plus taxes at 15%. A security deposit of $700 is also required.
   a) How much of her savings will remain if she chooses the used car?
   b) If she chooses option B, how much will she have to finance? What will her monthly payments be?
   c) If she chooses to lease the car, how much will she have to pay to drive the car away from the lot?

10. **Credit card** Pat's January credit card statement is shown.
   a) What is her new balance?
   b) Pat's credit limit is $2500. How much credit is available?
   c) If she paid off the new balance entirely, how much interest would she owe on the next statement?
   d) If Pat paid $400.00 on the due date, how would interest be calculated and charged on the next statement?

Previous balance	$305.62
Purchases	410.25
Cash advances	250.00
Interest	9.85
Fees	
Debit adjustments	95.00
Other	
Payments	300.00 CR

11. **Debit/credit card comparison** When is it better to use a credit card than a debit card? When is it better to use a debit card?

12. **Dream vacation** Don's once-in-a-lifetime holiday is a visit to Japan. He estimates that he will need 150 000 Japanese yen for his trip. The exchange rate is $0.014 282 Cdn per yen. How much, in Canadian dollars, will Don spend?

CHAPTER 9

ACCOMMODATION COSTS

Specific Expectations	Sections
• collect, organize, and analyze data involving the costs of various kinds of accommodation in the community	9.1, 9.6
• compare the costs of maintaining an apartment with the costs of maintaining a house	9.1, 9.6
• compare the advantages and disadvantages of renting accommodation with the advantages and disadvantages of buying accommodation	9.1, 9.6
• identify the common terminology and features associated with mortgages	9.2
• describe the manner in which interest is usually calculated on a mortgage (i.e., compounded semi-annually but calculated monthly) and compare this with the method of interest compounded monthly and calculated monthly	9.3
• generate an amortization table for a mortgage, using a spreadsheet or other appropriate software	9.4
• calculate the total amount of interest paid over the life of a mortgage, using a spreadsheet or other appropriate software, and compare the amount with the original principal of the mortgage or value of the property	9.3, 9.4, 9.5
• compare the effects of various payment periods, payment amounts, and interest rates on the length of time needed to pay off a mortgage	9.3, 9.4, 9.5
• demonstrate, through calculations, using technology, the effect on interest paid of retiring a loan before it is due	9.3, 9.4, 9.5
• summarize the findings of investigations in effective presentations, blending written and visual forms	9.1, 9.6
• describe a decision involving a choice between alternatives	9.1, 9.6
• collect relevant information related to the alternatives to be considered in making a decision	9.1, 9.6

*G*et Ready. . .

1. Rewrite each decimal as a percent.
   a) 0.43
   b) 0.7
   c) 0.008
   d) 0.0175
   e) 0.025
   f) 0.06

2. Rewrite each percent as a decimal.
   a) 6.5%
   b) 1.25%
   c) 0.5%
   d) 12%
   e) 2.75%
   f) 0.25%

3. Calculate.
   a) 3% of $52 000
   b) 32% of $40 000
   c) 40% of $86 500
   d) 1.5% of $92 500
   e) 15% of $2200
   f) 0.75% of $15 000

4. Find the percent increase if each amount has grown as indicated. Round your answers to one decimal place.
   a) $862 to $986
   b) $543 to $859
   c) $215 to $635
   d) $812 to $1015
   e) $843 to $943
   f) $360 to $940

5. Find the percent decrease if each amount has lost value as indicated. Round your answers to one decimal place.
   a) $1432 to $1134
   b) $987 to $634
   c) $1050 to $754
   d) $769 to $243
   e) $78 753 to $66 789
   f) $65 782 to $54 678

6. Express each time period in years.
   a) 65 weeks
   b) 144 months
   c) 75 months
   d) 26 weeks
   e) 78 weeks
   f) 261 months

7. Express each time period in months.
   a) 15 years
   b) 20 years
   c) 25 years

8. How many days are between the following dates? Do not count the last date shown.
   a) May 8 to June 15
   b) August 23 to September 30
   c) July 2 to August 1
   d) June 22 to July 17
   e) February 25 to March 15 (in a leap year)
   f) August 25 to October 7

9. Find each value. Round your answers to six decimal places.

a) $(1.06)^{\frac{2}{12}}$ **b)** $(1.075)^{\frac{2}{12}}$ **c)** $(1.10)^{\frac{3}{12}}$

d) $(1+0.005)^{\frac{2}{4}}$ **e)** $(1+0.0475)^{\frac{2}{52}}$ **f)** $(1+0.025)^{\frac{2}{4}}$

For questions 10 and 11, round your answers to six decimal places, if necessary.

10. For an annual interest rate of 12%, find

  a) the semi-annual interest rate   **b)** the quarterly interest rate
  c) the monthly interest rate   **d)** the daily interest rate

11. For an annual interest rate of 6.5%, find

  a) the semi-annual interest rate   **b)** the quarterly interest rate
  c) the monthly interest rate   **d)** the daily interest rate

12. You paid $36/month for 10 years on a $3500 loan.

  a) Calculate the total amount of interest you paid.
  b) Express the total amount of interest paid as a percent of the loan amount. Round your answer to one decimal place.

CASE STUDY

Designate several pages of your notebook or use a portfolio to keep all of your work on the Case Study described below together for easy reference.

Because of a company merger, several families are moving to another town. In looking for a new place to live, each family has different considerations. They need to make several decisions, including location, size, accommodation type, and whether to rent or buy. All of these decisions need to be made while keeping their budget constraints in mind.

Throughout the Case Study in this chapter, you will consider three families. Information about their current accommodation situation and financial picture is given. As you learn more about accommodation options and features, you will make recommendations to them about accommodation decisions. By the end of the chapter, you will have gathered enough information to suggest a plan for each family.

Accommodation Options

Unreal Estate

2 BEDROOM WITH VIEW AND UNFINISHED BASEMENT

© 1995 Rick Carlsen/Reprinted with permission.

You must make several decisions when you are finding a place to live. One of these is whether to rent or buy. You might consider some of the following accommodation factors.
- How much can I afford?
- Will I qualify for a mortgage?
- Is accumulating equity in a home important to me? **Equity** is the difference between the value of a property and the amount still owed on it.
- Am I prepared to take responsibility for maintenance?
- Do I expect my income to remain stable?
- Does my choice fit the needs of the people I am living with?
- How long do I intend to stay in this accommodation and/or this location?

DISCOVER

Considerations When Choosing Accommodation

Work with a partner. Read the list above carefully.

1. List at least two more factors that you might consider in your accommodation decision.
2. Rank the factors, including those you added, in order of importance, starting with the most important.
3. Compare your ranking with those of your classmates. Discuss any differences.
4. As a home owner, the types of expenses you pay differ from those of a person who rents. Brainstorm the different costs that are involved in each scenario, and record them on a concept map.

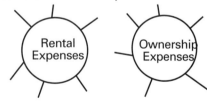

Rental Expenses   Ownership Expenses

A renter usually must sign a lease. This contract spells out what is or is not included in the rent, such as appliances, furniture, electricity, and heat.

EXAMPLE 1

Costs of Renting

Jed is looking for a one-bedroom apartment. Both apartments require first and last months' rent paid up front.

Apartment	Rent	Utilities
A	$750	included
B	$675	$700 per year

a) Calculate the up-front costs for each apartment.
b) Which apartment costs less?

Solution

a) Up-front costs:

Apartment A:

first and last months' rent = $750 + $750

= $1500

Apartment B:

first and last months' rent = $675 + $675

= $1350

b) Monthly expenses:

Apartment A:

$750

Apartment B:

$675 + $\dfrac{\$700}{12} \doteq \$675 + \$58.33$

= $733.33

Assuming utility costs do not change, Apartment B costs less.

EXAMPLE 2

Renting a House

Jay and Angela would like to rent a small house, but have very little furniture. Two options are given. Which option should they choose? Justify your answer.

Option A	Option B
• furnished house	• unfurnished house
• rent: $1500 + utilities	• rent: $1150 + utilities
• gas: $900/year	• furniture to rent: $200/month
• electricity: $500/year	• utilities: $1500 per year
• water: $300/year	

Solution

Option A

Total monthly costs

$= \$1500 + \dfrac{\$900}{12} + \dfrac{\$500}{12} + \dfrac{\$300}{12}$

$\doteq \$1500 + \$75 + \$41.67 + \$25$

$= \$1641.67$

Option B

Total monthly costs

$= \$1150 + \dfrac{\$1500}{12} + \$200$

$= \$1150 + \$125 + \$200$

$= \$1475$

Option B is the better choice for Jay and Angela. It costs less per month and they will be able to save to buy furniture of their own.

KEY CONCEPTS

- You need to consider many factors when making accommodation decisions.

- Rental expenses differ from the expenses of owning a home.

- Rent may or may not include utilities and parking.

- When comparing rental options, consider the overall cost per month.

- When you rent accommodation, you usually must pay first and last months' rent up front.

DISCUSS THE CONCEPTS

1. Mikayla is 21 years old and got a job 8 months ago working at a local tool and die company. She is ready to move out of her parents' house and has $5000 saved. Give at least two reasons why she should rent rather than buy accommodation.

2. Home ownership involves more responsibility than renting. Explain this statement.

PRACTISE

A 1. Give at least five advantages and five disadvantages to renting accommodation.

2. Where would you find information about rental properties? Identify three possible sources.

3. List at least six possible forms of accommodation, for example, a townhouse.

4. Where would you find information on homes for sale? Describe at least three sources.

5. Calculate the total average monthly costs for each rental situation.
   a) $675/month + utilities at $2000/year
   b) $925/month + water at $30/month + electricity at $80/month + gas at $110/month
   c) $1500/month + electricity at $450/year + water at $475/year + oil heating at $95/month
   d) $1100/month + electricity and water at $100/month + gas heating at $1400/year

6. Communication Copy and complete each sentence with at least three points.

   a) Renting a place to live instead of buying is better because ![?] .

   b) Buying a place to live instead of renting is better because ![?] .

B 7. The Ontario Rental Housing Tribunal (ORHT) is a government organization that monitors rental property. Disputes between landlords and tenants can be settled here. The ORHT permits a 2% increase in rent each year. Calculate the maximum monthly rents for the next 2 years if current rents are as follows.

   a) $675   **b)** $1215   **c)** $980

8. An apartment is available for $975/month plus utilities. The average costs for utilities are as shown.

   a) How much will you likely have to pay up front?

   b) What will the total monthly accommodation costs be?

Utility	Average Cost
water	$600/year
gas	$1200/year
electricity	$800/year

9. Heather has found two apartments that she likes. The first one costs $760 including utilities and free laundry facilities. The second one costs $725 including utilities but no laundry facilities. A nearby laundromat charges $2.25/load to wash and $2.00/load to dry. Heather estimates that she will have two loads per week. If she is on a very tight budget, which apartment should she choose? Justify your answer.

10. Application You and a friend are looking to rent two-bedroom accommodation in your own community. You have each saved $1750.

   a) List at least six conditions that you feel are necessary for your living arrangements.

   b) Use your local paper or other local resources to find three possible accommodations that meet your needs.

   c) Record the details for each option. Consider your conditions from part a) to rank these three options.

11. Problem Solving/Communication Sumit, Mauro, and Dan are college students. They plan to share rented accommodation. They have narrowed their search down to these three options.

Option A: Apartment	Option B: House	Option C: Duplex
• $1000 + utilities • gas: $120/month • electricity: $50/month • water: $40/month	• $1400 + electricity • electricity: $100/month	• $1175 + utilities • electricity: $175/month • water: $50/month

a) Calculate the monthly cost for each option.

b) Calculate the monthly cost per person if they select the least expensive option.

c) The cost of accommodation in the students' residence is $375/month per student for an 8-month period. What would the total monthly accommodation cost be for them to live in residence?

d) Compare the campus residence cost with the three off-campus choices.

   i) Which option is cheapest?

   ii) Make a list of the advantages and disadvantages of living on and off campus.

   iii) This would be the first time these three students have lived together. Describe three problems that might occur because of their sharing accommodation.

   iv) Choose one of the problems in part iii) and describe a solution.

12. Each family needs accommodation that best meets their needs. Consider carefully the details from the three families below. Brainstorm what features they might need in their accommodation.

Family	Details	Current Accommodation Situation	Accommodation Features Needed
Estey	• Aaron, 42 years old, registered nurse, $48 500 • Wendi, 44 years old, bank manager, $62 300 • Jerod, 14 years old, student • Mackenzie, 12 years old, student	• family owns house • lived in house for 8 years • house is a bit small for them at 1200 square feet	
Chu	• Darren, 24 years old, machinist, $30 500 • Jake, 6-month-old puppy	• one-bedroom apartment: $750/month + utilities • utilities: $150/month	
Lloyd	• Jen, 34 years old, mechanical engineer, $72 000 • Jason, 6 years old, student	• family owns house • lived in house for 2 years • would prefer a house within walking distance of Jason's school	

9.2 Costs of Buying: Introduction to Mortgages

Since cost is an important factor in accommodation choice, you need to understand the costs for both renting and buying.

DISCOVER

Mortgage Terminology

After renting an apartment for 2 years, Rosa would like to buy a home so that she can build some **equity**. Because she does not have enough money to pay for a home in full, she will combine some of her savings with a **mortgage** arranged through a bank or a **mortgage broker**. Rosa, as **mortgagor**, will then need to make **mortgage payments** to the **mortgagee**. These payments will apply to the **principal** and **interest** portions of the mortgage. She will use the property she buys as **collateral**.

1. Match the words in bold type in the paragraph above with the following definitions. Record your answers in your notebook.
   a) the borrower
   b) a special type of borrowing arrangement between a borrower and a lender
   c) the cost of borrowing money
   d) the lender
   e) regular installments made toward paying back the principal and interest on a mortgage
   f) the mortgage amount initially borrowed, or the portion still owing on the mortgage
   g) a licensed person who, for a fee, brings together a borrower in need of a mortgage and a lender willing to provide one
   h) a financial gain (value of home minus amount still owed on the home)
   i) property used to guarantee the repayment of a debt

2. Rosa has gathered information from banks and mortgage brokers to determine where she will get her mortgage. Define each of the words in bold type in the advertisement shown.

3. The advertisement says that the mortgage payments are monthly. The **payment frequency** is how often a mortgage payment is made. Although monthly payments are the most common, the following options are also available:
- semi-monthly
- weekly
- accelerated weekly
- bi-weekly
- accelerated bi-weekly

Discuss with a partner what each of these options means. Refer to the Glossary at the back of this text for help.

THIS MONTH'S SPECIAL
Make your monthly payments based on an 8.5% **interest rate** for a 10-year **term**, with an **amortization period** of 25 years. Pay down your mortgage early with our **prepayment privilege**. Moving soon? You will appreciate the **portability** of our mortgages.

EXAMPLE 1

Mortgage Payments

For a particular mortgage, Rosa will pay $585.58 per month.

a) Determine the payment amounts if the payment frequency is changed from monthly to
  i) semi-monthly   **ii)** weekly   **iii)** accelerated weekly
  iv) bi-weekly   **v)** accelerated bi-weekly

b) Which method of payment will cost most per year?

Solution

a)

	Payment Frequency	Definition	Payment Calculation	Amount of Payment
	monthly	once a month	M	$585.58
i)	semi-monthly	twice a month	$M \div 2$	$585.58 \div 2$ = $292.79
ii)	weekly	once a week	$M \times 12$ (months in a year) $\div 52$ (weeks in a year)	$585.58 \times 12 \div 52$ = $135.13
iii)	accelerated weekly	once a week	$M \div 4$ (weeks in a month)	$585.58 \div 4$ = $146.40
iv)	bi-weekly	every two weeks	$M \times 12$ (months in a year) $\div 52$ (weeks) $\times 2$	$585.58 \times 12 \div 52 \times 2$ = $270.27
v)	accelerated bi-weekly	every two weeks	$M \div 2$	$585.58 \div 2$ = $292.79

b) Compare the total amounts paid per year.

For semi-monthly payments, the total amount paid each year is
$292.79 × 24 = $7026.96.

For weekly payments, the total amount paid each year is
$135.13 × 52 = $7026.76.

For accelerated weekly payments, the total amount paid each year is
$146.40 × 52 = $7612.80.

For bi-weekly payments, the total amount paid each year is
$270.27 × 26 = $7027.02.

For accelerated bi-weekly payments, the total amount paid each year is
$292.79 × 26 = $7612.54.

Accelerated weekly payments cost the most per year.
They are also the fastest way to reduce the mortgage.

DISCOVER

Closing Costs

Rosa knows that on the **closing date**, which is the day that she legally takes
possession of her new home, she will need to pay part of the price of her home
as a **down payment**. In addition, Rosa will have to pay other expenses. These
other **closing costs** vary depending on the situation.

Use the glossary and/or other resources to find the meaning of each of these
other costs.

1. application fee
2. mortgage broker's fee
3. legal fees
4. land-transfer tax
5. home-inspection fee
6. CMHC (Canada Mortgage and Housing Corporation) fee

EXAMPLE 2

Calculate Closing Costs

Rosa has found a condominium that she would like to buy.

selling price	$89 500
legal fees	$1000 (including PST & GST)
land-transfer tax	0.75% of selling price
CMHC fee	$3000

As a first-time buyer, Rosa will pay a 5% down payment. Determine the amount of
money (down payment and closing costs) she will need on the closing date.

Solution

Down payment = 5% of $89 500

$\qquad$ = $0.05 \times \$89\ 500$

$\qquad$ = $\$4475$

Other closing costs = legal fees + land-transfer tax + CMHC fee

$\qquad$ = $\$1000 + 0.75\%$ of $\$89\ 500 + \$3000$

$\qquad$ = $\$1000 + 0.0075 \times \$89\ 500 + \$3000$

$\qquad$ = $\$4671.25$

Total closing costs = down payment + other closing costs

$\qquad$ = $\$4475.00 + \$4671.25$

$\qquad$ = $\$9146.25$

Rosa will need $9146.25 on the closing date.

KEY CONCEPTS

- A mortgage is a service offered by lenders that allows buyers to purchase homes.

- Mortgages can be arranged with a financial institution, such as a bank or credit union, or a mortgage broker.

- One important feature of a mortgage is its payment frequency. Payments can be made monthly, semi-monthly, weekly, accelerated weekly, bi-weekly, or accelerated bi-weekly. The more often a payment is made, the faster a mortgage is paid off.

- A down payment is paid by the buyer on the closing date. First-time buyers with good credit often qualify for a down payment option of 5% of the purchase price.

- Additional costs must also be paid on the closing date. These costs include application fee, mortgage broker's fee, legal fees, land-transfer tax, and CMHC fee.

DISCUSS THE CONCEPTS

1. Why are accelerated bi-weekly and accelerated weekly payments called accelerated?

2. Discuss the advantages and disadvantages of a large versus a small down payment.

3. Why do lenders offer a lower down payment option for first-time buyers?

4. Why do you think a mortgage broker charges a higher fee for someone with a poor credit rating?

5. Describe how the up-front costs of renting and buying differ.

A 1. Use the glossary or another source to describe the similarities and differences between the following types of mortgages.
   a) fixed-rate and variable-rate mortgages
   b) open and closed mortgages
   c) first and second mortgages

2. Copy and complete each sentence, using the mortgage terminology you have learned. Find the message written in numbers in the last line by replacing each number with the letter from the sentences.
   a) [?][?][1][?] fees can sometimes be avoided by making a down payment of 25% or more.
   b) A mortgage [?][?][2][?][?][?] is someone who matches lenders with borrowers.
   c) In a [3][?][?][?][?][?][?][?][?], the borrower uses property as a guarantee for the repayment of debt.
   d) [?][4][?][?]-[?][?][?][?][?][?][?][?] payments are made twice per month.
   e) The fee charged by lenders for the use of their money is called [5][?][?][?][?][?][?][?].
   f) A common closing cost is the [?][?][?][?]-[?][?][6][?][?][?][?][?][?][?] fee, the money charged to inspect a home.
   g) [?][?][?][?]-[7][?][?][?][?][?][?][?][?] [?][?][?] is the tax paid by anyone who buys property in Ontario.
   h) [?][?]-[8][?][?][?][?][?] payments are made every two weeks.
   i) The [9][?][?][?][?][?][?][?][?][?][?][?][?] period is the number of years required to repay an entire mortgage.
   j) The original amount borrowed is known as the [?][10][?][?][?][?][?][?][?].
   Message: 1, 2, 3, 4   5, 6   8, 1, 4, 10, 4   7, 1, 4   1, 4, 9, 10, 7   5, 6

3. Copy and complete the table to change the frequency of each monthly payment.

	Monthly	Weekly	Accelerated Weekly	Semi-monthly	Bi-weekly	Accelerated Bi-weekly
a)	$968.42					
b)	$843.15					
c)	$1248.89					

4. Find the total amount paid after 1 year for each payment schedule.
   a) monthly payments of $1120
   b) bi-weekly payments of $478.50
   c) accelerated weekly payments of $314.12

5. For a $987 monthly payment, find the difference in total amount paid after 1 year for each pair of payment frequencies.

a) weekly and accelerated weekly

b) bi-weekly and accelerated bi-weekly

c) semi-monthly and accelerated bi-weekly

6. Josh and Zadine would like to buy a home for $135 600. What is the minimum down payment if they

a) qualify for a first-time buyer's down payment of 5%?

b) require a 25% down payment?

Unreal Estate

NEW HOME WITH 2 CAR GARAGE.

TOO MANY UNIQUE FEATURES TO LIST.

© 1995 Rick Carlsen/Reprinted with permission.

APPLY THE CONCEPTS

7. Zac is buying a townhouse for $92 670. He estimates his legal expenses will be $1400. The bank is charging an application fee of $125. Land-transfer tax is 1% of the purchase price. Zac is making a down payment of 25%.

a) Calculate the land-transfer tax.

b) Calculate the down payment.

c) Calculate the mortgage amount.

d) Calculate the total amount Zac will need on the closing date.

B 8. How much more money is paid each week by accelerating a weekly payment of $226.42?

9. A mortgage broker advertises a mortgage that has accelerated bi-weekly payments of $278.00. What would the monthly payment be?

10. Karl is negotiating a $120 000 mortgage at an interest rate of 7% for a 10-year term. The monthly payment is $840.50. Calculate the payment for each payment frequency.

a) semi-monthly   **b)** accelerated weekly   **c)** bi-weekly

11. Meera needs a mortgage for $120 000. For a 10-year term amortized over 20 years at an interest rate of 7%, the monthly payment is $923.17.

a) Calculate the payment for a weekly payment frequency.

b) If Meera had negotiated more, she might have reduced her interest rate to 6.25%. The monthly payment would then have been $871.54.

i) Find the new weekly payment at this rate.

ii) How much would she have saved each week with this new interest rate?

Did You Know?

To get a mortgage from a bank you must have fire insurance on the property.

12. Eric is interested in a home selling for $126 500. He has put in an offer of $122 000. He qualifies for a first-time buyer's down payment of 5%.

   a) Determine the two possible down payments based on the selling price and the offer.

   b) How much will he save in down payment costs if his offer is accepted?

13. For the same mortgage amount, one bank offers bi-weekly payments of $512, while another bank offers accelerated weekly payments of $229.

   a) Find the total annual cost for each.

   b) Which option is less expensive and by how much per year?

14. **Problem Solving** Carter mistakenly estimates his closing costs to only include his 10% down payment of $13 500. He did not include estimates for legal fees ($3000), land-transfer tax (1% of purchase price), and other fees ($500).

   a) Determine the house price if $13 500 is 10% of the purchase price.

   b) Determine the land-transfer tax.

   c) Determine the true approximate total closing costs.

   d) By how much did Carter underestimate his closing costs?

15. **CMHC fees** CMHC fees depend on the amount of the loan provided. The loan amount is the difference between the full selling price of the house and the down payment. For example, a 15% down payment means that the remaining 85% of the purchase price needs to be borrowed. If the purchase price is $120 000, the loan amount will be 85% of $120 000 or $102 000. From the table, the fee in this case is 2.00% of the loan. Thus, the fee is 2.00% of $102 000 or $2040. Often, this fee is included in the mortgage and is not paid as part of the closing costs.

Loan Amount (as a percent of the total home value)	Fee (as a percent of the loan)
Up to and including 95%	3.75
Up to and including 90%	2.50
Up to and including 85%	2.00
Up to and including 80%	1.25
Up to and including 75%	0.75
Up to and including 65%	0.50

Determine the down payment and CMHC fee required in each case.

   a) $89 500 townhouse, 5% down payment

   b) $187 500 home, 40% down payment

   c) $126 900 semi-detached home, $15 000 down payment

16. The three families who are moving might decide to buy homes. Copy and complete the table using the following costs.
- Legal expenses average $2500.
- The land-transfer tax is about $2000.
- The home-inspection fee is about $250.
- There are no mortgage-broker or application fees.

Family	Cash Available to Buy Home	Closing Costs	Amount Available for Down Payment	Approximate Value of Home if Down Payment Is	
				5%	25%
Estey	$36 500				
Chu	$25 000				
Lloyd	$14 000				

Show your work and justify all the amounts you use.

17. a) A new home can be built at a cost of $87 per square foot (GST included). A 3400 square-foot home is built on a lot costing $40 000. Determine the total cost of the home, including the lot.

b) Use the CMHC table in question 15 to determine the fees based on each down payment.

i) 5%   **ii)** 10%   **iii)** 20%

18. A home is sold for $156 000. Real estate fees are 5.5% of the sale price. The seller receives the rest.

a) How much does the real estate agent receive?

b) How much does the seller receive?

19. Land-transfer tax is based on the selling price of the home, as shown in the table.

Home Selling Price	Land-transfer Tax
Up to and including $55 000	0.5%
Above $55 000, up to and including $250 000	1.0%
Above $250 000	1.5%

Draw a piecewise linear graph to show how the amount of land-transfer tax is related to the price.

Mortgage Interest

In Canada, mortgage interest rates are usually given as an annual percent. However, the interest is **compounded semi-annually** and **paid monthly**. Because the payment frequency is different from the compounding period, you need to use equivalent rates. **Equivalent interest rates** have different compounding frequencies, but yield the same amount of interest on a given principal for the same period of time.

EXAMPLE 1

Find Equivalent Interest Rates

What equivalent interest rate, compounded monthly, results in the same final amount as 6%, compounded semi-annually?

Solution

Step 1: Estimate.
Monthly compounding is 12 times a year, and semi-annual compounding is twice a year, so the equivalent interest rate will be lower than 6%.

Step 2: Use $A = P(1 + i)^n$ to write an equation to represent each investment:
$A = P(1.03)^2$ and $A = P(1 + i)^{12}$

The final amount, A, is the same for both investments, so,
$P(1.03)^2 = P(1 + i)^{12}$

Solve for i:

$$P(1.03)^2 = P(1 + i)^{12} \qquad \text{Divide each side by } P.$$

$$(1.03)^2 = (1 + i)^{12} \qquad \text{Evaluate } (1.03)^2.$$

$$1.0609 = (1 + i)^{12} \qquad \text{Raise each side of the equation to the exponent } \frac{1}{12}.$$

$$1.0609^{\frac{1}{12}} = [(1+i)^{12}]^{\frac{1}{12}} \qquad \text{Simplify.}$$

$$1.004\,938\,622 = 1 + i \qquad \text{Subtract 1 from each side.}$$

$$0.004\,938\,622 = i$$

So, the equivalent monthly interest rate is 0.493 862 2%.

Check using a principal of $100 and a term of 1 year:

0.493 862 2% per month, compounded monthly

$$A = 100(1.004\,938\,622)^{12}$$

$$A = 106.09$$

6% per year, compounded semi-annually

$$A = 100(1.03)^2$$

$$A = 106.09$$

An interest rate of approximately 0.494% per month, compounded monthly, is equivalent to 6%, compounded semi-annually.

Equivalent interest rates can be found in the tables on pages 349 to 353. The table on page 349 shows that the equivalent rate for 1 month, for 6%, compounded semi-annually, is 0.004 938 62.

Equivalent rates are useful when interest must be calculated for a time period of less than 1 year.

EXAMPLE 2

Calculate Interest Owed Between Two Dates

Tim recently purchased a home with a closing date of May 22. His mortgage is for $104 375 at 12% interest. His first mortgage payment is not due until June 1. How much interest does he owe for the days between the closing date and his first payment date?

Solution

Calculate the number of days for which interest is owed. Do not include the first day of payment.
May 22 to May 31 is 10 days.

Use the table on page 353.
For 12%, compounded semi-annually, the equivalent interest rate for 10 days is 0.003 197 92.

Interest = $104 375 × 0.003 197 92
         ≐ $333.78

The interest Tim owes for the 10 days is $333.78.

EXAMPLE 3

Calculate the Penalty for Early Discharge of a Mortgage

Carla is halfway through the 5-year term of her mortgage. She has noticed interest rates have dropped to the lowest they have been for some time. She would like to transfer her mortgage to take advantage of the better rate.

However, to do so before the end of the term she must pay a penalty equivalent to 3 months' interest. Her mortgage rate is 7.875% and the principal owing at the time of the transfer was $91 216.42. Calculate the penalty for discharging the mortgage early.

Solution

7.875% is not shown in the table. So, calculate a 3-month rate that is equivalent to 7.875%, compounded semi-annually.

For 7.875%, compounded semi-annually, $i = 0.07875 \div 2$ or 0.039 375.

To find the equivalent 3-month rate, solve for i in the following.

$(1+i)^4 = (1+0.039\ 375)^2$ For i, there are 4 compounding periods per year.

For 7.875%, there are 2 compounding periods per year.

$(1+i)^{\frac{4}{4}} = (1.039\ 375)^{\frac{2}{4}}$ Raise each side of the equation to the exponent $\frac{1}{4}$.

$1+i = (1.039\ 375)^{\frac{1}{2}}$ Simplify.

$1+i \doteq 1.019\ 497$

$i = 1.019\ 497 - 1$

$i = 0.019\ 497$

Penalty $= \$91\ 216.42 \times 0.019\ 497$

$\qquad = \$1778.45$

The penalty for discharging the mortgage early is $1778.45.

You can use the **TVM Solver** on the TI-83 Plus graphing calculator to find monthly payments for semi-annual and for monthly compounding. **C/Y** represents the number of compounding periods per year.

For semi-annual compounding, enter **C/Y**=2.

For monthly compounding, enter **C/Y**=12.

See pages 412 to 415 in the Technology Appendix for more details on the **TVM Solver**.

EXAMPLE 4

Compare Interest Paid With Monthly and Semi-annual Compounding

A mortgage of $80 000 at 9% is amortized over 25 years.

a) Find the monthly payment and the total amount of interest paid in 1 year if interest is compounded monthly.

b) How much less interest is paid each year by compounding semi-annually?

c) Find the total amount of interest paid over the 25-year amortization period with interest compounding semi-annually.

Solution

a) To find the monthly payment for monthly compounding:

Press (MODE) and set the number of decimal places to two.
Press (APPS), (ENTER), (ENTER) to access the **TVM Solver** screen.
Input the following values for the variables:

N=300   25 years at
I%=9   12 months/year
PV =80000
PMT =0
FV=0
P/Y=12
C/Y=12   compounding monthly, 12 times per year

Using the arrow keys, place the cursor beside **PMT**.
Press (ALPHA) (ENTER) for **SOLVE** to find the payment (**PMT**).
The payment is a negative amount. This indicates a cash outflow.

The monthly payment for monthly compounding is $671.36.

To find the total interest paid in 1 year, use the **ΣInt** function of the **Finance Applications**.

To exit the **TVM Solver** screen, press (2nd) (MODE) for **QUIT**.

Now, to access the **ΣInt** function, press (APPS) (ENTER) for the **Finance Applications** menu.
Using the arrows, cursor down to **A: ΣInt(** and press (ENTER).
Enter **1, 12, 2).**   (start payment number, end payment number, number of digits to round to)
Press (ENTER).

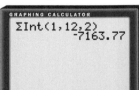

The total interest paid in 1 year is $7163.77.

b) To find the monthly payment for semi-annual compounding:
Use similar steps as in part a) except use **C/Y=2**.

If the mode is set to 2, the last entry is optional. ΣInt(1, 12) gives the same result.

The monthly payment for semi-annual compounding is $662.38 and the interest paid in 1 year is $7032.09.
The interest saved by semi-annual compounding is $7163.77 − $7032. 09 or $131.68.
By semi-annual compounding, $131.68 less interest is paid in 1 year.

c) To find the total interest paid at the end of 25 years with semi-annual compounding, use the **ΣInt** function of the **Finance Applications**. In 25 years, there are 25 × 12 or 300 monthly payments.
So, use **ΣInt(1,300,2)**.

The total interest paid in 25 years is $118 716.23.

KEY CONCEPTS

- Interest on mortgages in Canada is compounded semi-annually.

- Interest may be calculated for any time period by using a rate equivalent to the semi-annual rate of interest (see tables, pages 349 to 353).

- A penalty, often equivalent to 3 months' interest, is charged for paying off the balance of a closed mortgage before the term has expired.

DISCUSS THE CONCEPTS

1. When interest rates are low, it is good for the economy. Explain what this statement means.

2. The interest calculated with monthly compounding is greater than the interest calculated with semi-annual compounding, for the same interest rate. Explain.

3. Why might a homeowner consider paying a penalty for closing a mortgage before the end of its term?

A **1.** For each of the following interest rates, compounded semi-annually, determine the equivalent monthly interest rate.

a)   9%   b)   10.5%   c)   7.25%   d)   14%

2. For each of the following interest rates, compounded semi-annually, determine the equivalent interest rate, using the tables on pages 349 to 353.

a)   7.5% for 1 month   b)   10.25% for 3 months

c)   11% for 4 days   d) $11\frac{1}{4}$% for 9 days

e)   9% for 3 months   f)   6.75% for 1 week

3. Copy and complete the table.

	Principal	Quoted Interest Rate	Time Period	Equivalent Interest Rate	Interest Owing
a)	$47 500.00	6.50%	1 month		
b)	$29 000.00	10.00%	3 months		
c)	$114 275.63	9.25%	1 day		
d)	$154 716.09	8.75%	10 days		

APPLY THE CONCEPTS

B *Assume semi-annual compounding, unless otherwise specified.*

4. **a)** A mortgage amount of $68 415 at 9.4% for a 5-year term is amortized over 20 years. Use the **TVM Solver** to calculate the following for monthly and for semi-annual compounding:

i) the monthly payment for each type of compounding
ii) the total interest paid over the 5-year term (Hint: use the **ΣInt** function.)

b) How much less interest is paid, over the 5-year term, for semi-annual compounding?

5. The Bernsteins are paying $187 500 for their new home. They need a mortgage to cover 85% of the purchase price. The interest rate is 8.25%, amortized over 25 years, for a 10-year term. Calculate each of the following:

a) the monthly payment
b) the total interest for the 10-year term

6. The Nandas have a $105 000 mortgage at 8.75%. The closing date is July 14 but their first payment is not due until August 1. How much interest must they pay from closing to the first payment date?

7. Copy and complete the table to determine the interest owing from the closing date until the first payment date. If the time period is not included in the tables on pages 349 to 353, determine the equivalent rate separately. Recall that the first day of payment is not included in the number of days.

	Mortgage Amount	Interest Rate	Closing Date	First Payment	Number of Days	Interest Owing
a)	$71 210	9%	August 10	August 17		
b)	$142 250	10.5%	September 24	October 1		
c)	$104 000	$11\frac{1}{4}$%	January 4	January 15		
d)	$187 500	8.25%	March 3	April 1		

8. Verify some values in the interest tables on pages 349 to 353 by calculating the equivalent rate for each.
   a) 8% for 1 month   b) 6% for 3 months   c) 9.5% for 7 days

9. a) Determine the 3-months' interest penalty for paying off each mortgage early.
      i) $74 317.75 at 7% interest   ii) $104 300.06 at 8.25% interest
   b) Why do you think lenders penalize borrowers for paying off their debt early?

10. **Problem Solving** The Marten family owes $72 815.42 at 7.75% interest over a 10-year term. By changing their mortgage to a new lender, they will save $1500. If they will have to pay a 3-months' interest penalty, should they switch to the new lender?

11. Roma and Bill have just purchased a home with a closing date of May 8, and need to finance $163 215. Their payments start on June 15 of the same year.
   a) How many days' worth of interest will they be charged between the closing date and the first payment date?
   b) If the interest rate is 7.25%, determine the equivalent rate for the time period in part a).
   c) How much interest will they be charged for the time period in part a)?

12. The families have investigated mortgage options and decided that they need mortgages with the features shown in the table. In the past, each family has paid a mortgage payment or rent, and knows that it can continue to do so. Each family would like to maintain its current monthly payment.

Family	Mortgage Features for New Home	Current Monthly Payment	Amount That Can Be Borrowed to Maintain Monthly Payment	Amount Available for Down Payment	Approximate Price of Home That Family Can Afford
Estey	• 9.5%, compounded semi-annually • 5-year term • 25-year amortization	$587.60 semi-monthly			
Chu	• 9%, compounded semi-annually • 10-year term • 25-year amortization	$750/month			
Lloyd	• 9.25%, compounded semi-annually • 10-year term • 25-year amortization	$819.16/ month			

a) Use the **TVM Solver**, or another method, to calculate the most that each family can borrow to buy a home if they wish to maintain their current monthly payment.

b) Use the amounts available for down payment that you calculated in question 16 on page 340. Determine the approximate price of a home that each family can afford.

c) What conclusions can you make about the accommodation choices for these families?

ACHIEVEMENT Check *Knowledge/Understanding* Thinking/Inquiry/Problem Solving Communication Application

13. Rosa wants to borrow $100 000 for a mortgage. She wants to consider various payment options. Help her by reviewing the options available, using appropriate mortgage terminology. If Rosa wishes to pay off the mortgage as fast as possible, recommend which method of payment she should choose, with justifications.

Equivalent Interest Rates for Given Annual Rates
Compounded Semi-annually

Days	6.00%	6.25%	6.50%	6.75%	7.00%	Days
1	0.000 161 98	0.000 168 63	0.000 175 27	0.000 181 90	0.000 188 52	1
2	0.000 323 99	0.000 337 28	0.000 350 56	0.000 363 83	0.000 377 07	2
3	0.000 486 02	0.000 505 96	0.000 525 89	0.000 545 79	0.000 565 66	3
4	0.000 648 07	0.000 674 68	0.000 701 24	0.000 727 78	0.000 754 29	4
5	0.000 810 16	0.000 843 42	0.000 876 63	0.000 909 81	0.000 942 95	5
6	0.000 972 27	0.001 012 18	0.001 052 05	0.001 091 87	0.001 131 65	6
7	0.001 134 41	0.001 180 98	0.001 227 50	0.001 273 97	0.001 320 38	7
8	0.001 296 57	0.001 349 81	0.001 402 98	0.001 456 09	0.001 509 15	8
9	0.001 458 76	0.001 518 66	0.001 578 49	0.001 638 25	0.001 697 95	9
10	0.001 620 98	0.001 687 54	0.001 754 03	0.001 820 45	0.001 886 79	10
11	0.001 783 21	0.001 856 45	0.001 929 61	0.002 002 68	0.002 075 66	11
12	0.001 945 48	0.002 025 39	0.002 105 21	0.002 184 94	0.002 264 57	12
13	0.002 107 78	0.002 194 36	0.002 280 84	0.002 367 23	0.002 453 52	13
14	0.002 270 10	0.002 363 35	0.002 456 51	0.002 549 56	0.002 642 50	14
15	0.002 432 44	0.002 532 38	0.002 632 20	0.002 731 91	0.002 831 52	15
16	0.002 594 82	0.002 701 43	0.002 807 93	0.002 914 31	0.003 020 57	16
17	0.002 757 22	0.002 870 51	0.002 983 69	0.003 096 73	0.003 209 66	17
18	0.002 919 64	0.003 039 62	0.003 159 47	0.003 279 19	0.003 398 78	18
19	0.003 082 10	0.003 208 76	0.003 335 29	0.003 461 68	0.003 587 94	19
20	0.003 244 57	0.003 377 93	0.003 511 14	0.003 644 21	0.003 777 14	20
21	0.003 407 08	0.003 547 13	0.003 687 02	0.003 826 77	0.003 966 37	21
22	0.003 569 61	0.003 716 35	0.003 862 93	0.004 009 36	0.004 155 63	22
23	0.003 732 17	0.003 885 60	0.004 038 87	0.004 191 99	0.004 344 93	23
24	0.003 894 75	0.004 054 88	0.004 214 85	0.004 374 64	0.004 534 27	24
25	0.004 057 36	0.004 224 19	0.004 390 85	0.004 557 34	0.004 723 65	25
26	0.004 220 00	0.004 393 53	0.004 566 89	0.004 740 06	0.004 913 06	26
27	0.004 382 66	0.004 562 90	0.004 742 95	0.004 922 82	0.005 102 50	27
28	0.004 545 35	0.004 732 29	0.004 919 05	0.005 105 61	0.005 291 98	28
29	0.004 708 06	0.004 901 72	0.005 095 17	0.005 288 43	0.005 481 50	29
30	0.004 870 81	0.005 071 17	0.005 271 33	0.005 471 29	0.005 671 05	30

Months						Months
1	0.004 938 62	0.005 141 78	0.005 344 74	0.005 547 49	0.005 750 04	1
2	0.009 901 63	0.010 310 00	0.010 718 05	0.011 125 76	0.011 533 14	2
3	0.014 889 16	0.015 504 80	0.016 120 07	0.016 734 97	0.017 349 50	3

Equivalent Interest Rates for Given Annual Rates
Compounded Semi-annually

Days	7.25%	7.50%	7.75%	8.00%	8.25%	Days
1	0.000 195 13	0.000 201 74	0.000 208 34	0.000 214 93	0.000 221 51	1
2	0.000 390 31	0.000 403 52	0.000 416 72	0.000 429 91	0.000 443 08	2
3	0.000 585 52	0.000 605 34	0.000 625 15	0.000 644 93	0.000 664 69	3
4	0.000 780 76	0.000 807 21	0.000 833 62	0.000 860 00	0.000 886 35	4
5	0.000 976 05	0.001 009 11	0.001 042 13	0.001 075 12	0.001 108 06	5
6	0.001 171 37	0.001 211 06	0.001 250 69	0.001 290 28	0.001 329 82	6
7	0.001 366 74	0.001 413 04	0.001 459 29	0.001 505 49	0.001 551 63	7
8	0.001 562 14	0.001 615 07	0.001 667 94	0.001 720 74	0.001 773 49	8
9	0.001 757 58	0.001 817 13	0.001 876 62	0.001 936 04	0.001 995 40	9
10	0.001 953 05	0.002 019 24	0.002 085 35	0.002 151 39	0.002 217 35	10
11	0.002 148 57	0.002 221 39	0.002 294 13	0.002 366 79	0.002 439 36	11
12	0.002 344 12	0.002 423 58	0.002 502 95	0.002 582 22	0.002 661 42	12
13	0.002 539 71	0.002 625 81	0.002 711 81	0.002 797 71	0.002 883 52	13
14	0.002 735 34	0.002 828 08	0.002 920 71	0.003 013 24	0.003 105 67	14
15	0.002 931 01	0.003 030 39	0.003 129 66	0.003 228 82	0.003 327 87	15
16	0.003 126 71	0.003 232 74	0.003 338 65	0.003 444 45	0.003 550 13	16
17	0.003 322 46	0.003 435 13	0.003 547 69	0.003 660 12	0.003 772 43	17
18	0.003 518 24	0.003 637 57	0.003 756 77	0.003 875 84	0.003 994 78	18
19	0.003 714 06	0.003 840 04	0.003 965 89	0.004 091 60	0.004 217 18	19
20	0.003 909 92	0.004 042 56	0.004 175 06	0.004 307 41	0.004 439 63	20
21	0.004 105 81	0.004 245 11	0.004 384 27	0.004 523 27	0.004 662 12	21
22	0.004 301 75	0.004 447 71	0.004 593 52	0.004 739 17	0.004 884 67	22
23	0.004 497 72	0.004 650 35	0.004 802 82	0.004 955 12	0.005 107 27	23
24	0.004 693 73	0.004 853 03	0.005 012 16	0.005 171 12	0.005 329 91	24
25	0.004 889 78	0.005 055 75	0.005 221 54	0.005 387 16	0.005 552 61	25
26	0.005 085 87	0.005 258 51	0.005 430 97	0.005 603 25	0.005 775 35	26
27	0.005 282 00	0.005 461 31	0.005 640 44	0.005 819 38	0.005 998 15	27
28	0.005 478 16	0.005 664 15	0.005 849 95	0.006 035 57	0.006 221 00	28
29	0.005 674 36	0.005 867 04	0.006 059 51	0.006 251 79	0.006 443 88	29
30	0.005 870 61	0.006 069 96	0.006 269 11	0.006 468 07	0.006 666 82	30

Months						Months
1	0.005 952 38	0.006 154 52	0.006 356 46	0.006 558 20	0.006 759 73	1
2	0.011 940 20	0.012 346 93	0.012 753 33	0.013 159 40	0.013 565 16	2
3	0.017 963 65	0.018 577 44	0.019 190 86	0.019 803 90	0.020 416 58	3

Equivalent Interest Rates for Given Annual Rates
Compounded Semi-annually

Days	8.50%	8.75%	9.00%	9.25%	9.50%	Days
1	0.000 228 09	0.000 234 66	0.000 241 22	0.000 247 77	0.000 254 31	1
2	0.000 456 23	0.000 469 37	0.000 482 49	0.000 495 60	0.000 508 69	2
3	0.000 684 43	0.000 704 14	0.000 723 83	0.000 743 49	0.000 763 14	3
4	0.000 912 67	0.000 938 96	0.000 965 22	0.000 991 45	0.001 017 64	4
5	0.001 140 97	0.001 173 84	0.001 206 67	0.001 239 46	0.001 272 22	5
6	0.001 369 32	0.001 408 77	0.001 448 18	0.001 487 54	0.001 526 85	6
7	0.001 597 72	0.001 643 76	0.001 689 75	0.001 735 68	0.001 781 56	7
8	0.001 826 18	0.001 878 80	0.001 931 37	0.001 983 88	0.002 036 32	8
9	0.002 054 68	0.002 113 90	0.002 173 05	0.002 232 14	0.002 291 15	9
10	0.002 283 24	0.002 349 06	0.002 414 80	0.002 480 46	0.002 546 05	10
11	0.002 511 85	0.002 584 27	0.002 656 60	0.002 728 84	0.002 801 01	11
12	0.002 740 52	0.002 819 53	0.002 898 45	0.002 977 29	0.003 056 04	12
13	0.002 969 23	0.003 054 85	0.003 140 37	0.003 225 80	0.003 311 13	13
14	0.003 198 00	0.003 290 22	0.003 382 35	0.003 474 37	0.003 566 29	14
15	0.003 426 82	0.003 525 65	0.003 624 38	0.003 723 00	0.003 821 51	15
16	0.003 655 69	0.003 761 14	0.003 866 47	0.003 971 69	0.004 076 79	16
17	0.003 884 61	0.003 996 68	0.004 108 62	0.004 220 44	0.004 332 14	17
18	0.004 113 59	0.004 232 27	0.004 350 83	0.004 469 26	0.004 587 56	18
19	0.004 342 62	0.004 467 92	0.004 593 10	0.004 718 13	0.004 843 04	19
20	0.004 571 70	0.004 703 63	0.004 835 42	0.004 967 07	0.005 098 58	20
21	0.004 800 83	0.004 939 39	0.005 077 81	0.005 216 07	0.005 354 19	21
22	0.005 030 02	0.005 175 21	0.005 320 25	0.005 465 14	0.005 609 87	22
23	0.005 259 25	0.005 411 08	0.005 562 75	0.005 714 26	0.005 865 61	23
24	0.005 488 54	0.005 647 01	0.005 805 31	0.005 963 44	0.006 121 42	24
25	0.005 717 88	0.005 882 99	0.006 047 93	0.006 212 69	0.006 377 29	25
26	0.005 947 28	0.006 119 03	0.006 290 60	0.006 462 00	0.006 633 22	26
27	0.006 176 73	0.006 355 12	0.006 533 34	0.006 711 37	0.006 889 22	27
28	0.006 406 22	0.006 591 27	0.006 776 13	0.006 960 80	0.007 145 29	28
29	0.006 635 78	0.006 827 48	0.007 018 98	0.007 210 30	0.007 401 42	29
30	0.006 865 38	0.007 063 74	0.007 261 89	0.007 459 85	0.007 657 62	30

Months						Months
1	0.006 961 06	0.007 162 19	0.007 363 12	0.007 563 85	0.007 764 38	1
2	0.013 970 58	0.014 375 68	0.014 780 46	0.015 184 92	0.015 589 05	2
3	0.021 028 89	0.021 640 84	0.022 252 42	0.022 863 63	0.023 474 48	3

Equivalent Interest Rates for Given Annual Rates
Compounded Semi-annually

Days	9.75%	10.00%	10.25%	10.50%	10.75%	Days
1	0.000 260 85	0.000 267 38	0.000 273 90	0.000 280 41	0.000 286 92	1
2	0.000 521 77	0.000 534 83	0.000 547 88	0.000 560 91	0.000 573 92	2
3	0.000 782 76	0.000 802 35	0.000 821 93	0.000 841 48	0.000 861 00	3
4	0.001 043 81	0.001 069 95	0.001 096 05	0.001 122 13	0.001 148 17	4
5	0.001 304 93	0.001 337 61	0.001 370 25	0.001 402 85	0.001 435 17	5
6	0.001 566 12	0.001 605 35	0.001 644 53	0.001 683 66	0.001 722 75	6
7	0.001 827 38	0.001 873 16	0.001 918 88	0.001 964 55	0.002 010 16	7
8	0.002 088 71	0.002 141 04	0.002 193 30	0.002 245 51	0.002 297 56	8
9	0.002 350 10	0.002 408 99	0.002 467 90	0.002 526 55	0.002 585 24	9
10	0.002 611 57	0.002 677 01	0.002 742 38	0.002 807 68	0.002 872 90	10
11	0.002 873 10	0.002 945 11	0.003 017 03	0.003 088 88	0.003 160 64	11
12	0.003 134 70	0.003 213 27	0.003 291 76	0.003 370 16	0.003 448 47	12
13	0.003 396 37	0.003 481 51	0.003 566 56	0.003 651 52	0.003 736 38	13
14	0.003 658 10	0.003 749 82	0.003 843 44	0.003 932 95	0.004 024 37	14
15	0.003 919 91	0.004 018 20	0.004 116 39	0.004 214 47	0.004 312 44	15
16	0.004 181 78	0.004 286 66	0.004 391 42	0.004 496 06	0.004 600 60	16
17	0.004 443 72	0.004 555 18	0.004 666 52	0.004 777 74	0.004 888 84	17
18	0.004 705 73	0.004 823 78	0.004 941 70	0.005 059 49	0.005 177 16	18
19	0.004 967 81	0.005 092 45	0.005 216 95	0.005 341 32	0.005 465 56	19
20	0.005 229 96	0.005 361 19	0.005 492 28	0.005 623 24	0.005 754 05	20
21	0.005 492 17	0.005 630 00	0.005 767 69	0.005 905 23	0.006 042 62	21
22	0.005 754 45	0.005 898 88	0.006 043 17	0.006 187 30	0.006 331 27	22
23	0.006 016 80	0.006 167 84	0.006 318 72	0.006 469 44	0.006 620 01	23
24	0.006 279 22	0.006 436 87	0.006 594 35	0.006 751 67	0.006 909 83	24
25	0.006 541 71	0.006 705 97	0.006 870 06	0.007 033 98	0.007 197 73	25
26	0.006 804 27	0.006 975 14	0.007 145 84	0.007 316 36	0.007 486 71	26
27	0.007 066 89	0.007 244 39	0.007 421 70	0.007 598 83	0.007 775 78	27
28	0.007 329 59	0.007 513 70	0.007 697 63	0.007 881 37	0.008 064 93	28
29	0.007 592 35	0.007 783 09	0.007 973 64	0.008 164 00	0.008 354 16	29
30	0.007 855 18	0.008 052 55	0.008 249 72	0.008 446 70	0.008 643 48	30

Months						Months
1	0.007 964 71	0.008 164 85	0.008 364 78	0.008 564 52	0.008 764 05	1
2	0.015 992 87	0.016 369 36	0.016 799 53	0.017 202 38	0.017 604 91	2
3	0.024 084 96	0.024 695 08	0.025 304 83	0.025 914 23	0.026 523 26	3

Equivalent Interest Rates for Given Annual Rates
Compounded Semi-annually

Days	11.00%	11.25%	11.50%	11.75%	12.00%	Days
1	0.000 293 42	0.000 299 91	0.000 306 39	0.000 312 87	0.000 319 33	1
2	0.000 586 92	0.000 599 91	0.000 612 87	0.000 625 83	0.000 638 77	2
3	0.000 880 51	0.000 899 99	0.000 919 45	0.000 938 89	0.000 958 30	3
4	0.001 174 19	0.001 200 17	0.001 226 12	0.001 252 05	0.001 277 94	4
5	0.001 467 95	0.001 500 44	0.001 532 89	0.001 565 31	0.001 597 68	5
6	0.001 761 80	0.001 800 79	0.001 839 75	0.001 878 66	0.001 917 53	6
7	0.002 055 73	0.002 101 24	0.002 146 70	0.002 192 11	0.002 237 47	7
8	0.002 349 75	0.002 401 78	0.002 453 75	0.002 505 66	0.002 557 52	8
9	0.002 643 86	0.002 702 41	0.002 760 89	0.002 819 31	0.002 877 67	9
10	0.002 978 92	0.003 044 90	0.003 068 13	0.003 133 06	0.003 197 92	10
11	0.003 232 33	0.003 303 93	0.003 375 46	0.003 446 91	0.003 518 27	11
12	0.003 526 70	0.003 604 83	0.003 682 88	0.003 760 85	0.003 838 73	12
13	0.003 821 15	0.003 905 82	0.003 990 40	0.004 074 89	0.004 159 29	13
14	0.004 115 68	0.004 206 90	0.004 290 02	0.004 389 03	0.004 479 05	14
15	0.004 410 31	0.004 508 07	0.004 605 72	0.004 703 27	0.004 800 71	15
16	0.004 705 02	0.004 809 33	0.004 913 52	0.005 017 61	0.005 121 58	16
17	0.004 999 82	0.005 110 68	0.005 221 42	0.005 332 04	0.005 442 55	17
18	0.005 294 70	0.005 412 12	0.005 529 41	0.005 646 58	0.005 763 62	18
19	0.005 589 67	0.005 713 65	0.005 837 49	0.005 961 21	0.006 084 79	19
20	0.005 884 73	0.006 015 27	0.006 145 67	0.006 275 94	0.006 406 07	20
21	0.006 179 87	0.006 316 98	0.006 453 94	0.006 590 77	0.006 727 44	21
22	0.006 475 10	0.006 618 70	0.006 762 31	0.006 905 69	0.007 048 93	22
23	0.006 770 42	0.006 920 68	0.007 070 77	0.007 220 72	0.007 370 51	23
24	0.007 065 82	0.007 222 66	0.007 379 33	0.007 535 84	0.007 692 20	24
25	0.007 361 31	0.007 524 73	0.007 687 98	0.007 851 07	0.008 013 98	25
26	0.007 656 89	0.007 826 90	0.007 996 73	0.008 166 39	0.008 335 88	26
27	0.007 952 56	0.008 129 15	0.008 305 57	0.008 481 81	0.008 657 87	27
28	0.008 248 31	0.008 431 50	0.008 614 50	0.008 797 33	0.008 979 97	28
29	0.008 544 14	0.008 733 93	0.008 923 53	0.009 112 94	0.009 302 17	29
30	0.008 840 07	0.009 036 46	0.009 232 66	0.009 428 66	0.009 624 47	30

Months						Months
1	0.008 963 39	0.009 162 54	0.009 361 49	0.009 560 24	0.009 758 79	1
2	0.018 007 13	0.018 409 03	0.018 810 61	0.019 211 87	0.019 612 82	2
3	0.027 131 93	0.027 740 24	0.028 348 19	0.028 955 78	0.029 563 01	3

9.4 Mortgage Amortization Tables

A mortgage payment is a blend of payments toward the interest and the principal. It is often referred to as a blended monthly payment. The amount from each monthly payment directed toward each portion is shown in an **amortization table**. Amortization tables give important information about the amount of interest being paid and the principal remaining.

DISCOVER

Build an Amortization Table

Part of an amortization table is shown below. The monthly payment has been given and the first few calculations have been done for you. Interest is at 12%, amortized over 25 years. Remember, each month's interest portion is calculated on the previous month's principal remaining.

See pages 416 to 427 in the Technology Appendix for specific spreadsheet instructions.

Spreadsheet 1

	A	B	C	D	E
1	Payment	Monthly	Interest	Principal	Principal
2	Number	Payment	Portion ($)	Portion ($)	Remaining ($)
3		Amount ($)	(I = PRT)		
4	Opening Balance	————————	————————	————————	112 450.00
5	1	1184.35	1124.50	59.85	112 390.15
6	2	1184.35	1123.90	60.45	112 329.70
7	3	1184.35			
8	4	1184.35			
9	5	1184.35			
10					

1. The formula in cell C5 is =E4*0.12/12*1. Explain this calculation.
2. Describe the operations being performed in columns D and E.
3. Write the operations in question 2 in spreadsheet formula format.
4. Copy and complete the table to line 9.
5. What do you notice about the interest amounts as you go down the table? Explain why this happens.
6. An amortization table can be used for various payment methods, such as weekly or bi-weekly. What would you need to change to allow for weekly payments?
7. Is interest in this spreadsheet calculated in the same way as interest on mortgages in Canada? Explain.
8. Where can you obtain amortization tables?

Amortization tables for Canadian mortgages are more complicated than they appear in Spreadsheet 1, because Canadian mortgages are compounded semi-annually, but paid monthly. Special tables, called **blended monthly payment factor tables,** are used to simplify the calculations and reduce human error. See page 361 for a sample.

See page 361 for a sample.

DISCOVER

Amortization Table for a Canadian Mortgage

Reconsider the information from the spreadsheet, using semi-annual compounding.

Step 1: Calculate the blended monthly payment.

principal = $112 450, interest = 12%, amortization period = 25 years

From the blended monthly payment factor table on page 361, a payment of $10.319 per month is required for every $1000 borrowed.

Payment for $112 450 = (112 450 ÷ 1000) × 10.319
$$= 1160.371\ 55$$

The blended monthly payment is $1160.37.

Step 2: Calculate the interest portion.

From the equivalent interest table on page 353, for a 12% interest rate, the interest rate for 1 month is 0.009 758 79.

Interest = 0.009 758 79 × $112 450
$$\doteq \$1097.38$$

The amount of interest paid in 1 month is $1097.38.

1. Set up a spreadsheet as shown, using values based on semi-annual compounding. Complete the spreadsheet to line 8.

Spreadsheet 2

	A	B	C	D	E
1	Payment	Monthly Payment	Interest	Principal	Principal
2	Number	Amount ($)	Portion ($)	Portion ($)	Remaining ($)
3	Opening Balance	————	————	————	112 450.00
4	1	1160.37	1097.38	62.99	112 387.01
5	2	1160.37			
6	3	1160.37			
7	4	1160.37			
8	5	1160.37			

2. Compare your completed Spreadsheet 2 to Spreadsheet 1. How is the interest portion of the spreadsheet different? Why does this difference occur?

Use a Graphing Calculator to Calculate Mortgage Values

A Canadian mortgage of $95 400 has an interest rate of 8.75%, a 5-year term, and an amortization period of 25 years. Use the financial functions on a graphing calculator to determine each of the following:

a) the monthly payment   **b)** the principal owing after the first year

c) the amount to be refinanced at the end of the term

d) the total interest paid after 5 years   **e)** the total principal paid after 5 years

Solution

a) Go to the **TVM Solver** screen and enter the following values for the variables:

N=300

I%=8.75

PV=95400

PMT=0

FV=0

P/Y=12

C/Y=2

PMT:END BEGIN

See pages 412 to 415 in the Technology Appendix for more details on the **TVM Solver**.

Using the arrow keys, cursor up to **PMT**. Then, press (ALPHA)(ENTER) for **SOLVE**. The monthly payment is $774.28.

b) The principal owing after the first year is the balance after 12 monthly payments.
Quit the **TVM Solver**.
Use the **bal(** function of the **Finance Applications**.
Press (APPS)(ENTER), and then, cursor down to **9: bal(**.
Then, press (ENTER).

Enter the values **12, 2** and a closing bracket, and then, press (ENTER).
The value 12 is **N**, or the number of payments.
The value 2 represents the number of decimal places the balance is rounded to.
The principal owing after the first year is $94 264.85.

c) The amount to be refinanced at the end of the term is the balance after the 5-year term. 60 monthly payments will have been made. Use the **bal(** function again.
Press (APPS)(ENTER), and then, cursor down to **9: bal(**.
Then, press (ENTER).
Enter the values **60, 2** and a closing bracket, and then, press (ENTER).
The amount to be refinanced at the end of the 5-year term is $88 608.45.

d) To find the total interest paid after 5 years, use the **ΣInt(** function.
Press (APPS)(ENTER), and then, cursor down to **A: ΣInt(**.
Then, press (ENTER).
Enter **1, 60, 2)**, and then, press (ENTER).
The value 1 is the starting payment number, the value
60 is the end payment number, and 2 is the rounding
value.
The total interest paid after 5 years is $39 665.25.

e) To find the total principal paid after 5 years, use the **ΣPrn(** function.
Press (APPS)(ENTER), and then, cursor down to **0: ΣPrn**.
Then, press (ENTER).
Enter **1, 60, 2)** and press (ENTER).
The value 1 is the starting payment number, the value
60 is the end payment number, and 2 is the rounding
value. The total principal paid after 5 years is $6791.55.

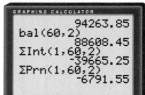

KEY CONCEPTS

- An amortization table shows the amount of each payment that goes toward the interest and the amount that goes toward the remaining principal of a mortgage.

- An amortization table is a tool for financial decision-making. It allows you to determine the principal owing or the total interest paid at any time.

- To account for interest compounding and payment periods being different, tables can be used to determine the blended monthly payment (see page 361) and to find the equivalent interest rate (see pages 349 to 353).

DISCUSS THE CONCEPTS

1. Describe when a borrower might want to calculate the total interest on a mortgage.

2. What is meant by a blended monthly payment?

3. Will the balance of a mortgage, halfway through its amortization period, be more than, less than, or equal to half of the original amount? Explain.

4. Explain how the amortization period and the term of a mortgage affect the payment.

5. What technology-related skills would a real estate agent need to have?

A *Assume semi-annual compounding unless otherwise specified.*

1. Determine each blended monthly payment factor using the table on page 361.

a) 7.5% amortized over 25 years

b) 6.25% amortized over 25 years

c) 7.5% amortized over 20 years

2. Explain why the answer to question 1, part a) is less than the answer to part c).

3. Determine the blended monthly payment for each mortgage.

a) $85 000 mortgage at 12% amortized over 20 years

b) $115 000 mortgage at 7.25% amortized over 25 years

c) $45 000 mortgage at 10.5% amortized over 15 years

APPLY THE CONCEPTS

B **4.** **Application** Use the spreadsheet.

	A	B	C	D	E
1	Mortgage Amount ($)		125 000		
2	Annual Interest Rate (%)		10.25		
3	Amortization Period (years)		20		
4	Monthly Payment Factor		9.67524		
5	Monthly Interest Factor		0.00836478		
6					
7	Payment Number	Monthly	Interest	Principal	Balance
8		Payment	Portion	Portion	
9	0				
10	1				
11	2				
12	3				

a) Determine the monthly payment. Explain how to copy this down the column using the spreadsheet software.

b) Determine the formula that will calculate the interest portion of each payment. In what cell will this be located?

c) Determine the formula that will calculate the principal portion of each payment. In what cell will this be located?

d) Determine the formula that will calculate the balance owing. Where will this formula be in the spreadsheet?

e) List the steps required to copy these formulas down each column.

5. A $74 500 mortgage at $7\frac{3}{4}$% interest is amortized over 25 years.

a) Calculate the monthly payment using the **TVM Solver**.

b) Calculate the monthly payment using the payment table on page 361. Compare this answer to your answer for part a).

c) Change **C/Y** to 12 and calculate the monthly payment using the **TVM Solver**. Explain why your answer is different from your answer in part b).

d) Which answer is correct? Explain.

HERMAN®

by Jim Unger

NEXT TIME
BLACK
NO SUGAR

8-31

© 1987 Jim Unger

"I spilled my coffee on the keyboard!"

6. Problem Solving/Communication Three mortgages have the same interest rate of 9.25% and the same principal of $124 500, but different amortization periods of 15, 20, and 25 years.
   a) Which mortgage do you expect to have the greatest monthly payment? Explain.
   b) Over a 5-year term, how much interest is paid on each mortgage?

7. As part of a mortgage agreement, the borrower should receive an annual statement outlining the details of the mortgage. For an $85 000 mortgage at 7% amortized over 20 years, determine what the first annual statement should list for the total interest paid, total principal paid, and balance owing.

8. Application Claude has just finished the second year of his mortgage of $83 200 at 9.25% amortized over 20 years.
   a) Determine the monthly payment for this mortgage.
   b) Determine the interest and principal he has paid so far.
   c) Determine the balance still owing.

9. The McLearys bought a $162 000 home. They needed a 25% down payment to qualify for a 25-year mortgage at 10.25% for a 5-year term.
   a) Determine the amount that they financed.
   b) Determine the monthly payment.
   c) Determine the amount to refinance at the end of the 5-year term.
   d) Determine the total interest paid after 5 years.
   e) Interest rates drop to 7.75% at the end of their first 5-year term. Find the new monthly payment if they renew for a 20-year amortization.
   f) What is the total interest paid for this 5-year term?
   g) Compare your answers in parts d) and f). Explain the difference.

10. Communication Three years ago, the McGowans negotiated a $136 000 mortgage at 8.5% for a 5-year term, amortized over 25 years. Today, interest rates are 6.5%. The McGowans could lock their mortgage in at 6.5% for another 5-year term by paying a 3-months' interest penalty. Calculate how much this penalty would be. Should they renegotiate the mortgage now? Explain.

11. Marcia and Ravi are buying their first home for $109 500. They have saved a 5% down payment and have been approved for a mortgage at 9.5% interest, amortized over 25 years, for a 10-year term.

   a) How much is their down payment?

   b) How much is the CMHC fee if it is 3.75% of the loan?

   c) Find the amount to be financed, including the CMHC fee.

   d) Determine their monthly payment.

   e) How much will Marcia and Ravi need to refinance at the end of the term?

   f) Calculate the total interest after 25 years.

   g) If Marcia and Ravi had amortized their mortgage over 20 years, how much money would they have saved?

12. The Estey family and the Lloyd family each owns a home. Each family has decided to switch to a new lender and will have to pay a penalty for changing lenders before the term expires. The current mortgage situation for both families is shown.

Family	Original Amount of Mortgage	Amount Owing	Terms of Original Mortgage	Length of Term Remaining	Penalty for Closing Mortgage
Estey	$136 752		9.5%, 25-year amortization, 10-year term	2 years	3 months' interest
Lloyd	$105 835		8.25%, 25-year amortization, 5-year term	3 years	2 months' interest

   a) Use the **TVM Solver** to find the balance owing for each family.

   b) Calculate the penalty for each family.

   c) How could each family have avoided this penalty?

13. In reality, it is unlikely that a mortgage will have the same interest rate over the entire amortization period. Calculate the total interest paid for the following mortgage.

   • The original principal is $132 500, amortized over 25 years, at 7.9% interest for a 5-year term.

   • After this term, the mortgage is renewed at 9.6% for 3 years, amortized over 25 years.

   • Then, for 10 years, 7.4% interest is charged, amortized over 20 years.

   • The final renewal is amortized over 15 years, at a rate of 10.25% for 3 years, with the balance being paid in full at the end of the term.

Blended Monthly Payment Factors
for a Loan of $1000

Interest Rate	Amortization Period (years)				Interest Rate
	10	15	20	25	
6.00%	11.065 10	8.398 83	7.121 89	6.398 07	6.00%
6.25%	11.187 69	8.530 77	7.262 82	6.547 42	6.25%
6.50%	11.310 94	8.663 70	7.405 01	6.698 24	6.50%
6.75%	11.434 84	8.797 61	7.548 45	6.850 50	6.75%
7.00%	11.559 40	8.932 50	7.693 11	7.004 16	7.00%
7.25%	11.684 61	9.068 35	7.838 98	7.159 19	7.25%
7.50%	11.810 47	9.205 14	7.986 03	7.315 55	7.50%
7.75%	11.936 97	9.342 88	8.134 23	7.473 22	7.75%
8.00%	12.064 10	9.481 53	8.283 58	7.632 14	8.00%
8.25%	12.191 85	9.621 11	8.434 04	7.792 29	8.25%
8.50%	12.320 24	9.761 58	8.585 60	7.953 64	8.50%
8.75%	12.449 24	9.902 95	8.738 22	8.116 15	8.75%
9.00%	12.578 86	10.045 19	8.891 90	8.279 78	9.00%
9.25%	12.709 09	10.188 30	9.046 60	8.444 50	9.25%
9.50%	12.839 92	10.332 27	9.202 31	8.610 28	9.50%
9.75%	12.971 35	10.477 07	9.359 00	8.777 08	9.75%
10.00%	13.103 37	10.622 70	9.516 65	8.944 88	10.00%
10.25%	13.235 98	10.769 15	9.675 24	9.113 63	10.25%
10.50%	13.369 18	10.916 41	9.834 74	9.283 30	10.50%
10.75%	13.502 95	11.064 45	9.995 13	9.453 87	10.75%
11.00%	13.637 29	11.213 27	10.156 40	9.625 30	11.00%
11.25%	13.772 20	11.362 86	10.318 52	9.797 55	11.25%
11.50%	13.907 67	11.513 21	10.481 46	9.970 61	11.50%
11.75%	14.043 70	11.664 29	10.645 21	10.144 44	11.75%
12.00%	14.180 27	11.816 10	10.809 75	10.319 00	12.00%

Compare Your Mortgage Options

Home buyers should find a mortgage that suits their needs. Institutions offering mortgages often have flexibility in features such as interest rate, payment frequency, and prepayment options.

Changing features of a mortgage can dramatically affect the overall amount of money paid. You can show this with a graphing calculator or amortization tables.

DISCOVER

Effect of Changing the Amortization Period, Using a Graphing Calculator

The table shows the monthly payments for an $80 000 mortgage at 11% for different amortization periods.

Amortization Period	15 years	20 years	25 years
Monthly Payment	$897.06	$812.51	$770.02
Total Interest	ΣInt(1,180,2) = $81 471.43		

1. Use the **ΣInt** function on a graphing calculator to find the total interest paid when the amortization period is 20 years, and then, 25 years. Recall that the calculator requires the following information to calculate total interest: (first payment number, last payment number, number of decimal places)
   a) What happens to the total amount of interest paid if the amortization period is shortened?
   b) Why might someone still choose an amortization period of 25 years?
2. Compare the three different amortization periods. Describe a situation for which each amortization period would be best.

EXAMPLE

Calculate the Time to Pay Off and the Total Interest Paid

An $80 000 mortgage at 11% interest is amortized over 25 years. Compare the time required to pay it off and the total interest paid for monthly or weekly payments. How much interest is saved by making weekly payments?

Solution

Use the **TVM Solver** to calculate the monthly payment.
The monthly payment is $770.02.
Then, each weekly payment is $770.02 × 12 ÷ 52 or $177.70.
In the **TVM Solver**, **N** represents the time required to pay off a mortgage. The units of **N** are the same as the units of the payment frequency.

To determine the time required to pay off a mortgage, set all of the variables in the **TVM Solver**, except **N**.

Enter
N=0
I%=11
PV=80 000
PMT=−177.70
FV=0
P/Y=52
C/Y=2

Move the cursor back up to **N** and press (ALPHA)(ENTER) for **SOLVE**.

See pages 412 to 415 in the Technology Appendix for more details on the **TVM Solver**.

The table shows the calculated value for **N**.
Then, you can use the **ΣInt** function to find the total interest. The results are shown in the table below.

Payment Frequency	P/Y	PMT	N	Total Interest
Monthly	12	$770.02	25 years	ΣInt(1,300,2) = $151 011.32
Weekly	52	$177.70	1277.87 weeks ÷ 52 weeks/year = 24.57 years	ΣInt(1,1278,2) = $147 077.91

By making weekly payments, the savings are $151 011.32 − $147 077.91 or $3933.41.

Changes in Payment Amounts Using Spreadsheet Software

Increasing the payment amounts or making annual lump-sum payments can also decrease the amount of interest paid and the amount of time it takes to pay off a mortgage because all of the extra payment goes toward the principal remaining. This is best demonstrated with the use of spreadsheet software.

An $80 000 mortgage is amortized over 25 years at 11% interest. The amortization table demonstrates the effects of payments over time.

See pages 416 to 427 in the Technology Appendix for specific spreadsheet instructions.

Spreadsheet A

	A	B	C	D	E
1	Payment	Payment	Interest	Principal	Principal
2	Number	($)	Portion ($)	Portion ($)	Remaining ($)
3					80000.00
4	1	770.02	717.07	52.95	79947.05
5	2	770.02	716.60	53.42	79893.63
6	3	770.02	716.12	53.90	79839.73
301	298	770.02	20.38	749.64	1524.54
302	299	770.02	13.67	756.35	768.18
303	300	770.02	6.89	763.13	5.05
304					
305			Total		
306			Interest		
307			$151 011.05		

What if the buyer doubles up payments after 2 years into the mortgage? These payments can be input in the spreadsheet. The Principal Remaining column will then become zero sooner, as shown in Spreadsheet B. A new value for N, the number of payments, can then be calculated.

Spreadsheet B

	A	B	C	D	E
26	23	770.02	705.59	64.43	78654.23
27	24	770.02	705.01	65.01	78589.22
28	25	1540.04	704.43	835.61	77753.6
29	26	1540.04	696.94	843.1	76910.5
95	92	1540.04	20.69	1519.35	788.82
96	93	1540.04	7.07	1532.97	−744.15
97	94	1540.04	−6.67	1546.71	−2290.86

1. According to Spreadsheet B, when will the last payment be?

2. What exact amount for the last payment would be required to make the balance zero?

3. How much sooner is the mortgage paid off by doubling up payments?

4. Describe a way to easily determine the total amount of interest paid with this spreadsheet.

DISCUSS THE CONCEPTS

1. When making monthly payments or weekly payments, the overall amount paid in a year is equal. However, when weekly payments are made, the amount of total interest paid in a year is less. Explain.

2. What assumption is being made when using an amortization spreadsheet like the one shown in the second Discover activity above?

3. In Spreadsheet A, the balance owing after the last payment is still shown as $5.05. Why?

4. When comparing different mortgage features, why do you only need to compare the total interest paid and not the sum of all of the actual payments?

PRACTISE

A *Assume semi-annual compounding unless otherwise specified.*

1. For each value of **N** for the **TVM Solver**, determine the total number of years.
   a) N=300, monthly payments
   b) N=180, monthly payments
   c) N=408, semi-monthly payments
   d) N=524, bi-weekly payments
   e) N=910, weekly payments
   f) N=1125, accelerated weekly payments

2. For each mortgage, use the **TVM Solver** or the blended monthly payment table on page 361 to determine the monthly payment. Then, determine the payment for the payment frequency indicated.
   a) $48 500 at 10.25% amortized over 25 years, weekly payments
   b) $114 210 at 8% amortized over 20 years, accelerated weekly payments
   c) $158 000 at 9.5% amortized over 25 years, accelerated bi-weekly payments
   d) $74 000 at 7.75% amortized over 15 years, bi-weekly payments
   e) $196 200 at 11% amortized over 25 years, semi-monthly payments

3. Use the **TVM Solver** and the values given to determine the missing values for each mortgage. Round your answers to two decimal places.

	N	I%	PV	PMT	FV	P/Y	C/Y	Payment Frequency
a)	300	7.4	97 500		0		2	monthly
b)		10.35	72 850	−159.00	0		2	weekly
c)	1100	9.8		−665.23	0	24	2	
d)	780	11.25	129 400		0		2	accelerated weekly
e)	510	10.75	142 750		0	12	2	

APPLY THE CONCEPTS

B **4.** Meena recently took out a mortgage of $106 700 at 9.9% amortized over 25 years.
   a) Use the **TVM Solver** to determine her monthly payment and **ΣInt** to determine the total interest paid.
   b) If Meena had taken the time to shop around, she might have been able to find an interest rate of 0.9% less. In that case, what would her payment and total interest paid have been?
   c) How much would she have saved in interest overall if she had found the reduced rate?

5. **Communication** Give one advantage and one disadvantage for each of the following.
   a) 20-year amortization period
   b) accelerated weekly mortgage payments
   c) paying a large lump sum toward the principal of a mortgage each year

6. A mortgage of $95 980 is amortized over 20 years at 6.5%.
   a) Determine the monthly and semi-monthly payments for this mortgage.
   b) Compare the total amount of money paid for each payment frequency.
   c) Compare the amount of time required to pay off the mortgage for each payment frequency.
   d) Which payment frequency is better? Explain.

7. A mortgage of $73 480 is amortized over 25 years at 8.5%.
   a) Use the monthly payment to calculate the semi-monthly and bi-weekly payments.
   b) Calculate the total interest paid for each payment frequency.
   c) Use the information on money and time saved to explain which method is better.

8. A $65 470 mortgage, at an interest rate of 9%, is amortized over 20 years.
   a) Calculate the weekly and bi-weekly payments.
   b) Calculate the total interest paid for each payment frequency.
   c) Which option is best? Use your answers from parts a) and b) to support your choice.

9. The Fongs have purchased a home for $154 000, and want to minimize their payments for 3 years so they can afford renovations. Their mortgage is 75% of the purchase price. For the first 3-year term, they make monthly payments at 9.4% amortized over 25 years.
   a) Find the amount to be financed.
   b) Find the total interest paid at the end of the first term and the amount that they will need to refinance.

10. Application Tony and Missumi have a mortgage of $81 230 at 7% interest amortized over 25 years. Their lender allows them to increase their monthly payment by up to 10%. In the first year, the couple made only regular payments. In the second year, they increased their payments by 5%. In years 3, 4, and 5, they increased their payments by 10% over the payments at the beginning of the term.
   a) Determine the payments made in each year.
   b) Set up an amortization table using the increased payments to determine the total interest paid over a 5-year term.
   c) Determine the total interest if the payments were increased by 10% from the beginning of the term.

11. Ruth and Hamish have a mortgage balance of $98 754.13 at an interest rate of 10.25%. They would like to renew.
   a) Calculate their monthly payment for a 15-, a 20-, and a 25-year amortization period.
   b) Calculate the total interest paid, assuming the same interest rate for each amortization period.

12. Problem Solving The Tran family can afford a maximum of $1025 per month for mortgage payments. Current interest rates are 8.75%. Use the **TVM Solver** to determine the maximum mortgage they can afford for each amortization period.
   a) 15 years
   b) 20 years
   c) 25 years

13. A mortgage of $142 500 is amortized over 20 years at an interest rate of 9.15%.

   a) Calculate the monthly payment.

   b) Calculate the total interest paid.

   c) If the same mortgage was offered at 10.15% interest, what would the amortization period need to be for the same monthly payment?

ACHIEVEMENT Check   Knowledge/Understanding Thinking/Inquiry/Problem Solving *Communication* *Application*

14. Pat has a mortgage of $100 000 that she needs to renew. She has two options to consider.

A: She can pay $1200 a month on the mortgage amortized over 20 years.

B: She can pay $300 a week on the mortgage amortized over 25 years.

Use a graphing calculator or a spreadsheet to find the interest rates being charged and the total interest to be paid in each case. Based on your calculations, which option would you advise Pat to choose?

15. The interest rate on a $100 000 mortgage is 10%.

   a) Calculate the monthly payment for a 15-, a 20-, and a 25-year amortization period.

   b) Calculate the total interest paid over the entire amortization period for each case in part a).

   c) By what percent does the monthly payment increase for a 20-year amortization instead of a 25-year amortization?

   d) By what percent does the total interest decrease for a 20-year amortization instead of a 25-year amortization?

   e) Which change in amortization period gives you more interest savings compared to payment increase? Explain.

16. A recent option is the cash-back mortgage, where the lender gives the borrower an up-front bonus cash payment. For a 3% cash-back mortgage of $100 000, you would receive $3000 to use toward the down payment or for other purposes. However, with cash-back mortgages, you are unlikely to negotiate an interest rate reduction. Which option would you suggest a borrower choose, Option A or Option B? Assume monthly payments are made over a 25-year amortization period. Use your calculations to justify your answer.

Option A: $80 000 mortgage at 6.75% interest

Option B: 3% cash-back mortgage of $80 000 at 7.5% interest

9.6 | Make Accommodation Decisions

As you learned in 9.1 Accommodation Options, there are several factors involved in making accommodation decisions. One major advantage of buying is the opportunity to build equity. However, in order to buy, you will need to be approved for a mortgage. Lenders use several calculations to determine whether or not you can afford to buy.

DISCOVER

Can You Afford to Buy?

You must meet two basic conditions for your mortgage application to be approved.

- Your mortgage payment plus taxes plus heating should not be more than 32% of your gross income. This is called the **gross debt service ratio** or **GDS ratio**.
- Your total monthly debts should not be more than 40% of your gross income. This is called the **total debt service ratio** or **TDS ratio**.

1. If your gross income is $25 000 per year, what is the most you should spend on your mortgage, taxes, and heating per year? per month?
2. If you and your partner have a combined annual gross income of $80 000, what is the most you should spend on your mortgage, taxes, and heating per year? per month?
3. Your monthly gross income is $2700. You have debts of $400/month. You would like to purchase a home that requires a monthly mortgage payment of $1015. Heating expenses are estimated to be $100/month. Is a lender likely to approve this mortgage? Why or why not?

EXAMPLE 1

Decide Whether to Buy or to Rent

Armin and Jackie have two children in elementary school. The couple earns $70 000. Armin has a 1-year contract as an engineering consultant, while Jackie works part-time as a nurse. They are moving from their small two-bedroom rental to be closer to Armin's new contract job. They have $10 000 in savings. Their credit cards are all paid off, but their monthly debt payment on their two cars is $600. Armin and Jackie have narrowed down their accommodation search to two options. Which option would you recommend?

Option A: Buy	Option B: Rent
• 3 bedrooms, 1 bathroom, large kitchen, no appliances, medium-sized living room, unfinished basement, garage • 1250 square feet of living space • price: $128 819 (Armin and Jackie anticipate they will get this back if they sell the house in 1 year.) • interest rate: 10.5% • term: 5 years • amortization period: 25 years • down payment: 5% • mortgage payment: $1136.07/month • property taxes: $1950/year • utilities: $377/month	• 3 bedrooms, 2 bathrooms, medium kitchen (includes appliances), large living room, finished basement, big backyard • 1175 square feet of living space • rent: $1100/month • utilities: $175/month • must sign a 1-year lease • landlord appears friendly and responsible

Solution

Organize the information using a Pros (for) and Cons (against) table.

Option A: Buy

Pros	Cons
• can build equity in home • has garage • finances within range (see calculations below) • can resell at any time	• big financial commitment when Armin only has a contract job • only one bathroom • need to purchase appliances • possibility of extra home-repair costs

Monthly Cost Calculations:

Mortgage + heating + taxes = $1136.07 + $377.00 + $1950.00 ÷ 12

$$\doteq \$1675.57$$

Total monthly debt = housing costs + car payments

$$= \$1675.57 + \$600$$
$$= \$2275.57$$

Monthly income = $70\ 000 ÷ 12$

$$\doteq \$5833.33$$

$$\text{GDS ratio} = \frac{\text{mortgage + heating + taxes}}{\text{income}} \qquad \text{TDS ratio} = \frac{\text{total monthly debt}}{\text{income}}$$

$$= \frac{\$1675.57}{\$5833.33} \qquad\qquad\qquad\quad = \frac{\$2275.57}{\$5833.33}$$

$$\doteq 0.29 \text{ or } 29\% \qquad\qquad\qquad \doteq 0.39 \text{ or } 39\%$$

The GDS is less than 32% and the TDS is less than 40%. However, the TDS is very close to the maximum. Armin and Jackie meet the financial conditions for mortgage approval, but the financial commitment of buying this house is risky.

Option B: Rent

Pros	Cons
• only a 1-year commitment • appliances included • two bathrooms • big backyard • lower monthly costs ($1275 versus $1675.57; see below) • no maintenance responsibilities	• no equity after 1 year (see below) • no garage • slightly less space • smaller kitchen than other option • must sign a 1-year lease

Monthly Cost Calculations:

Costs = rent + utilities

= $1100 + $175

= $1275

The money Armin and Jackie would spend in the first year on each option can be compared visually using a double bar graph.

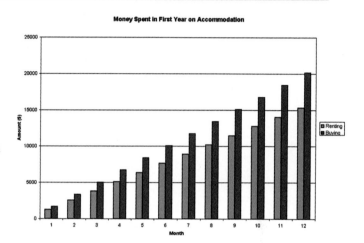

Another factor that Armin and Jackie might consider to help them make their choice is the equity they would have for each option.

Equity = value of the house − balance owed on mortgage

Option A: Buy

Assume that the value of the house, $128 819, does not change. The balance owing at any point in the mortgage can be determined using the **TVM Solver**. The starting principal of the mortgage is 95% of $128 819 or $122 378.05.

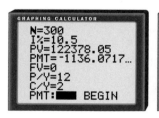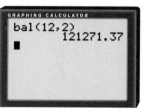

Equity at the end of year 1 = $128 819 − $121 271   Round to the nearest dollar.

= $7548

The calculations can be continued over the number of years being considered and are shown for the first 5 years in the table below. Amounts have been rounded to the nearest dollar.

At the end of...	Year 1	Year 2	Year 3	Year 4	Year 5
Balance owing	$121 271	$120 045	$118 687	$117 183	$115 516
Equity	$7 548	$8 773	$10 132	$11 636	$13 303

Note: This assumes that the value of the house does not change over 5 years. Often, real estate values increase slowly over time, so, the equity might be slightly higher.

Option B: Rent
You build no equity when you rent.

The line graph shows the growth of equity over 5 years for both options.

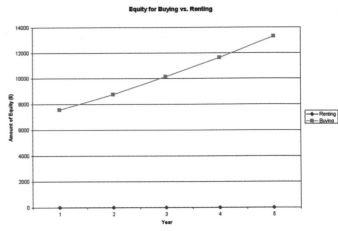

With Armin's contract position, the financial commitment of a mortgage is risky. Though Armin and Jackie meet both the GDS and TDS ratio requirements, their TDS ratio is very close to the maximum. This suggests that they cannot take on any more debt. They might find it difficult to buy appliances for their new home. Buying a home is probably not in their best interest at this time. They could revisit this idea if they reduced their monthly debt, saved a larger down payment, or increased their monthly income.

EXAMPLE 2

Make a Choice About Accommodation

Sarah and her son live in a small two-bedroom apartment. They would like to move to a larger place that has a yard for their dog.
- Sarah has worked for a computer company for 12 years.
- She has an annual gross income of $58 500.
- Her monthly debt is approximately $695.
- She has $6000 in savings.
- She has a preapproved mortgage from a lender at a rate of 7% for a 10-year term, amortized over 25 years.

Sarah is excited about the thought of home ownership because she loves home decorating. However, she is also nervous about the responsibility and financial commitment. Sarah has narrowed her choices down to three options. Based on the information, which option would you recommend?

Option 1: Buy a Semi-Detached Home	Option 2: Rent a Duplex	Option 3: Buy a Townhouse
• initial cash required: 5% down payment, rest to be mortgaged • price: $105 000 (includes taxes and fees) • 2 bedrooms, $1\frac{1}{2}$ bathrooms, unfinished basement, cement patio, own backyard • utilities: $175/month • 10 years old • 1250 square feet • property taxes: $1512/year	• first + last months' rent required • monthly cost: rent of $850 + utilities • 1350 square feet • utilities: $250/month • 3 bedrooms, 1 bathroom, • backyard shared with lower unit • must sign a minimum of a 1-year lease • 8 years old • parking: $30/month	• 2 bedrooms, 1 bathroom, fireplace, unfinished basement, shared courtyard, wood patio • Initial cash required: 5% down payment, rest to be mortgaged • price: $132 900 • monthly maintenance fees: $100 • new • 1100 square feet • utilities: $180/month • property taxes: $2006/year

Solution

First, calculate the total monthly expenses for each option.

	Option 1	Option 2	Option 3
Mortgage/rent payment	$699	$850	$884
Monthly utilities	$175	$250	$180
Taxes and other fees	$126	$30	$267
Total Monthly Costs	$1000	$1130	$1331

Option 1, buying the semi-detached home, is the least expensive per month.

Second, consider the factors that are important to Sarah. Rank each option (poor, satisfactory, or good) on each factor.

Factor	Option 1	Option 2	Option 3
up-front costs	satisfactory ($5250)	good ($1700)	poor ($6645)
monthly expense	good	satisfactory	satisfactory
space	good	good	satisfactory
maintenance	satisfactory	good	good
building equity	good	poor	good
ability to meet financial commitment	poor	good	poor
opportunity for decorating	good	poor	good
yard	good	satisfactory	satisfactory

Option 1 has the most good evaluations and the least poor evaluations.

Third, consider the big financial picture. Sarah meets the GDS and TDS ratios for both purchasing options. However, the down payment in Option 3 would reduce Sarah's savings to zero. Sarah would be unable to cover closing costs or any other maintenance expenses that might be needed in the first few months. As a result, eliminate Option 3.

Sarah's employment is stable, and her debt is relatively low. By buying instead of renting, Sarah can build equity, and possibly improve her financial picture. By applying her home-decorating talents to a purchased home, she may make a profit if she sells this home in the future. The monthly expenses for the semi-detached home are lower than renting the duplex, and the features of the semi-detached home best meet the needs of Sarah and her son. Thus, Sarah should be encouraged to choose Option 1.

KEY CONCEPTS

You should consider a number of factors when making accommodation decisions.

- Rental expenses differ from home ownership expenses.

- Two conditions usually need to be met before a mortgage application will be approved.
   Gross debt service ratio (GDS): Mortgage payments + taxes + heating should be no more than 32% of gross income.
   Total debt service ratio (TDS): All monthly debts (including mortgage) should be no more than 40% of gross income.

- Using lists, organization charts, graphs, and mathematical calculations effectively leads to good decision-making.

DISCUSS THE CONCEPTS

1. Study Example 1 on pages 369 to 372. Give at least two reasons why Armin and Jackie should rent instead of buy.

2. Ken is 21 years old. He started work 8 months ago and has $4000 saved. He is ready to move out of his parents' house. Should he rent or buy his accommodation? Give at least two reasons for your choice.

A 1. Based on the GDS ratio of 32%, what is the maximum that you can spend on mortgage + taxes + heating for each gross income?

a) $28 500 annually **b)** $3150 monthly **c)** $560 per week

2. For which of the following situations is the TDS ratio less than 40%?

a) gross monthly income: $1950; car payment: $432/month; rent: $850/month; utilities: $175/month; student loan: $76/month; car payments: $98/month

b) annual income: $62 100; loan: $250/month; mortgage payment: $965/month; taxes: $1100/year; utilities: $235/month; car payments: $575/month

3. Copy and complete the table. Each mortgage is amortized over 25 years.

	Cost of House + Taxes + Charges	Down Payment	Interest Rate	Mortgage Term	Monthly Mortgage Payment
a)	$136 000	5%	7.5%	10 years	
b)	$93 780	8%	7%	10 years	
c)	$182 500	10%	8%	15 years	
d)	$112 800	$12 000	6.5%	10 years	

4. Calculate the total monthly costs for each rental situation.

a) rent: $675/month; total annual utilities: $2000

b) rent: $1500/month; electricity: $450/year; water: $475/year; heating: $1200/year

c) rent: $1100/month; electricity and water: $100/month; heating: $1400/year

5. Give at least five advantages and five disadvantages of buying accommodation.

6. How would you find information about homes for sale? List at least three sources.

7. Make a larger copy of the diagram shown.
Record in your diagram all accommodation costs. Place any costs that apply to both renting and buying in the overlapping section of the circles.

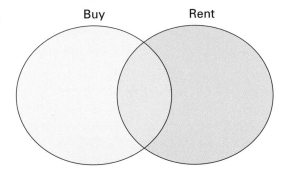

Buy   Rent

Did You Know?

The average resale value of homes in Toronto rose from $57 583 in 1987 to $238 511 in 2000.

Assume semi-annual compounding unless otherwise specified.

8. a) You bought a house 5 years ago for $140 000 and took out a $105 000 mortgage at 7.5% interest amortized over 20 years. You can sell the house now for $115 000. By how much has your equity increased?

b) You have rented an apartment for 5 years, paying $675/month. How much equity do you have?

c) What conclusion can you draw about renting versus buying in terms of equity?

B 9. A house is priced at $132 000. Your offer of $128 000 is accepted. You are putting 5% down, and have arranged a mortgage on the balance at a rate of 7.5% amortized over 10 years.

a) How much is the monthly mortgage payment?

b) Determine the principal owed after 5 years.

c) How much equity will you have after 5 years? Assume the value of the house does not change.

10. These are the costs for an apartment.
rent: $1275/month; water: $680/year; heating: $1475/year; electricity: $1000/year; parking: $40/month

a) How much will you likely have to pay up front?

b) How much will your total monthly accommodation costs be?

c) Assuming that you have no other debts, what would you have to earn per month to stay within the 40% TDS ratio?

11. Sharon and Zev have a combined gross annual income of $75 000.

a) Based on the GDS ratio, what is the most they should spend per year on their mortgage + taxes + heating?

b) Estimate the value of house that Sharon and Zev can afford. Describe the assumptions you made to obtain your answer.

c) What advice would you give them about accommodation?

12. Madison earns a gross income of $1200 bi-weekly. She has $13 000 in savings. She is not sure whether to rent or buy her accommodation. What would you advise her to do? Why?

13. You would like to purchase a home for $96 500. A mortgage broker offers a 10-year term mortgage with monthly payments at 7.5% amortized over 20 years. Heating and taxes are about $437/month. In order to stay within 32% of your gross income (GDS ratio), what must your minimum monthly income be?

14. Application Eric and Monique and their three children are moving to your area. Monique has a gross income of $40 000 per year. Eric is starting a new job with a gross salary of $50 500. Their debt load is about $700/month. Financing is available at 7% for a 10-year term amortized over 25 years. They need a minimum of 15% for a down payment. They have $15 000 from the sale of their current home. They would like to have a room for each child. However, two of the girls can share a room if necessary. They would prefer to live close to a school. They also need two bathrooms, and would like a garage. Both Eric and Monique have experience with home improvement.

a) Provide two accommodation options in your community using real information from local sources. Include the amount of down payment that will be required and show all of your calculations.

b) Decide which of the two options is better. Use a minimum of two visual tools in your argument.

ACHIEVEMENT Check   Knowledge/Understanding   Thinking/Inquiry/Problem Solving   Communication   Application

15. Thomas and Anne want to rent a house or apartment, or possibly buy a house with at least three bedrooms. Their combined annual gross income is $110 000. If they buy a house, they will need a down payment of 10%. They have $16 000 saved and they can get financing at 7% for a 10-year term amortized over 25 years. Anne and Thomas enjoy a very active social life, travel often, and work out regularly. They have narrowed their decision down to three options. Which option would you recommend? Justify your answer.

Rent a House	Buy a House	Rent an Apartment
• $1500/month + utilities	• price: $149 900	• $950/month + utilities
• utilities: $4200/year	• property taxes: $2000/year	• utilities: $200/month
• first and last months' rent required	• utilities: $4000/year	• first and last months' rent plus refundable security deposit of $1000 required
• 4 bedrooms, fireplace, big backyard, $1\frac{1}{2}$ bathrooms	• 3 bedrooms, big front yard, back deck, large kitchen, 2 bathrooms	• 3 bedrooms, enclosed sundeck, fitness facilities on site, 2 bathrooms

CAREER PROFILE

Realtor

Are you the type of person who likes to work for commission or do you prefer a regular fixed income? Realtors are paid commission. The average commission rate is 5% of the selling price of the property. 5% of a $200 000 home is $10 000! Most realtors receive half of that amount. The other half goes toward expenses and real estate fees.

To become a realtor you must complete a course of study specified by the Real Estate Act of Ontario. The courses can be completed by correspondence, on-line, or at your local college.

1. Go to *www.school.mcgrawhill.ca/resources/* and follow the links to obtain information on how to become a realtor.

   a) What three phases need to be completed to become a registered real estate salesperson?
   b) What three articling courses are required?
   c) What do you have to do to maintain your registration?

2. To be a realtor you need to drive a reliable car. List at least two other expenses involved in being a successful realtor.

3. Depending on where you live, the ability to speak more than one language can be a great asset to you as a realtor. Describe other characteristics or qualities that might help make you more successful as a realtor.

4. If a realtor would like to earn about $3000 per month after expenses and fees, on average, approximately what must his or her total annual sales be? List the assumptions that you made in arriving at your answer.

CASE STUDY WRAP-UP

Your task is to recommend new choices of accommodation for each family.

Points to Consider

1. The Esteys sold their house for $153 700. The Lloyds sold their house for $114 600. Refer to your earlier work on the Case Study. Determine how much each family has available for a down payment on their new accommodation. Remember that closing costs must be paid when purchasing a home.

2. Keep in mind the information that you have found concerning each family's accommodation needs and their financial situation. Use the real estate listings shown to find two suitable new homes for each family.

3. Prepare a report for each family and give reasons for your recommendations.
   - For rental accommodation, show how you calculated the monthly costs.
   - For buying, include calculations and data to find the down payment available, the amount of the mortgage needed, and the interest rate that will be charged if current monthly payments are to be maintained.

   Justify all your decisions and explanations with calculations, mathematical analysis, and graphics. Use technology where appropriate.

For Rent

Bachelor apt $550 + utilities, appliances included, near downtown, permit parking available.

2-Bedroom apt in 16-unit building, near school, $850/month + hydro, fridge & stove included, 1 bathroom.

1-bedroom apt in highrise, furnished, appliances included. $785 + utilities. Laundry and exercise room incl.

Lower Duplex: 2-bedroom, pkg available, fenced yard, laundry facilities in basement, appliances included, $800/month + utilities

Semi-Detached House: 2 bedrooms, $1\frac{1}{2}$ baths, large kitchen, basement, fireplace, new carpeting, large backyard, no pets please, $1000/month + utilities

3-bedroom house: ranch style, in great neighbourhood, 1400 sq. ft. inground swimming pool, 2 bathrooms, one newly finished, paved driveway, patio, $1150/month + heating. References please.

To Buy

2-bedroom house: Spacious living room, large kitchen, in subdivision near school. Small backyard, fridge and stove incl. $106 500.

2-bedroom house: Open concept with finished basement. Heated garage, garden. Good area. $104 800.

2-bedroom house: In the country, 1100 sq. ft., fridge and stove incl. Large porch, shed. $99 800.

3-bedroom house: Newly refinished kitchen, no appliances. $2\frac{1}{2}$ baths, 1400 ft^2, finished basement with fireplace. Garage. $172 500.

3-bedroom house: near high school, unfinished basement, garage. Two baths, kitchen with pantry. Large backyard with pool. $148 700

2-bedroom semi-detached : one bathroom, large backyard, unfinished basement, no appliances. Close to schools. $103 000

3-bedroom semi-detached: Two floors plus half-finished basement. New kitchen and bathroom, 1180 sq. ft. $129 000

3-bedroom condominium: 2 bathrooms, large kitchen. Fridge and stove included. Shared courtyard, pool, and exercise room. 1400 sq. ft. $169 900.

Duplex: 2 units, fixer-upper. Upper unit has 2 bedrooms, large bathroom with old-fashioned tub, appliances. Lower unit has 2 bedrooms, appliances, fireplace, large living room. Located near school. Excellent investment opportunity, $124 750.

4-bedroom house: Two levels, $2\frac{1}{2}$ baths, large kitchen with appliances, master bedroom has balcony overlooking spacious backyard. Large wooden deck. Garage. $182 500.

Review

9.1 Accommodation Options, pages 328–332

1. Describe at least five responsibilities that a homeowner would face that a renter would not.

2. Hanna is looking for an apartment and has found two possibilities. How much will be required up front for each apartment if the first and last months' rent is required? Which apartment would be the better choice. Why?

Apartment A	Apartment B
• rent: $645/month	• rent: $615/month
• hydro: $945/year	• gas: $650/year
• parking: $300/year	• hydro: $900/year
	• parking: included

9.2 Costs of Buying: Introduction to Mortgages, pages 333–340

3. For a monthly mortgage payment of $842.08, determine each amount.
   a) the bi-weekly payment
   b) the semi-monthly payment
   c) the accelerated weekly payment
   d) the difference in annual payments between the greatest and least payments from parts a), b), and c)

4. Raja purchased a $94 600 home. These were his costs:
   • legal fees: $1275
   • land-transfer tax: 1% of purchase price
   • CMHC fee: 2.5% of the loan amount based on a 10% down payment
   a) Determine the down payment and closing costs.
   b) Determine the CMHC fee and total principal to be borrowed.

9.3 Mortgage Interest, pages 341–353

5. a) Determine the monthly rate of interest equivalent to 9%, compounded semi-annually.
   b) Determine the rate of interest for a 12-day period that corresponds to 10.25%, compounded semi-annually.

6. A $184 500 mortgage at 10.94% is amortized over 25 years. Use the **TVM Solver** to find each amount.
   a) the monthly payment if the mortgage is compounded semi-annually
   b) the monthly payment if the mortgage is compounded monthly
   c) the difference in annual costs to the borrower between parts a) and b)

9.4 Mortgage Amortization Tables, pages 354–361

7. A $105 000 mortgage at 9.25% is amortized over 20 years.

	A	B	C	D	E
1	Payment	Monthly	Interest	Principal	Balance
2	Number	Payment	Portion	Portion	Owing
3	0				
4	1				
5	2				
6	3				

State the cell location of and determine a formula to calculate

a) the monthly payment

b) the interest portion of each payment

c) the principal portion of each payment

d) the balance owing

8. Two mortgages have the same interest rate of 10.25%, but are amortized over 20 and 25 years, respectively. If the principal is $84 750, determine

a) the monthly payment for each

b) the total interest paid for each

c) the percent increase in monthly payment for the 20-year amortization

d) the percent of interest saved for the 20-year amortization

9.5 Compare Your Mortgage Options, pages 362–368

9. Copy and complete the table for a $70 000 mortgage at 11% amortized over 25 years.

	Payment Method	Payment	Time Required to Pay Off Mortgage	Total Interest
a)	monthly		25 years	
b)	semi-monthly			
c)	bi-weekly			

10. If the Benoit family can afford to spend $1200/month on their mortgage, and they borrow $152 000 at 7.2% interest, which amortization period should they choose: 15, 20, or 25 years? Explain.

9.6 Make Accommodation Decisions, pages 369–379

11. A family has an annual income of $66 200. They are considering buying a home that has annual taxes and heating costs of $2710. The family has other debts averaging $442/month.

a) What maximum monthly mortgage payment will satisfy the GDS ratio of 32%?

b) What maximum monthly mortgage payment will satisfy the TDS ratio of 40%?

c) If interest is 9.5%, amortized over 25 years, what maximum mortgage will satisfy both?

Practice Test

Achievement Chart Category Connections

Category	Knowledge/Understanding	Thinking/Inquiry/Problem Solving	Communication	Application
Questions	1–11	9b, 10, 11	1, 3, 9b, 10, 11	8, 9a, 11

1. List three advantages of buying a home instead of renting.

2. What are the total average monthly costs for an apartment that rents at $874/month, with utilities that average $1950/year and parking at $32.50/month?

3. Copy and complete the sentences by inserting the most appropriate terms.
   a) When borrowing more than 65% of the home's value, a ▨ ? ▨ fee is usually added to the mortgage.
   b) A mortgage is renegotiated at the end of each ▨ ? ▨. The ▨ ? ▨ (life of the mortgage) and the interest rate are used to determine the monthly payment.
   c) Each mortgage payment consists of a(n) ▨ ? ▨ portion and a(n) ▨ ? ▨ portion.

4. A mortgage of $139 417 has a closing date of September 14 with payments beginning October 16. If interest is 7.35%, determine the interest owing for this time period.

5. A $75 000 mortgage at 8.5% is amortized over 25 years. Use the **TVM Solver**, or another method, to compare monthly and semi-annual compounding by determining
   a) the monthly payment for each case
   b) the total interest paid for each case
   c) the total interest paid at the end of the first year in each case
   d) the amount saved in each case by semi-annual compounding instead of monthly compounding

6. A $77 350 mortgage at 7.5% for a 5-year term is amortized over 25 years.
   a) What is the monthly payment?
   b) What is the total interest paid by the end of the term?

c) How much will need to be refinanced at the end of the term?

7. For a $68 400 mortgage at 8% amortized over 25 years, determine
   a) the blended monthly payment factor
   b) the monthly payment
   c) the monthly interest factor
   d) the interest and principal portions of the first payment

8. Rehan and Joe each purchased half of a semi-detached home. Each of them has the same mortgage of $105 000 at 10.25%. Joe chose a 20-year amortization period, while Rehan chose a 25-year amortization period.
   a) What is the monthly payment for each person?
   b) Who will pay less total interest over the life of the mortgage and by how much?

9. The Dubois family wishes to maintain their $875/month mortgage payment. The interest rate is 12.25%.
   a) What is the most they could borrow for their next home if the mortgage is amortized over 20 years?
   b) What could the family do differently if they need to borrow $80 000 and still keep the same payment? Explain.

10. Which do you think would save more interest?
A: Pay off $2100 of a mortgage each year on the anniversary date.
B: Pay an extra $175 at the end of each month.
Justify your answer.

ACHIEVEMENT Check   Knowledge/Understanding   Thinking/Inquiry/Problem Solving   Communication   Application

11. Brett and Carla have three children. Their combined income is $85 000 and they both work full-time. They own one car. They will be moving to your area and will need accommodation. Their bank is offering a mortgage at 9.35% for a 25-year amortization period.
   a) Assume taxes and heating costs are $3000/year, and their other debts total $450/month. Determine the maximum mortgage they can afford that satisfies both the GDS and TDS ratios.
   b) Use this maximum mortgage and a 15% down payment to determine the most expensive home they can afford.
   c) List at least five criteria that Brett and Carla should probably consider to help them choose a home.

CHAPTER 10

PERSONAL FINANCIAL DECISIONS

Specific Expectations	Sections
• identify the advantages and disadvantages of a variety of occupations of personal interest	10.1, 10.4
• compare the expected income for a variety of occupations with the costs of the education or training required	10.2, 10.4
• analyze employment trends to identify some occupations that are in high demand, and identify the skills required and the education paths recommended in order to qualify for these occupations	10.3, 10.4
• design an effective financial plan to facilitate the achievement of a long-term goal	10.4
• describe a decision involving a choice between alternatives	10.1, 10.2, 10.3, 10.4
• collect relevant information related to the alternatives to be considered in making a decision	10.1, 10.2, 10.3, 10.4
• summarize the advantages and disadvantages of the alternatives to a decision, using lists and organization charts	10.1, 10.2, 10.3, 10.4

What are you looking for in a career? What attracts you to a certain career may be different from what attracts your friends. It is important to identify the factors that will influence the type of career you choose and whether each factor is an advantage or a disadvantage.

DISCOVER

Factors Influencing Career Choices

There are many factors, besides salary, that may influence your career choice. Work with a partner to discuss some of them.

1. **Hours**
   a) Why do most people work regular hours, for example, Monday to Friday, 9 to 5? Would you prefer this routine? Explain.
   b) List some types of careers that involve irregular hours. Would you accept a position offering and perhaps expecting lots of overtime hours? Does shift work appeal to you? Give reasons for your answers.

2. **Opportunities for advancement**
   a) Many companies offer training programs to their employees. Why do you think they do this?
   b) Many companies try to promote their own employees to more responsible positions. They will advertise openings inside the company first, before advertising in the newspaper or elsewhere. What are the advantages to the company of this strategy?

3. **Benefits**
   a) Some employers provide benefits, such as medical and dental packages. The amount and range of the benefits can vary greatly. It is important to determine what is and is not included when you are considering a job offer. Is a good benefits package important to you? If benefits are not important to you now, when do you think they might be? Why?
   b) What other benefits may be provided?

4. Job security Most people look for financial stability and do not want to be laid off because of downsizing, mergers, or closures. Describe at least two ways that you can learn whether a job in a company that you are interested in working for is secure.

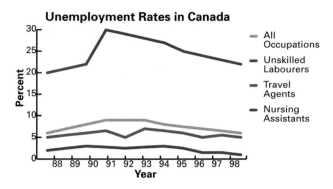

Unemployment Rates in Canada

- All Occupations
- Unskilled Labourers
- Travel Agents
- Nursing Assistants

5. Travel

a) Some people are willing to spend up to an hour commuting to work. Do you think this is an advantage or a disadvantage? Explain.

b) Some careers involve a lot of travelling. Do you think this is an advantage or a disadvantage? Explain. Is travelling a factor you will need to consider in the career you choose?

EXAMPLE

Demonstrate Flexibility

When you are starting out in a career, it is often necessary to be flexible to get a job that interests you. You may have to accept a job with less pay or with fewer responsibilities and challenges. But this may be the first step on the way to obtaining a better position.

List some other ways you might show an employer that you are flexible and eager to get the job.

Solution

Other ways that show flexibility and eagerness to obtain a job are

- moving to another town or city
- accepting shift work, weekend work, or overtime
- doing work that does not require all of your qualifications
- accepting part-time work
- volunteering while still in school

APPLY THE CONCEPTS

B 1. a) Refer to the Discover. Identify three more factors that might influence your career choices.

b) For each factor from part a), describe how or when it might be an advantage or a disadvantage, giving reasons.

2. Decide whether each of the following job features is an advantage or a disadvantage. Explain your reasoning, and describe scenarios in which it could be considered either way.

   a) The benefits package includes $200 for eyeglasses or contact lenses every 2 years.

   b) Employees are expected to work 5 to 10 h of overtime most weeks, at an overtime rate of 1.5 times the hourly rate.

   c) Once a month employees can buy up to $200 of company goods at greatly reduced prices.

   d) The employer provides a training program that leads to advancement.

   e) The pay is a flat rate of $285 per week plus 2.25% of the weekly retail sales. The company specializes in chemical fertilizers and its agents average $5000 to $10 000 per week in sales. The fertilizers are sold during the spring and fall only.

   f) The work is mostly in the office in Toronto but regular visits to other offices in Ottawa and North Bay must be made.

3. Look through the help-wanted advertisements in a newspaper or on the Internet. Choose an advertisement that appeals to you. Copy and complete the table for the job you chose.

Job:	
Advantages	**Disadvantages**

4. Repeat question 3, but this time, use a job-search web site. Go to *www.school.mcgrawhill.ca/resources/* and follow the links to select an area that interests you.

5. Describe two other strategies not listed in the Example that you might need to use to "get your foot in the door" of a career that you are interested in.

6. Some possible disadvantages for occupations are listed below. Describe a situation in which each could be an advantage.

   a) The hourly wage is $2 less than you hoped for.

   b) You are expected to work every Saturday in January to prepare the year-end report.

   c) You are qualified as an early childhood educator and are offered a position as an assistant to an early childhood educator.

   d) A company vehicle is not provided for driving from the office to construction sites to conduct surveying.

   e) You are presented with a great employment opportunity in another city.

   f) The company is very busy and asks you to put off your holidays.

10.2 Expected Income

Your lifestyle should correspond to the amount of money you earn. Unfortunately, many people spend more than they earn. In fact, the average Canadian spends 10% more than he or she earns, which results in a heavy debt load.

It is easy to overspend. A sporty new car is more attractive than a used compact model. Many people charge more to their credit cards than they can pay back each month, so the interest charges build up. The "buy now, pay later" philosophy is not in the consumer's best interest. It is a way for banks and finance companies to make money.

There is such a thing as "good debt," though. An example of a good debt is a loan for investment purposes in a registered retirement savings plan (RRSP). Many people borrow from financial institutions during income tax preparation time to make an RRSP investment. This type of investment will often result in an income tax refund that can be used to quickly repay the loan.

Sometimes you cannot help getting into debt. This may happen because of a family illness, unemployment, rising interest rates, a mortgage renewal, or family members who need financial assistance.

Before you start a career, you need to investigate how much money you will earn. Consider the starting salary as well as the income potential. What can you expect to earn in 5 to 10 years?

EXAMPLE

Salary Expectations

Some jobs may have a good benefits package to make up for a lower salary. Other jobs have a higher salary, but not a very good benefits package. It is important to consider all of the factors involved in an offer of employment, not just the salary. Sometimes people will lower their salary expectations as a trade-off for other advantages. What might these other advantages be?

Solution

You might accept a lower-paying job because it has one or more of the following advantages:

- You can gain valuable work experience.
- The job is related to your favourite activity.
- The job is at a large company with growth opportunities.
- The location is close to home.
- The job is with a small company in a relaxed work environment.

 APPLY THE CONCEPTS

B **1.** **a)** Prepare a list of six careers that interest you.

    b) Beside each career write what you think the salary would be.

 Σ-STAT

2. Go to *www.school.mcgrawhill.ca/resources/* and follow the links to use the Government of Canada's Job Futures database or E-STAT, ask people in the field, or research advertisements to find the actual starting salaries of people in the careers you chose in question 1.

Did You Know?

The average weekly earnings of all full-time Canadian workers in December 2000 were $631.87.

3. For each career you listed in question 1, use the Job Futures database to find the low, average, and high starting salaries of graduates in that field.

4. Compare the income you expected to the averages you found in question 3. Which of the careers are you still interested in?

5. Find advertisements for three occupations that interest you.

    a) Organize the information in the advertisements using the following headings:

        Position
        Company
        Job Description
        Salary

    b) Which position interests you the most? Why? Did the salary influence your choice?

6. **Five-year plan** The income that you earn needs to match the lifestyle that you expect to lead. Write a paragraph describing the lifestyle you hope to have in 5 years and in 10 years.

7. **Lifestyle** Do you expect to have a better lifestyle than your parents do, as past generations usually have? Write a paragraph to explain your thoughts.

10.3 Employment Trends

In the past, people usually had one career in their lifetime. These days, many people will have more than one career. This is due to a quickly growing and changing society and the greater number of career options available. People are more willing to take risks and start over in new careers. The level and type of education you obtain can influence your ability to move from one career to another.

Employment can be classified as goods-producing or service-producing. The number of people employed to provide services is increasing.

Goods-producing Areas	Distribution of Employed People in Ontario in 2000 (Total 5 872 100)	Service-producing Areas
farming		transportation
construction	27% Goods-Producing	real estate
manufacturing	73% Service-Producing	education
mining		health care
forestry		accommodation
fishing		food services
		trade

DISCOVER

Stable or Growing Career Areas

Stable occupations are those where the number of employed people has not traditionally changed very much and is not expected to change much in the future. Some stable occupations are listed below:

- cashier
- nurse
- janitor/cleaner
- general manager
- teacher's aid
- waiter/waitress
- education assistant
- truck driver
- marketing representative
- retail sales representative

Two of the major changes in society are an aging population and great advances in technology. There is a growing demand for people to work in careers having anything to do with these two areas.

1. Describe five occupations associated with an aging population. Be specific.
2. List five occupations associated with technology.

3. List your three top career interests. Discuss how they fit into the stable or growth areas.

4. Make a list of five occupations that require some level of mathematics. Classify each as a stable, growing, or decreasing area of employment.

5. Give two types of occupations that are in decreasing demand. Explain.

EXAMPLE

Advantages of Education

People who have only a high school diploma or have completed only part of their high school education may find themselves in the **secondary labour market**. Occupations in the secondary labour market include store clerks, labourers, cleaners, food servers, and factory workers.

a) Describe some advantages and some disadvantages of working in the secondary labour market.

b) How could a person move from a job in the secondary labour market to one in the primary market?

Solution

a) The advantages of jobs in the secondary market are that they may have little or no education requirements. The work is probably fairly stress-free with little or no responsibility or decision-making involved. Once you leave the place of work you can forget the job until the next day. The disadvantages include low pay, limited or no advancement opportunities, and having to do what the boss tells you.

b) Education is the key to the primary labour market. Going back to school after being in the labour force for a while can be difficult but well worth the effort. Many new employment opportunities can be found with better education or specialized training.

APPLY THE CONCEPTS

 1. a) Create a mind map of possible career paths for you.
- Start in the centre with your first career choice.
- Make branches to other related career interests.
- If you are also interested in a second career, unrelated to your first choice, start another mind map.

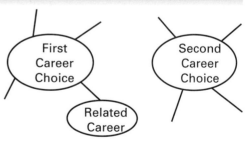

b) Using a highlighter, mark the path on your mind map that you think you will most likely take if you have two careers.

c) What type of courses could you take to upgrade for career changes? Where would you take these courses?

2. Do you think you will have more than one career in your lifetime? Give reasons for your response.

3. **a)** Give three benefits, related to career choices and employment opportunities, of having a good education.
   b) What other advantages are there to having a good education? Brainstorm with a partner or small group.

4. Investigate why people change careers.
   a) List reasons why people might have to change careers.
   b) Survey at least 10 adults. How many have already made career changes in their lives? How many expect to soon?

5. Identify other possible paths in your career.
   a) Make a list of five careers that you are interested in.
   b) Beside each career list three occupations. One example is shown.
   c) Beside each occupation, describe where and how a knowledge of mathematics might be useful.

Career	Occupations
Film and Television Production	film director
	sound-recording technician
	cinematographer

6. Many people, such as foreign aid workers, food bank assistants, and other charity employees, have job satisfaction in careers where they are not very well paid. Musicians and artists who are just starting out are not well paid, either. Why might these people make these career choices?

7. Self-employment is a growing trend. More people are choosing to run their own businesses. Write two paragraphs to outline some of the advantages and some of the disadvantages of self-employment.

8. Another growing trend is for companies to let their employees have flexible work hours, and to telecommute, or work from home. Some people telecommute even though they are full-time employees of a company. For example, when you phone to place a catalogue order, or to ask about a service, the person who takes your call could be anywhere in Canada, or even in another country!
   a) Would this type of arrangement suit you? Why or why not?
   b) What are the advantages of full-time telecommuting to the employee? the employer?
   c) What are the disadvantages to the employee? the employer?

10.4 | Finance Your Future: A Case Study

You have learned how to use consumer mathematics to help you make decisions in your life. In this section you will prepare a plan for the future, to guide you through the next few years. Store your answers to the questions and research in a portfolio. Your portfolio will have three parts.

Part 1: Career Interests
- Post-Secondary Institutions: Training Centres, Colleges, and Universities
- Prerequisites: Select the Right Courses
- Finance Your Post-Secondary Education
- The Job Search

Part 2: Accommodation and Living Costs
- Accommodation
- Transportation
- Credit Cards

Part 3: Investing: Pay Yourself First
- Savings and Investments
- Other Expenses

PART 1

Career Interests

Like many students, you may not be sure what you want to do after high school. Your student services department can probably help you. Software packages are available that lead you through a number of questions to determine your career aptitude. Based on your answers to the questions, a number of possible careers will be proposed.

Post-Secondary Institutions: Training Centres, Colleges, and Universities

Where do you want to go to continue your education? If you want to live at home, your post-secondary institution choices may be reduced. Otherwise, you will have many post-secondary institutions to choose from.

1. List your career choice(s).
2. List the colleges in your area.

3. List the colleges that specialize in your career interests.
4. Use the Internet to visit the web sites of the colleges you listed. Alternatively, use the college brochures available in your student services department.
5. Print or copy the pages describing the program(s) related to your career choices.
6. Highlight the following information:
   a) prerequisites
   b) length of program
   c) related career opportunities
7. Search the college web site or brochure to determine the cost per course or per year.
8. Are there any additional costs associated with your courses? If so, list them.
9. How much do you need to budget for incidental fees (e.g., student council, athletic fees)?
10. How much does the college suggest you should budget for textbooks?
11. Calculate the annual cost of your post-secondary education.

Prerequisites: Select the Right Courses

To graduate from high school in Ontario, you need 18 compulsory credits and 12 optional credits. You must also complete 40 h of community service. If you do not meet the admission requirements, some colleges may offer bridging courses that allow you to upgrade. Read the college admission requirements to determine whether this option is available to you.

12. List the courses you plan to take in grade 12.
13. Will these courses give you the necessary prerequisites for the college program that you have selected?
14. If you do not have 30 credits or are missing one or more prerequisites, how will you get caught up? Be specific.

Finance Your Post-Secondary Education

15. Where will you get the money to pay for your post-secondary education? Be specific.
    a) Will your parents help you?
    b) How much of your education cost will you be expected to contribute?

16. Are you planning to apply for a loan from the Ontario Student Assistance Plan (OSAP)? If so, answer the following questions.
    a) How do you apply for OSAP?
    b) How much money do you intend to apply for?
    c) When do you have to pay an OSAP loan back?

d) What is the current interest rate for OSAP loans?

e) What will you do if you are denied an OSAP loan?

17. Refer back to your college information.

a) Does the college offer any scholarships or bursaries?

b) What is the difference between scholarships and bursaries? Your college brochure will explain.

c) Are you eligible for scholarships or bursaries?

d) Where else can you obtain scholarships or bursaries?

18. If you would like to have $2000 to help pay for your post-secondary education, calculate how much you need to invest each month, starting now, compounded monthly, at the current rate of interest. Refer to 5.5 Payment of an Ordinary Annuity to review this calculation.

19. a) Predict how much you will owe when you are finished your post-secondary education.

b) Use your amount from part a).
- You intend to pay off the loan in equal monthly payments over 5 years.
- Interest is 9.00%, compounded monthly.

How much is each payment? Refer to 5.5 Payment of an Ordinary Annuity.

The Job Search

20. a) Find an advertisement for a job in your chosen field of study.

b) Place a copy of the advertisement in your portfolio.

21. Based on the salary in the advertisement, calculate the monthly salary.
- Assume you will start at the low end if a range is given.
- If an hourly range is given, assume a 40-h workweek, unless stated otherwise.
- Use your research skills to find a likely salary range if one is not given.

22. Taxes are deducted from your gross monthly salary. Obtain an income tax guide from the post office, or use the Internet to research the federal and Ontario provincial taxes for the current year.

   a) Calculate how much federal tax will be deducted from your predicted monthly pay.

   b) Calculate how much provincial tax will be deducted from your monthly pay.

   c) List other deductions that you can expect to see on your pay statement. Estimate the amount for each.

   d) Calculate your approximate net monthly pay after deductions from your gross monthly pay.

PART 2

Accommodation and Living Costs

Accommodation

This section will focus on renting accommodation. Refer to 9.1 Accommodation Options.

23. a) Search the rental section of a newspaper for rental accommodation suitable for your income and location. Place a copy of the advertisement in your portfolio.

   b) Below the copy of the advertisement, describe the type of accommodation you will be renting.

24. a) Estimate other expenses related to renting. Make a list of the expenses and the cost of each.

   b) Subtract the cost of renting and related monthly costs from your net monthly income. What is your remaining balance?

Transportation

Keeping in mind your remaining balance, you must now consider how you will get to work. Some alternatives are

A: public transportation

B: new or used vehicle

C: leased vehicle

D: car pool

E: walk

F: bicycle

G: motorcycle

Refer to Chapter 7 to review transportation costs.

If you live in a densely populated city, using public transportation might be the best way to get to work, as well as the most economical. If you work in a more rural location, having a vehicle might be essential.

25. a) Identify your choice of transportation.
   b) Give two advantages of the method of transportation you chose.
   c) Give two disadvantages of the method of transportation you chose.

26. If you decide to buy a new or used vehicle, search through the newspaper for an advertisement for a suitable vehicle.
   a) Calculate the cost of buying the vehicle. See Chapter 7 to review the additional costs of buying a vehicle. Be sure to include an estimate for insurance.
   b) Describe how you will finance the purchase. Calculate a payment schedule that fits your budget.

27. If you decide to lease a vehicle, find an advertisement for one that suits your needs. Contact the dealer for further information if necessary.
   a) Describe the conditions of the lease. Be specific.
   b) How many kilometres can you drive per year without being charged an additional fee?

28. If you decide to use public transportation, find out the cost of travelling from your rented accommodation to the college of your choice.
   a) Calculate your monthly expenses for using public transportation.
   b) Describe what you will do if you need to carry large items occasionally.
   c) Most people eventually would like to own a car. Design a savings plan to purchase a new car. Calculate how much you can contribute to your savings plan and how long it will take you to save enough to buy a car.

Credit Cards

When you graduate from college you may automatically receive a credit card application in the mail. Be sure to read the fine print. Interest rates vary from card to card, as do the annual fees and any extra reward points for using the card.

29. Look back at the research you did on different types of credit cards for 8.2 Managing Debit and Credit Cards.
   a) What type of credit card might you apply for?
   b) What is the interest rate on the credit card you chose?
   c) How will you keep track of your credit card purchases?
   d) What type of purchases do you intend to use your card for?
   e) Identify the advantages and disadvantages of using a credit card.

PART 3

Investing: Pay Yourself First

Savings and Investments

You have learned about the benefits of investing. The challenge is finding that extra $50 or $100 each month to save and invest.

30. a) What type of investment will you choose? Refer to Chapter 4 to review the options. If you intend to make regular investments, how much can you afford to invest each month?
   b) Calculate how much you will have if you invest $50 each month in a mutual fund over a 15-year period, with interest at 7.75%, compounded monthly.

Other Expenses

31. You may need to deal with other expenses. Working other expenses into your budget will ease the process. You will not have to deal with too many unexpected bills. Some other expenses you could expect are car maintenance, gym membership, and holidays.
   a) Prepare a list of other expenses you might encounter in the first few years of working.
   b) Prepare a brief summary of your possible income and expenses in your first year of full-time employment. Illustrate with a circle graph.

Review Your Portfolio

32. It is a good idea to review your spending and investing habits regularly. Do it often to keep track of where your money goes. Review the personal plan that you made through this Case Study. Describe how you might reduce costs and save more.

33. Keep your portfolio in a safe place at home. Make a statement of your current income and expenses. Review and modify the statement at least once a year, or whenever your circumstances change in any major way.

*C*umulative Review

Chapters 1–10

1. Enzo works part-time and earns $1500 per month. He is saving to buy a used motorcycle for $4000. His monthly budget includes these expenses:

   Transportation: $90   Entertainment: $200   Rent and Food: $500
   Clothing: $100   Miscellaneous: $60

   a) How much does Enzo save each month?
   b) Draw a circle graph to show Enzo's budget.
   c) How long will it take for Enzo to save enough for the motorcycle? What assumptions did you make?

2. After 24 months, Danielle's investment of $1250.00 had grown to $1462.50. What rate of simple interest did her investment earn?

3. Evaluate.
   a) 3^{-3}
   b) 7^0
   c) $25^{-\frac{1}{2}}$
   d) $32^{\frac{3}{5}}$
   e) $(-2)^3$

4. Solve for x.
   a) $2^x = 16$
   b) $9^x = 27$
   c) $\dfrac{1}{8} = 32^x$
   d) $27^{2x} = \dfrac{1}{27}$

5. Identify each sequence as arithmetic, geometric, or neither. Write the next two terms in each.
   a) $-2, 2, 6, 10, 14, \ldots$
   b) $0, 1, 3, 6, 10, \ldots$
   c) $1024, 512, 256, 128, 64, \ldots$

6. Ruta is trying to exercise more. Each day she increases the distance that she walks by 0.5 km. The first day she walked 2 km.
   a) Write an expression for the distance she will walk on the nth day.
   b) How far will she walk on the 10th day?
   c) How far will she walk altogether in the first 20 days?

7. José borrowed $2800 at 11%, compounded semi-annually, for 3 years.
   a) How much will José owe in 3 years?
   b) How much of the amount he owes will be interest?

8. Glenda is opening an investment account for her newborn granddaughter. She wants the money to grow to $5000 by the girl's 18th birthday. If the investment earns an average of 8%, compounded quarterly, how much will Glenda need to invest?

9. Stavro has $3500 to invest for 2 years. Which investment option should he choose? Justify your answer.
A: simple interest at 10%
B: 9.5%, compounded semi-annually
C: 9%, compounded monthly

10. Morag invested $2750 at 7.5%, compounded semi-annually. How long will it take for the investment to

a) grow to $4000?   **b)** double?

11. i) Identify each series as arithmetic or geometric.
   ii) Develop a formula for S_n, the sum of the series.
   iii) Calculate the indicated sum.
   a) $6 + 12 + 18 + 24 + \ldots$; $S_{12} = $ ❓
   b) $3 + 6 + 12 + 24 + 48 + \ldots$; $S_{10} = $ ❓
   c) $6 + 3 + 0 + (-3) + (-6) + \ldots$; $S_{15} = $ ❓

12. Tuzo has to make 10 more monthly payments of $280.15 to pay off a loan. The interest rate on the loan is 15%, compounded monthly. What is the present value of the loan?

13. Freya would like to save $8000 in 3 years to go on her dream vacation to New Zealand. How much does she need to deposit at the end of every month into a savings account that earns interest at 6%, compounded monthly?

14. Graph each function. Classify each as increasing or decreasing. State the y-intercept of each.

a) $y = 3^x$ **b)** $y = \left(\dfrac{1}{3}\right)^x$ **c)** $y = 0.3^x$

15. State the domain and the range of each function. If there is an asymptote, give its equation.

a) 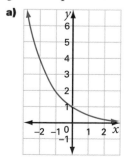   **b)** 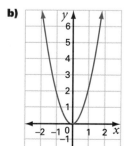   **c)**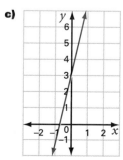

16. The cost of gasoline is $0.729/L. If the increase in the Consumer Price Index is 3.2% per year, predict the price of 1 L of gasoline each year for the next 5 years.

17. A type of bacterium divides into two every 15 min. There are now 100 bacteria in a culture.
   a) How many will be in the culture after 30 min? 1 h? 3 h?
   b) After approximately how many minutes will there be more than 10 000 bacteria in the culture?

18. The population of Toronto in 1999 was 4 680 000. The growth rate was 2.1% per year.
   a) Write an exponential function to model the population growth of Toronto.
   b) Use this function to predict the population of Toronto in 2020.
   c) How reliable do you think this prediction is? Suggest reasons why it might be incorrect. Discuss with a partner.

19. The population of Newfoundland has been decreasing at an annual rate of 0.8%. In 1999 the population was about 541 000.
   a) Write an exponential function to model the population of Newfoundland.
   b) Use this function to predict the population of Newfoundland in 2015.
   c) Using a graph, or another method, predict when the population will drop below 500 000.

20. Jason has chosen to buy a new car with a base price of $18 320. The extra options that he has selected will cost $1200. Other charges, including freight and delivery, amount to $965.
   a) Find the total cost of his car after the taxes at 15% have been added.
   b) Jason has $6000 saved as a down payment. The dealership will finance the balance at 3%, compounded monthly, over 4 years. How much will each monthly payment be?

21. MaeTze drives her compact car an average of 2500 km per month. She budgets $200 for regular maintenance of the car and allows $400 for unexpected repairs. She pays $202 per month for insurance and $74 per year for the car licence. If gas is approximately $0.83/L and her car uses 5.9 L/100 km, how much should she budget for transportation for the year?

22. Ray has just started his first full-time job.
   a) Give two reasons why he might need a new car rather than a used one.
   b) Give a possible reason why Ray might choose to lease a new car rather than buy one.

23. Retail choices Most items can be bought in a variety of ways:

A: in person at a store

B: ordered from a catalogue

C: ordered over the Internet

For each item, describe which retail source you would recommend. Give reasons for your choices.

a) computer software   **b)** flowers   **c)** shoes

24. Erin's March credit card bill is shown.

a) What is her new balance?

b) Erin's credit limit is $2000. How much credit is still available?

c) If Erin paid her new balance entirely, how much interest would she owe on her next statement?

d) If she paid only $200 of the new balance, how would the interest be calculated and charged?

Previous balance	$305.75
Purchases	239.52
Cash advances	100.00
Interest	4.28
Fees	
Debit adjustments	55.00
Other	
Payments	250.00 CR

25. Shopping trip This weekend Harry plans to go to the United States to do some shopping. He plans to convert $300 Cdn into U.S. dollars. The exchange rate is $1.5294 Cdn per U.S. dollar. How much, in U.S. dollars, will he receive?

26. Compare buying a condominium and renting an apartment. List two advantages and two disadvantages of each accommodation choice.

27. Beth's offer to buy a condominium for $135 000 has been accepted. She has $30 000 for a down payment and is getting a mortgage for the balance. She is considering two mortgage options. Interest is compounded semi-annually.

A: 7.5% for a 5-year term amortized over 25 years

B: 8.25% for a 1-year term amortized over 25 years

Use the **TVM Solver**, or another method, to compare the two options.

a) Find the monthly payment for each option.

b) Find the balance at the end of 1 year for each option.

c) Even though each monthly payment is greater, what reason might Beth have for choosing option B?

28. Write a two-paragraph summary of your 5-year plan. Describe your accommodation plans, means of transportation, the courses you hope to take, and the work you hope to do. How will you finance this plan?

TECHNOLOGY APPENDIX

CONTENTS

TI-83 and TI-83 Plus Graphing Calculators

A graphing calculator can be used as alternative tool for many of the required calculations in this course. This appendix provides detailed instructions and chapter references.

Spreadsheets

Spreadsheets are used in Chapters 1, 3, 4, and 9. General spreadsheet instructions are provided in each of the chapters. This appendix provides more specific instructions for two spreadsheet software programs.

	Microsoft® Excel	Corel® Quattro® Pro 8
THE BASICS		
Delete	416	422
Enter Information	415	422
Open	415	422
Print	416	422
Save	416	422
The Screen	415	422
SELECTING CELLS, COLUMNS, AND ROWS		
Adjacent Cells	417	423
Adjacent Columns	417	423
Adjacent Rows	417	423
Non-adjacent Cells	417	423
Non-adjacent Columns	417	423
Non-adjacent Rows	417	423
Single Cell	416	423
Single Column	417	423
Single Row	417	423
PREPARING THE SPREADSHEET		
Column Width	417	423
Currency ($)	419	423
Decimal Places—Set the Number	418	423
Format Characters (**Bold**, *Italics*, etc.)	419	423
Percent (%)	418	423
Row Height	418	423
Space for Thousands (## ### not ##,###)	418	423
SPECIAL FEATURES		
Copy Cell Contents	419	424
Formulas and Functions	420	424
GRAPHS		
Circle Graph (Pie Chart)	421	425

TI-83 AND TI-83 PLUS GRAPHING CALCULATORS
THE BASICS
The Keyboard

The keys are colour-coded to make it easier to locate them.

The Home Screen or Graph Viewing Window

To access the **Finance Applications** on the TI-83 Plus, press APPS. On the TI-83, press 2nd x^{-1}.

These five blue keys are used when graphing.

The four blue arrow keys are used to move the cursor.

Each key has three functions:
- The **primary function** is on the key. For example, the primary function of x^2 is x^2. To evaluate 3^2, press 3 x^2 ENTER.
- The **secondary function** is above the key in yellow. For example, the secondary function of x^2 is $\sqrt{}$. To evaluate $\sqrt{9}$, press 2nd x^2 9) ENTER.
- The **alpha function** is also above the key but in green. For example, the alpha function of x^2 is the letter I. To display I on the screen, press ALPHA x^2.

The $\wedge$ key is used for exponents. For example, to evaluate 3^4, press 3 $\wedge$ 4 ENTER.

These five blue keys are the math operations. Note the following:
- ENTER is the same as $=$ on other calculators.
- When you press $\div$, a slash, /, appears on the screen.
- When you press $\times$, an asterisk, *, appears on the screen.

The twelve light grey keys include the numbers, decimal point, and negative sign.

Don't confuse these two keys:
- $-$ is for subtraction
- $(-)$ is for negative values

Contrast—Increase and Decrease

To increase the contrast, press 2nd, and then, hold ▲.
To decrease the contrast, press 2nd, and then, hold ▼.
Alternatively, press 2nd ▲ or 2nd ▼ to increase or decrease the contrast one increment at a time.

GRAPHING CALCULATOR
LOW CONTRAST SCREEN

GRAPHING CALCULATOR
HIGH CONTRAST SCREEN

Decimal Places—Set the Number

You can set the calculator to display numbers with 0 to 9 decimals, or with a number of decimal places that floats, that is, varies with the number.

To set the number of decimal places to 2 for calculations involving money, press (MODE) (▼)(▶)(▶)(▶)(ENTER).

To return to the Home Screen, press (2nd)(MODE).

EFFICIENT CALCULATIONS

Editing—Delete and Insert Characters

The (◀), (▶), (DEL), and (2nd)(DEL) keys are used to delete and insert characters.

For example, to change **359(1+0.11*40)^6** to **359(1+0.11/4)^{16}**, follow these steps:

Step 1: To delete the **0** in **40**, use the arrow keys to move the cursor to the **0**. Then, press (DEL):

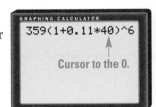

Cursor to the 0.

The zero has been deleted.

Step 2: To replace ***** (×) with **/** (÷), cursor to the *****. Then, press (÷):

The * has been replaced with /.

Step 3: To insert a **1** to the left of the **6**, cursor to the **6**. Then, press (2nd)(DEL) **1**.

The 1 has been inserted.

Step 4: To evaluate the expression, press (ENTER):

The edited expression has been entered, or evaluated

Last Expression—Recall to Edit

You can recall the last expression entered in order to edit it.

For example, the expression $\dfrac{2000[(1+0.02)^{10}-1]}{0.02}$ has been entered incorrectly:

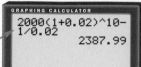

Brackets are missing.

To recall the expression, press (2nd)(ENTER):

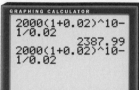

Use the arrow keys and (2nd)(DEL) to insert the missing brackets. Then, press (ENTER) to evaluate the expression:

Brackets have been inserted and the expression has been evaluated.

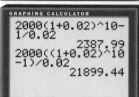

Last Answer—Recall for Next Calculation

You can recall the last answer to use it in the next calculation.

For example, to calculate the amount owed (principal and interest) after 3 years on a $1000 loan with simple interest charged at 6%, follow these steps:

To calculate the interest, press
1000(×)**0.06**(×)**3**(ENTER):

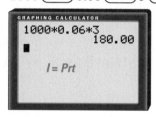

To add the principal and interest, press
1000(+)(2nd)((–))(ENTER):

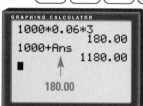

Multiply Without (×)—Use Brackets

When brackets are used in a calculation, the (×) key is optional.

For example, to calculate $500(1 + 0.06 \div 4)^6$:

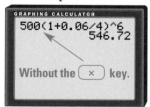

Without the (×) **key.**

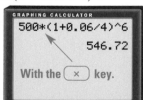

With the (×) **key.**

SEQUENCES AND SERIES

The *n*th Term in a Sequence

If you know the formula for t_n in a sequence, you can determine any term in the sequence.

For example, to determine the 12th term in the sequence defined by $t_n = 4 + (n-1)7$, follow these steps:

Step 1: To access the sequence function, **seq(**, press 2nd STAT ▶ **5.**

Step 2: To enter the formula for t_n, press
4 + (ALPHA LOG − 1) 7 , .

Step 3: To enter the variable **N**, press ALPHA LOG , .

Step 4: To enter the term number twice, press **12** , **12.**

Step 5: To close the sequence function and display the term, press) ENTER .

Formula for t_n in an Arithmetic Sequence

Enter the sequence as a table of values in the **Stat List Editor**, and then, use Linear Regression (**LinReg**) to determine a formula. This works because there is a linear relationship between the term numbers and term values.

For example, to determine a formula for t_n in 3, 7, 11, 15, … , follow these steps:

Step 1: To open the **Stat List Editor**, press STAT **1.**

Step 2: Enter the term numbers in **L1**, pressing ENTER after each entry:

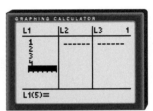

Step 3: Enter the term values in **L2**, pressing ENTER after each entry:

To clear existing lists, cursor to the list head. Then, press CLEAR ENTER .

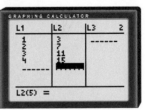

Step 4: To use **LinReg**, press STAT ▶ **4** ENTER :

$$t_n = 4n - 1$$

Sum of a Series, S_n

If you know the formula for t_n in a sequence, you can determine the sum of the first n terms.

For example, to determine the sum of the first 15 terms, S_{15}, in the sequence defined by $t_n = 4 + (n - 1)7$, follow these steps:

Step 1: To access the sum function, **sum(**, press
[2nd] [STAT] [◀] **5.**
Step 2: To access the sequence function, **seq(**, press
[2nd] [STAT] [▶] **5.**
Step 3: To enter the formula for t_n, press
4 [+] [( ] [ALPHA] [LOG] [−] **1** [ )] **7** [,].
Step 4: To enter the variable **N**, press [ALPHA] [LOG] [,].
Step 5: To enter the beginning and ending term numbers, press **1** [,] **15.**
Step 6: To close the sequence and sum functions and display the sum, press
[ )] [ )] [ENTER].

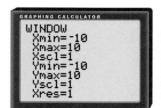

GRAPHING

Graph an Equation (Standard Window)

Enter the equation into the **Y= Editor**, and then, use the standard window option from the **Zoom** menu to graph it.

For example, to graph $y = 2^x$ in the standard window, follow these steps:

Press [Y=] and enter $y = 2^x$ To graph in the standard
by pressing **2** [∧] [X,T,θ,n]:   window, press [ZOOM] **6:**

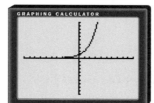

To clear existing equations, cursor to the right of the equal sign. Then, press [CLEAR].

The Variables of the Standard Window

Graph Window—Change the Settings

The minimum and maximum x- and y-values of the graph viewing window can be changed, in addition to the scales of the axes and the resolution.

For example, to graph $y = 2^x$ in the first quadrant with an axes scale of 2, follow these steps:

Enter $y = 2^x$ into the
Y= Editor:

Press (WINDOW), and then,
enter these values:

To graph, press (GRAPH):

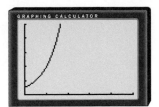

Trace a Graph

The **Trace** instruction is used to determine the coordinates of a graph.

For example, to determine x- and y-values along the graph of $y = 2^x$,
press (TRACE), and then, use the (◀) and (▶) keys:

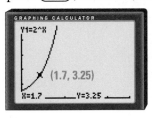

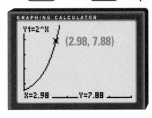

**The x- and y-coordinates of
the current cursor location
are displayed at the bottom
of the window.**

Table of Values

When a graph is displayed, a table of values is created in the **Table Editor.**

The graph of $y = 2^x$ is displayed:

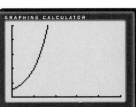

To display its table of values, press (2nd) (GRAPH):

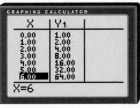

**To scroll through
the table, use the
(▲) and (▼) keys.**

To change the setup of the table, press (2nd) (WINDOW):

The TVM SOLVER

About the Finance Applications

The **TVM Solver** is used to work with annuities (for example, loans and investments with regular payments, and mortgages), and can also be used for non-annuities (for example, loans or investments with no regular payments). **TVM** stands for **T**ime **V**alue of **M**oney. The Balance function (**bal**), the Principal function (**ΣPrn**), and the Interest function (**ΣInt**) are used with the **TVM Solver** to work with mortgages.

Open the TVM Solver

On the TI-83, press (2nd)(x^{-1}) **1 1**.
On the TI-83 Plus, press (APPS) **1 1**.

What the TVM Solver Variables Represent

When There Are Regular Payments (Ordinary Annuities and Mortgages):

N	Number of Payments
I%	Annual Interest Rate
PV	Present Value
PMT	Payment
FV	Future Value
P/Y	Number of Payments/Year
C/Y	Number of Compounding Periods/Year
PMT: **END** BEGIN	Payments at End of Payment Interval

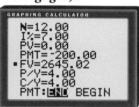

A savings annuity invested at 7%, compounded quarterly, with quarterly deposits of $200, for 3 years is $2645.02.

When There Are No Regular Payments:

N	Number of Years
I%	Annual Interest Rate
PV	Present Value, or Principal
PMT	Always set **PMT=0.00**.
FV	Future Value, or Final Amount
P/Y	Always set **P/Y=1.00**.
C/Y	Number of Compounding Periods/Year
PMT: **END BEGIN**	**END** or **BEGIN**

$1000 invested at 5%, compounded monthly, for 7 years is $1418.04.

Important Points About the TVM Solver

- Set the number of decimal places to 2 (see page 407).
- A value must be entered for each variable.
- Money paid out (cash outflow), such as a loan payment, is negative.
- Money received (cash inflow), such as the final amount of an investment, is positive.
- To quit the **TVM Solver** and return to the Home Screen, press (2nd)(MODE).

Investments and Loans (No Regular Payments)

Final Amount If you know the principal, or present value, interest rate, compounding frequency, and term of an investment or loan, you can determine its final amount.

For example, to determine the final amount of a **$2500** investment earning **5%** interest, **compounded semi-annually**, for **3 years**, follow these steps:

Open the **TVM Solver**, and then, enter the values as shown:

To solve for **FV**, cursor to **FV=0.00**, and then, press (ALPHA)(ENTER):

Term is **3** years.
Annual interest rate is **5%**.
Principal is **$2500**.
Final amount is unknown.
2 compounding periods/year

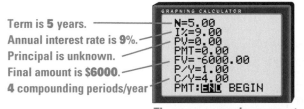

There are no regular payments, so, **PMT=0.00** and **P/Y=1.00**.

The Final amount is **$2899.23**.

Present Value, or Principal If you know the final amount, interest rate, compounding frequency, and term of an investment or loan, you can determine its present value, or principal.

For example, to determine the principal of a **$6000** debt at **9%** interest, **compounded quarterly**, for **5 years**, follow these steps:

Open the **TVM Solver**, and then, enter the values as shown:

To solve for **PV**, cursor to **PV=0.00**, and then, press (ALPHA)(ENTER):

Term is **5** years.
Annual interest rate is **9%**.
Principal is unknown.
Final amount is **$6000**.
4 compounding periods/year

There are no regular payments, so, **PMT=0.00** and **P/Y=1.00**.

The principal was **$3844.90**.

Interest Rate To find the annual interest rate, enter the known values for **N**, **PV**, **FV**, and **C/Y**. Set **I%= 0.00**, **PMT= 0.00**, and **P/Y=1.00**. Then, cursor to **I%=0.00** and press (ALPHA)(ENTER). (See page 141 in Chapter 4.)

Term To find the term, in years, enter the known values for **I%**, **PV**, **FV**, and **C/Y**. Set **N= 0.00**, **PMT= 0.00**, and **P/Y=1.00**. Then, cursor to **N=0.00** and press (ALPHA)(ENTER). (See page 147 in Chapter 4.)

Ordinary Annuities (Regular Payments)

Future Value Enter the known values into the **TVM Solver** for **N, I%, PMT, P/Y,** and **C/Y** and set **PV=0.00, FV=0.00,** and **PMT:END**. Then, cursor to **FV=0.00** and press ALPHA ENTER . (See page 190 in Chapter 5.)

Present Value Enter the known values into the **TVM Solver** for **N, I%, PMT, P/Y,** and **C/Y** and set **PV=0.00, FV=0.00,** and **PMT:END**. Then, cursor to **PV=0.00** and press ALPHA ENTER . (See page 199 in Chapter 5.)

Payment To find the payment given the present value or the future value, enter the known values into the **TVM Solver** for **N, I%, PV** or **FV, P/Y,** and **C/Y** and set **FV=0.00** or **PV=0.00, PMT=0.00,** and **PMT:END**. Then, cursor to **PMT=0.00** and press ALPHA ENTER . (See page 204 (if the future value is given) and page 206 (if the present value is given) in Chapter 5.)

Mortgages

Payment Enter the known values for **N, I%, PV, P/Y,** and **C/Y** into the **TVM Solver** and set **FV=0.00, PMT=0.00** and **PMT:END**. Then, cursor to **PMT=0.00** and press ALPHA ENTER . (See pages 344 and 345 in Chapter 9.)

See page 412 for details on what the **TVM Solver** variables represent for ordinary annuities and mortgages.

Interest Paid Ensure values are entered into the **TVM Solver** for **N, I%, PV, PMT, P/Y,** and **C/Y** and set **FV=0.00** and **PMT:END**. Press 2nd MODE to exit the **TVM Solver** and then, press APPS **1** ALPHA MATH to access the Interest function, **ΣInt(**. Enter the start payment number, press **,** , enter the end payment number, and then, press **)** ENTER . (See page 344 in Chapter 9.)

Principal Balance Owing Ensure values are entered into the **TVM Solver** for **N, I%, PV, PMT, P/Y,** and **C/Y** and set **FV=0.00** and **PMT:END**. Press 2nd MODE to exit the **TVM Solver** and then, press APPS **1 9** to access the Balance function, **bal(**. Enter the number of payments and then, press **)** ENTER . (See page 357 in Chapter 9.)

Principal Paid Ensure values are entered into the **TVM Solver** for **N, I%, PV, PMT, P/Y,** and **C/Y** and set **FV=0.00** and **PMT:END**. Press 2nd MODE to exit the **TVM Solver** and then, press APPS **1 0** to access the Principal function, **ΣPrn(**. Enter the start payment number, press **,** , enter the end payment number, and then, press **)** ENTER . (See page 358 in Chapter 9.)

Time to Pay Off Enter the known values for **I%, PV, PMT, P/Y,** and **C/Y** into the **TVM Solver** and set **N=0.00, FV=0.00,** and **PMT:END**. Cursor to **N=0.00** and press ALPHA ENTER . Use the number of payments, **N,** and the length of the payment interval to calculate the time. (See page 363 in Chapter 9.)

MICROSOFT® EXCEL SPREADSHEETS
THE BASICS
Open

You can access Microsoft® Excel from the **Start/Programs** menu or directly from the desktop.

The Screen

The Microsoft® Excel spreadsheet screen is called a worksheet.

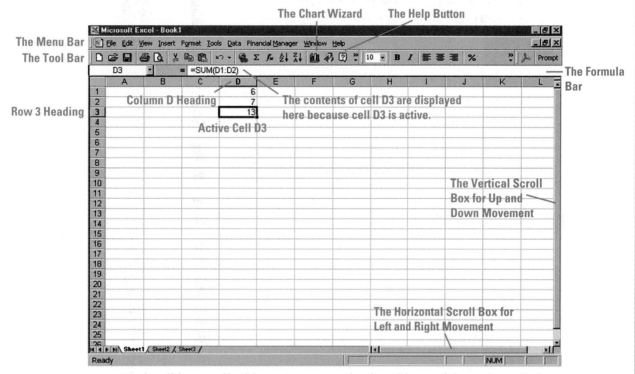

- Each cell has a **cell address**. For example, the address of the active cell above is D3 (column D, row 3).
- The **Tool Bar** contains the most commonly used functions also found in the **Menu Bar**, such as **Save**, **Print**, **Copy**, and **Paste**.
- The **Formula Bar** displays the address and the contents of the cell in which you are currently working.
- The **Chart Wizard** takes you through the steps of creating a chart (graph) that displays the data in the spreadsheet.

Enter Information

To enter information in a cell, click in the cell, and then, use the keyboard to type your heading, data, or formula. Finally, click on the checkmark or press Enter on the keyboard.

Delete

Select the cell(s), column(s), or row(s) for which you want to delete the contents (see *Selecting Columns, Rows, and Cells*), and then, press **Delete** on the keyboard.

Save

To save a spreadsheet, go to **Save as** in the **File** menu or click on the floppy disk icon on the toolbar. Enter a name for your file, and then, save it in an appropriate folder.

Print

To print a spreadsheet, go to **Print** in the **File** menu. You have several printing options to choose from, such as **Number of copies** and **Print range**. The default settings are **1 copy** and **all pages**. Click **OK** when you are ready to print. (Note that clicking on the printer icon on the toolbar will automatically print using the default settings.)

SELECTING CELLS, COLUMNS, AND ROWS

In order to perform many of the spreadsheet functions, you must first select or highlight the appropriate cells, columns, or rows.

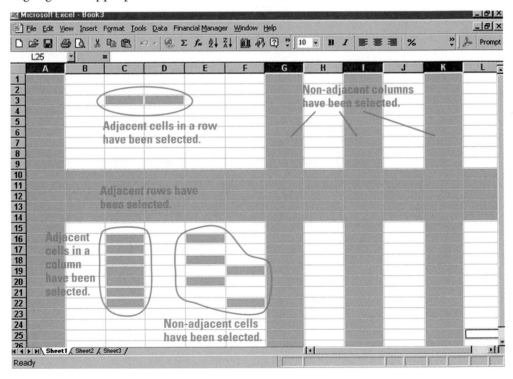

Single Cell

To select a single cell, click on the cell.

Single Column or Single Row

To select a single column or single row, click on the column heading or row heading.

Adjacent Columns or Adjacent Rows

To select a group of adjacent columns or adjacent rows, you can do either of the following:
- Click and hold on the middle of the first column or row heading in the group, and then, drag to highlight all the other columns or rows in the group.
- Click on the first column or row heading in the group, hold the **Shift** key, and then, click on the last column heading or row heading in the group.

Non-adjacent Columns or Non-adjacent Rows

To select a group of columns or rows that are not adjacent, click on the first column heading or row heading in the group, hold the **Ctrl** key down, and then, click on each of the other column headings or row headings in the group.

Adjacent Cells

To select a group of adjacent cells, you can do either of the following:
- Click and hold on the first cell in the group. Then, drag to highlight the other cells in the group.
- Click on the first cell in the group, hold the **Shift** key, and then, click on the last cell in the group.

Non-adjacent Cells

To select a group of cells that are not adjacent, click on the first cell in the group, hold the **Ctrl** key down, and then, click on each of the other cells in the group.

PREPARING THE SPREADSHEET

Column Width

To change the width of a column, you can do either of the following:

The width of column C has been increased.

- Cursor to the far right of the column heading until the cursor changes appearance. Click, hold, and drag to the right to change the width.
  (NOTE: Dragging all the way to the left deletes the column.)
- Right click on the column heading and select **Column Width** from the menu that appears. Enter the width of the column, and then, click **OK**.

To change the width of a group of columns Select all the columns in the group. Then, follow the directions for changing the width of a column for the first column in the group.

Row Height

To change the height of a row, you can do either of the following:

- Cursor to the bottom of the row heading until the cursor changes appearance. Click, hold, and drag down to change the height. (NOTE: Dragging all the way up deletes the row.)

The height of row 3 has been increased.

- Right click on the row heading and select **Row Height** from the menu that appears. Enter the height of the row, and then, click **OK**.

To change the height of a group of rows Select all the rows in the group. Then, follow the directions for changing the height of a row for the first row in the group.

Decimal Places—Set the Number

To set the number of decimal places, select the appropriate column(s). Choose **Cells** from the **Format** menu (or right click on the column heading and choose **Format Cells**). Click on the **Number** tab. Choose **Number** from the list that appears, and then, choose the number of decimal places. Click **OK**.

Percent (%)

To express numbers as percentages, select the appropriate column(s), and then, do either of the following:

- Choose **Cells** from the **Format** menu (or right click on the column heading and choose **Format Cells**). Click on the **Number** tab. Choose **Percentage** from the list that appears, and then, choose the number of decimal places. Click **OK**.
- Click on the % button at the far right of the tool bar.

Space for Thousands (## ### not ##,###)

To insert a space instead of a comma to show thousands, select the appropriate column(s). Choose **Cells** from the **Format** menu (or right click on the column heading and choose **Format Cells**). Click on the **Number** tab. Choose the **Custom** category. Choose **#,##0** from the list that appears, delete the comma, and then, press the spacebar to insert a space in its place. The result will appear as **# ##0**. Click **OK**.

	A	B	C	D
1	2 decimal places	percents with 2 decimal places	dollar signs with 0 decimal places	space for thousands
2	45.00	8.00%	$100	100
3	45.60	80.00%	$23	1 000
4	45.06	800.00%	$427	10 000

Currency ($)

To express numbers with dollar signs, select the appropriate column(s). Choose **Cells** from the **Format** menu (or right click on the column heading and choose **Format Cells**). Click on the **Number** tab. Choose **Currency** from the list that appears, and then, choose **0** or **2** decimal places. Click **OK**.

Format Characters (Bold, *Italics*, etc.)

To format characters, select the column(s), row(s), or cell(s) that contain the characters to be formatted, and then, use the formatting buttons on the tool bar: **B** (for bold), *I* (for italics), or use the font size menu. For more formatting options, choose **Cells** from the **Format** menu, and then, click on the **Font** tab.

SPECIAL FEATURES

Copy Cell Contents

To copy into the cells below Select the cell with the contents you want to copy and the cells in the same column into which you want the contents copied. Choose **Fill** from the **Edit** menu, and then, choose **Down** from the menu that appears.

Select the cell and the cells below it.

	A	B
1	Fill Down	
2		
3		
4		
5		
6		

Choose **Fill**, and then, **Down** from the **Edit** menu.

	A	B
1	Fill Down	
2	Fill Down	
3	Fill Down	
4	Fill Down	
5	Fill Down	
6		

To copy into the cells to the right Select the cell with the contents you want to copy and the cells in the same row into which you want the contents copied. Choose **Fill** from the **Edit** menu, and then, choose **Right** from the menu that appears.

Select the cell and the cells to its right.

	A	B	C	D
1	Fill Right			
2				

Choose **Fill**, and then, **Right** from the **Edit** menu.

	A	B	C	D
1	Fill Right	Fill Right	Fill Right	Fill Right
2				

Formulas and Functions

Formulas If you enter a formula into a cell, the spreadsheet will perform the calculations for you. Formulas always begin with an equal sign (=). For example, if you enter the formula =**A1+A2+A3+A4** into cell A5, the contents of cells A1 to A4 will be automatically added, and then, displayed in cell A5.

A5	▾	=	=A1+A2+A3+A4	
	A	B	C	D
1	1			
2	2			
3	3			
4	4			
5	10	1 + 2 + 3 + 4 = 10		

A5			=	=SUM(A1:A4)
	A			
1	10			
2	2			
3	3			
4	4			
5	19	10 + 2 + 3 + 4 = 19		

If the formula =A1+A2+A3+A4 in cell A5 is copied into cell B5, it will automatically change to =B1+B2+B3+B4.

If the contents of cells A1 to A4 are changed, the formula in A5 will automatically update the contents of cell A5.

Functions A function is a shortcut formula. For example, instead of the formula =**A1+A2+A3+A4**, you could use the function =**SUM(A1:A4)**.

Functions can be used alone, as in =**SUM(A1:A4)**, or they can be part of a formula, for example, **A1*SUM(A1:A4)**.

A5	▾	=	=SUM(A1:A4)	
	A	B	C	D
1	1			
2	2			
3	3			
4	4			
5	10	1 + 2 + 3 + 4 = 10		

Some of the basic symbols used in formulas and functions are shown here:

Symbol	Meaning	Keyboard Keystrokes
+	Addition	[Shift] [=]
-	Subtraction	[-]
*	Multiplication	[Shift] 8
/	Division	[/]
^	Exponent	[Shift] 6
:	A range of cells	[Shift] [;]
=	Formula/Function	[=]

GRAPHS

Circle Graph (Pie Chart)

Select the cells that contain the data to be graphed. Then, click on the **Chart Wizard** button, or choose **Chart** from the **Insert** menu, and follow these steps:

	A	B	C
	Section	Amount	
	A	120	
	B	60	
	C	30	
	D	15	

Step 1: Select a **Pie Chart type** and **Chart sub-type**. Then, click **Next**.

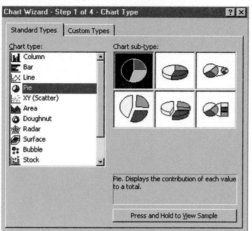

Step 2: Make sure the correct cells (**Data range**) and **Series** have been selected.

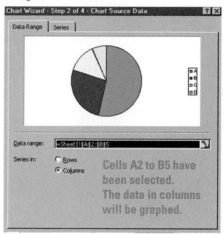

Cells A2 to B5 have been selected.
The data in columns will be graphed.

Step 3: Click on the **Titles** tab and enter the **Chart title**. Click on the **Legend** tab and choose the **Placement** of the legend. Click on the **Data Labels** tab and choose the **Data labels** to display. Then, click **Next**:

Step 4: Choose to locate the chart **As an object in** the worksheet. Then, click **Finish**:

The pie chart will appear on the worksheet.

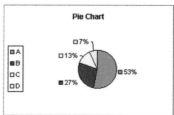

COREL® QUATTRO® PRO 8 SPREADSHEETS
THE BASICS
Open
You can access **Corel® WordPerfect® Suite 8** from the **Start/Programs** menu. Then, click on **Corel® Quattro® Pro 8**.

The Screen
The Quattro® Pro screen is called a notebook.

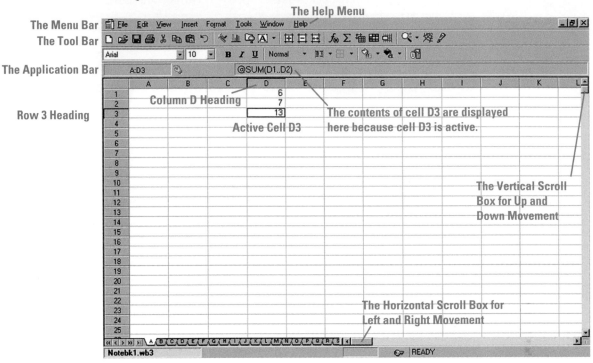

- Each cell has a **cell address**, for example, the address of the active cell above is D3 (column D, row 3).
- The **Tool Bar** contains the most commonly used functions also found in the **Menu Bar**, such as **Save**, **Print**, **Copy**, and **Paste**.
- The **Application Bar** displays the address and the contents of the cell in which you are working.

Enter Information
See Microsoft® Excel instructions on page 415.

Save
See Microsoft® Excel instructions on page 416.

Delete
See Microsoft® Excel instructions on page 416.

Print
See Microsoft® Excel instructions on page 416.

SELECTING CELLS, COLUMNS, AND ROWS
See Microsoft® Excel instructions on pages 416–417.

FORMATTING
Column Width
See Microsoft® Excel instructions on page 417.

Row Height
See Microsoft® Excel instructions on page 418.

Decimal Places—Set the Number
To set the number of decimal places, select the appropriate column(s). Choose **Selection** from the **Format** menu (or right click on the column head and choose **Column Properties**). Then, click on the **Numeric Format** tab. From the same menu, choose **Fixed**, and then, choose the number of decimal places. Click **OK**.

Percent (%)
To express numbers as percents, select the appropriate column(s). Choose **Selection** from the **Format** menu (or right click on the column head and choose **Column Properties**). Then, click on the **Numeric Format** tab. Then, choose **Percent**. From the same menu, choose the number of decimal places. Click **OK**.

Space for Thousands (## ### not ##,###)
To use a space instead of a comma to show thousands, select the appropriate column(s). Choose **Selection** from the **Format** menu (or right click on the column head and choose **Column Properties**). Choose **Comma**, and then, click **OK**. Now, choose **Settings** from the **Tools** menu and click on the **International** tab. Choose **Punctuation**, and then, choose **1 234.56 (a1, a2)** from the list that appears. Finally, click **OK**.

Currency ($)
To express numbers with dollar signs, select the appropriate column(s). Choose **Selection** from the **Format** menu (or right click on the column head and choose **Column Properties**). Then, click on the **Numeric Format** tab. Then, choose **Currency**. On the same menu, choose **0** or **2** decimal places. Click **OK**.

Format Characters (Bold, *Italics*, etc.)
To format characters, select the column(s), row(s), or cell(s) that contain the characters to be formatted, and then, use the formatting buttons on the tool bar: **B** (for bold), *I* (for italics), (U for underline), or the font size and font type menus. For more formatting options, choose **Selection** from the **Format** menu, and then, click on the **Cell Font** tab.

SPECIAL FEATURES

Copy Cell Contents

Select the cell(s) with the contents you want to copy. Choose **Copy Cells** from the **Edit** menu. The address(es) of the cell(s) you want to copy should be listed in the **From** box and also in the **To** box. Delete the contents of the **To** box and then, enter the address of the first cell in the group of cells you want to copy into. Then, click **OK**.

Formulas and Functions

Formulas If you enter a formula into a cell, the spreadsheet will perform the calculations for you. Formulas always begin with an addition sign (+). For example, if you enter the formula **+A1*(A2+A3+A4)** into cell A5, the contents of cell A1 will be multiplied by the sum of the contents of cells A2 to A4, and then, the result will be displayed in cell A5.

A:A5			+A1*(A2+A3+A4)
	A	B	C	D
1	1			
2	2			
3	3			
4	4			
5	9	1 × (2 + 3 + 4) = 9		

A:A5	
	A
1	10
2	2
3	3
4	4
5	90

10 × (2 + 3 + 4) = 90

If the formula **+A1*(A2+A3+A4)** in cell A5 is copied into cell B5, it will automatically change to **+B1*(B2+B3+B4)**.

If the contents of cells A1 to A4 are changed, the formula in A5 will automatically update the contents of cell A5.

Functions A function is a shortcut formula. For example, instead of using **A2+A3+A4** in the formula **+A1*(A2+A3+A4)**, the function **@SUM(A2..A4)** could be used: **+A1*@SUM(A2..A4)**.

A:A5			+A1*@SUM(A2..A4)
	A	B	C	D	E
1	10				
2	2				
3	3				
4	4				
5	90	10 × (2 + 3 + 4) = 90			

Functions can be used alone, or they can be part of a formula.

Some of the basic symbols used in formulas and functions are shown here:

Symbol	Meaning	Keyboard Keystrokes
+	Addition	**Shift** **=**
-	Subtraction	**-**
*	Multiplication	**Shift** 8
/	Division	**/**
^	Exponent	**Shift** 6
..	A range of cells	**.** **.**
+	Formula	**Shift** **=**
@	Function	**Shift** 2

If = is entered at the beginning of a formula instead of **+** or **@**, the appropriate symbol, **+** or **@**, will be substituted.

GRAPHS

Circle Graph (Pie Chart)

Select the cells that contain the data to be graphed. Then, choose **Chart** from the **Insert** menu and follow these steps:

	A	B	C
1	Section	Amount	
2	A	120	
3	B	60	
4	C	30	
5	D	15	
6			

Step 1: Make sure the correct cells (**Chart data**) are selected, and then, click **Next**.

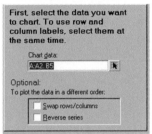

Steps 2 and 3: Choose **Pie** chart, click **Next**, and choose a **specific** pie **chart type**. Then, click **Next**:

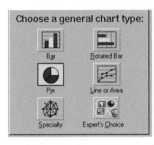
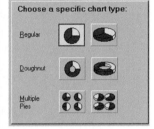

Step 4: **Choose a color scheme** and click **Next**:

Step 5: Enter the chart **Title** and **Subtitle**. Choose **Current Sheet** for **Destination**. Then, click **Finish**:

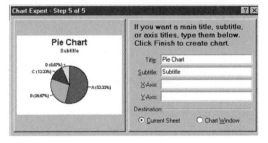

Step 6: Click on the notebook and the chart will appear.

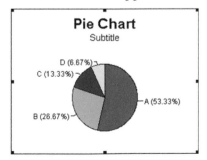

If you want to make changes, left click on one of the wedges of the pie, and then, right click. Choose **Pie Chart Properties** and the following window will appear:

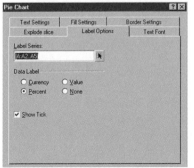

ANSWERS

Chapter 1 – Personal Financial Planning

Get Ready, pp. 2–3

1. a) 45.65 **b)** 3.12 **c)** 156.10 **d)** 201.00 **2. a)** 16.67% **b)** 66.67%
c) 0.25% **d)** 54.69% **3. a)** 115.2 **b)** 190.8 **c)** 36 **d)** 18 **4. a)** 0.06
b) 0.11 **c)** 0.045 **d)** 0.125 **e)** 0.085 **f)** 0.1025 **g)** 0.12625
h) 0.0325 **5. a)** 6.77% **b)** 12.38% **c)** 0.85% **d)** 8.38% **e)** 25%
f) 33.33% **g)** 37.5% **h)** 83.33% **6. a)** 15 **b)** 60 **c)** 7 **d)** 7 **e)** 10
f) 6 **7.** Keys in brackets are optional. **a)** scientific calculator:
15 $-$ 3 $\times$ 4 $+$ 12 $=$; graphing calculator: 15 $-$ 3
$\times$ 4 $+$ 12 (ENTER) **b)** scientific calculator: (15 $-$ 3
) $\times$ 4 $+$ 12 $=$; graphing calculator: (15 $-$ 3
) ($\times$) 4 $+$ 12 (ENTER) **c)** scientific calculator: 55 $-$
3 $\times$ (4 $+$ 12) $=$; graphing calculator: 55 $-$ 3
($\times$) (4 $+$ 12) (ENTER) **d)** scientific calculator: 315
$\div$ (4 $\times$ 12 $-$ 3) $=$; graphing calculator: 315 $\div$
(4 $\times$ 12 $-$ 3) (ENTER) **e)** scientific calculator: 360
$\div$ ((4 $\times$ (12 $-$ 3))) $=$; graphing calculator:
360 $\div$ ((4 ($\times$) (12 $-$ 3)) (ENTER)
f) scientific calculator: 120 $\div$ ((4 $+$ 2 $\times$ 8) $=$;
graphing calculator: 120 $\div$ ((4 $+$ 2 $\times$ 8
) (ENTER) **8. a) i)** $l = \dfrac{V}{wh}$ **ii)** 3 cm **b) i)** $w = \dfrac{V}{lh}$ **ii)** 4 m

c) i) $h = \dfrac{V}{lw}$ **ii)** 10 mm **9. a)** $\dfrac{3}{4}$ years, or 0.75 years

b) $\dfrac{3}{2}$ years, or 1.5 years **c)** $\dfrac{1}{2}$ years, or 0.5 years

d) $\dfrac{1}{4}$ years, or 0.25 years **10. a)** $\dfrac{90}{365}$, or $\dfrac{18}{73}$ years

b) $\dfrac{120}{365}$, or $\dfrac{24}{73}$ years **c)** $\dfrac{180}{365}$, or $\dfrac{36}{73}$ years

1.1 Understand Financial Planning, pp. 8–10

1. Answers will vary, for example: **a) i)** He may not have to
reduce his expenses as much. **ii)** He may have to delay college
for 3 years. **b)** an increase in tuition; an increase in current
expenses **2. a)** Answers will vary, for example: find out about
tuition and other college expenses; open savings account; get
summer job; save money from summer job; get part-time job;
research scholarships; apply for student loan; ask parents for
loan; pay first year's tuition. **3. b)** Answers will vary, for
example: Life insurance should be part of a financial plan for
someone with dependants, such as children.

6. a) Answers may vary, for example: If something happens to
Lyle, the money from the life insurance will support the
children financially. **7.** An emergency fund must be safe and
easily available. A retirement fund is a long-term investment,
so, it can tolerate more risk in order to potentially earn more
interest. **8. a)** Answers may vary, for example: credit card;
furniture; car loan; student loan. **b)** In Erin's case, it might
mean a loan of between $28 000 and $31 500 at an interest rate
of less than 9%. **9. c)** 3 years: $556; 5 years: $333

1.2 Budgeting: Part 1, pp. 15–18

2. a) $2545

b)

Donald's Monthly Budget

	Current
Monthly Net Income	$2545
Monthly Living Expenses:	
Telephone	$80
Food	$430
Transportation	$590
Clothing	$40
Rent	$825
Savings	$75
Loan payment	$320
Vacation fund	$85
Spending money	$100
Total Living Expenses	$2545
Left Over	$0

3. b) Answers may vary, for example: Liquid assets are those
that can be cashed easily. Non-liquid assets are those that
cannot be cashed easily. Both liquid and non-liquid assets are
included as assets in a net worth statement.

4. a)

Franco and Gayle's Monthly Budget

	Current
Monthly Net Income	$5525
Monthly Living Expenses:	
Mortgage and taxes	$1320
Clothing	$167
Charity	$100
Loan payments	$200
Vacation fund	$100
Gifts	$100
Day care	$650
Food	$650
Utilities	$500
Entertainment	$250
Savings	$433
Transportation	$542
Spending money	$520
Total Living Expenses	$5532
Left Over	−$7

7. a)

Soni's Current Net Worth Statement

Assets	$	Liabilities	$
Car	15 000	Debt to parents	15 000
Furniture	8 500	Car loan	8 500
Coin collection	3 200	Furniture loan	5 800
Bank account balance	2 800	Student loan	9 600
Investments	9 100		
Total Assets	**38 600**	**Total Liabilities**	**38 900**

Net Worth = –$300

b) He can earn money, either through investments or working, and use this income to pay off debts.

9. a) Jamal and Olivia's Monthly Budget

	Current
Monthly Net Income	$3252
Monthly Living Expenses:	
Rent	$750
Car loan payments	$375
Car expenses	$325
Entertainment	$379
Food	$867
Student loan payments	$400
Clothing	$125
Credit card payments	$100
Health/Personal	$433
Total Living Expenses	**$3754**
Left Over for Savings	**–$502**

Jamal and Olivia's Current Net Worth Statement

Assets	$	Liabilities	$
Car	15 000	Car loan	8 000
Furniture	2 500	Student loan	12 000
		Credit card balance	2 000
Total Assets	**17 500**	**Total Liabilities**	**22 000**

Net Worth = –$4500

13. a) question 1: 0%; question 2: 2%; question 4: 6%; question 9: 0% **15. c)** question 7: 31%; question 9: 0%

1.3 Budgeting: Part 2, pp. 21–23

1. a) She eliminated half of her food and entertainment expenses and all of her clothing expenses and debt repayment.
c) These may only be temporary changes.

2. a)   Doreen's Revised Net Worth Statement

Assets	$	Liabilities	$
Furniture	1000		
Jewellery	1500		
Savings bonds	3600		
Total Assets	**6100**	**Total Liabilities**	**0**

Net Worth = $6100

b) There is no change to her net worth because the change in assets is equal to the change in liabilities.

7. a) i) Donald: 26.1%; Franco and Gayle: 17.6%; Jamal and Olivia: 16.4% **ii)** Donald: 13.6%; Franco and Gayle: 8.7%; Jamal and Olivia: 18.9% **iii)** Donald: 18.6%; Franco and Gayle: 7.2%; Jamal and Olivia: 15.3%

8. a) Food: $178.50; Savings: $89.25; Tuition: $282.63; Transportation: $252.88; Clothing: $44.63; Rent: $416.50; Left over: $223.13 **d)** Measure with a protractor, and then, divide the angle that corresponds to each expense by 360°. Then, multiply the result by the monthly net income. For example, the angle corresponding to the Left Over section of the circle is 54°. $\frac{54°}{360°}$ = 15%, and 15% of $1487.50 is $223.13.

1.4 Simple Interest, pp. 28–29

1.

	Principal ($)	Interest Rate (%)	Time	Interest Earned ($)	Amount ($)
	P	r	t	I	$A = P + I$
a)	2 000	8.0	3 years	480.00	2 480.00
b)	3 000	6.5	9 months	146.25	3 146.25
c)	5 500	6.0	180 days	162.74	5 662.74
d)	10 000	5.5	30 months	1375.00	11 375.00
e)	6 000	5.0	2.5 years	750.00	6 750.00
f)	7 003	1.5	5 weeks	10.10	7 013.10
g)	1 650	3.5	18 months	86.63	1 736.63
h)	1 675	6.75	9 months	84.80	1 759.80

2. a) $336 **b)** $936 **3.** 10.5% **4.** $950 **5.** 9 months **6.** $516.27
7. 4.25% **8.** 3 months **9. a)** $5600 **b)** $25 **10. b)** As the term increases, so does the interest rate. **11. a)** $140 **b)** They will need an interest rate of 8.57% or less. **c)** $70; $70; $70; The interest payments are the same. **13.** $1250 **14. a)** $5316.85 **b)** $5015.30

Review, pp. 32–33

1. a) Step 1: Identify goals and state objectives. Step 2: Collect information on the current situation. Step 3: Design a plan. Step 4: Put the plan into action. Step 5: Monitor and adjust the plan. **2. a)** Answers will vary, for example: create a current budget; examine spending habits; pay off high-interest debts; begin an emergency fund; make a will; take out life insurance; begin a retirement plan; investigate the cost of a vacation; begin a vacation fund; take out a low-interest loan and consolidate debts.

3. a)   Justin and Hannah's Current Net Worth Statement

Assets	$	Liabilities	$
House	150 000	Mortgage	125 000
Two cars	16 000	Car loan	8 000
Furniture	6 000	Credit card balance	5 500
Retirement savings	10 000	Loan to parents	10 000
Savings bonds	5 000		
Savings in bank	500		
Total Assets	**187 500**	**Total Liabilities**	**148 500**

Net Worth = $39 000

b) Answers will vary, for example: Pay off their high-interest debts with their low-interest savings. **c)** Net worth will not change.
4. a) $833; $556 **6.** Answers will vary, for example: Many financial goals require changes to spending habits and expenses.
7. a) $900 **b)** $5900 **c)** $37.50 **8.** 3.5 years **9.** $950 **10.** 8.75%

Practice Test, pp. 34–35

3. a) $166.67

b) Paul's Current Monthly Budget

	Current
Monthly Net Income	$433
Monthly Living Expenses:	
Entertainment	$87
Health/Personal	$43
Transportation	$43
Clothing	$100
Food	$87
Total Living Expenses	$360
Left Over for Savings	$73

4. Rent: $996.67; Food: $433.33; Transportation: $195; Clothing: $108.33; Entertainment: $216.67; Health/Personal: $21.67; Debt repayment: $108.33; Left over for savings: $86.67 **6.** $6.51 **7.** 16 years and 8 months **8.** 8.8% **9.** $16 666.67 **10.** No; Examples will vary. **11. a)** $20

Chapter 2 – Exponential Expressions

Get Ready, pp. 38–39

1. a) 25 **b)** 81 **c)** 64 **d)** 216 **e)** 32 **f)** 4096 **2. a)** 32 **b)** 32 **c)** 32 **3. a)** The student multiplied the bases instead of keeping them the same. **b)** The student multiplied the exponents instead of adding them. **c)** 3^8 **4. a)** 5^5 **b)** 4^{12} **c)** 3^{16} **d)** 5^{10} **e)** 8^6 **f)** x^8 **g)** a^9 **h)** a^5 **5. a)** 27 **b)** 27 **c)** 27 **6. a)** 2^2 **b)** 5^8 **c)** 6^1 **d)** 7^4 **e)** x^4 **f)** a^6 **7. a)** 64 **b)** 64 **c)** 64 **8. a)** 2^{12} **b)** 5^6 **c)** 4^{18} **d)** 6^{20} **e)** x^8 **f)** a^9 **9.** No; explanations may vary, for example: If $x = 1$ and $y = 2$, $(x + y)^2 = 9$, whereas $x^2 + y^2 = 5$. **10. a)** 3 **b)** 7 **c)** 10 **d)** 8 **e)** 12 **f)** 15 **g)** 4 **h)** 11 **i)** 20 **j)** 1 **k)** $\frac{3}{5}$ **l)** $\frac{2}{9}$ **11. a)** -2 **b)** -4 **c)** 3 **d)** 1 **e)** -2 **f)** 4 **g)** -11 **h)** 0 **12. a)** -2 **b)** -7 **c)** 11 **d)** 2 **e)** 4 **f)** -4 **g)** 0 **h)** -8 **13. a)** -8 **b)** 9 **c)** 0 **d)** -20 **e)** 1 **f)** -10 **g)** -6 **h)** -40 **14. a)** $t = 6$ **b)** $k = 8$ **c)** $m = 7$ **d)** $y = 3$

2.1 Evaluate Powers With Integral Exponents, pp. 43–45

1. a) 49 **b)** 125 **c)** 10 000 **d)** 1 **e)** 1 **f)** 1 **g)** 1 **h)** 1 **i)** -1 **j)** -125 **2. a)** $\frac{1}{25}$ **b)** $\frac{1}{64}$ **c)** $\frac{1}{16}$ **d)** $\frac{1}{121}$ **e)** $\frac{1}{27}$ **f)** $\frac{1}{81}$ **g)** $\frac{1}{32}$ **h)** $\frac{1}{1000}$ **i)** $\frac{1}{125}$ **j)** $\frac{1}{64}$ **3. a)** $2^2 = 4$ **b)** $7^1 = 7$ **c)** $3^{-1} = \frac{1}{3}$ **d)** $5^0 = 1$ **e)** $8^0 = 1$ **f)** $6^2 = 36$ **g)** $4^{-1} = \frac{1}{4}$ **h)** $2^3 = 8$ **i)** $5^{-2} = \frac{1}{25}$ **j)** $3^{-2} = \frac{1}{9}$ **4. a)** $5^2 = 25$ **b)** $3^3 = 27$ **c)** $4^{-3} = \frac{1}{64}$ **d)** $5^{-3} = \frac{1}{125}$ **e)** $2^{-3} = \frac{1}{8}$ **f)** $4^3 = 64$ **g)** $7^4 = 2401$ **h)** $5^1 = 5$ **i)** $10^2 = 100$ **j)** $6^0 = 1$ **5. a)** $2^6 = 64$ **b)** $5^{-2} = \frac{1}{25}$ **c)** $3^0 = 1$ **d)** $3^{-4} = \frac{1}{81}$

e) $4^{-2} = \frac{1}{16}$ **f)** $7^2 = 49$ **g)** $6^0 = 1$ **h)** $11^1 = 11$ **i)** $2^{-6} = \frac{1}{64}$ **j)** $10^{-9} = \frac{1}{1\,000\,000\,000}$ **6.** When n is even, $(-1)^n$ is +1, and when n is odd, $(-1)^n$ is -1. **7. a)** k^7 **b)** b^9 **c)** $3x^5$ **d)** $10t^4$ **e)** n **f)** x^6 **g)** a^{-10} **h)** $125p^6$ **i)** $3a^6$ **j)** $9a^6$ **k)** x^{-6} **l)** a **m)** $4a^3$ **n)** $6n^3$ **o)** x^{-1} **p)** m **8. a)** a^3b^3 **b)** $2x^3y$ **c)** $3m^2n^{-2}$ **d)** x^4y^4 **e)** $2a^{-2}b^{-4}$ **f)** $2d^6k^{-1}$ **9. a)** 2^{a+b+c} **b)** 2^{2a} **c)** 2^c **10.** next two A notes above middle A: 1760 Hz, 3520 Hz; four A notes below middle A: 220 Hz, 110 Hz, 55 Hz, 27.5 Hz **11.** Greg's playing is 10 times as loud as the vacuum cleaner.

12. a)

Distance from Light (m)	1	2	4	8	16	32
Intensity of Light (lm)	3200	800	200	50	12.5	3.125

b) Intensity is divided by 4. **c)** Intensity is multiplied by 4. **d)** Intensity is doubled. **13. a) i)** 15 **ii)** 16 **iii)** 195 **iv)** 185 **b) i)** 1000 **ii)** 1011 **iii)** 11101 **iv)** 1110101 **14. a)** 2^6 **b)** 2^6 **c)** 2^{-8}

2.2 Powers With Rational Exponents, pp. 48–50

1. a) 7 **b)** 30 **c)** 4 **d)** 3 **e)** 10 **2. a)** 8 **b)** 10 **c)** 20 **d)** 2 **e)** 5 **3. a)** 6 **b)** 11 **c)** 3 **d)** 2 **e)** 5 **4. a)** $\frac{1}{5}$ **b)** $\frac{1}{6}$ **c)** $\frac{1}{3}$ **d)** $\frac{1}{2}$ **e)** $\frac{1}{10}$ **5. a)** $\frac{1}{5}$ **b)** $\frac{1}{2}$ **c)** $\frac{1}{15}$ **d)** $\frac{1}{6}$ **e)** $\frac{1}{10}$ **6. a)** 125 **b)** 216 **c)** 8 **d)** 8 **e)** 9 **7. a)** $\frac{1}{16}$ **b)** $\frac{1}{27}$ **c)** $\frac{1}{32}$ **d)** $\frac{1}{100}$ **e)** $\frac{1}{27}$ **8. a)** 30 **b)** 726 **c)** 25 **d)** 6 **9. a)** $2^1 = 2$ **b)** $100^{\frac{1}{2}} = 10$ **c)** $5^1 = 5$ **d)** $16^{\frac{1}{2}} = 4$ **11. a)** $V = 12$ V **b)** $V = 120$ V **12. a)** $L = 48$ cm **b)** $L = 260$ cm **13. a)** $S = 64$ km/h **b)** $S = 55$ km/h **c)** $S = 78$ km/h **14. a)** 2^{100} **b)** 4^{26} **c)** 20^{100} **d)** $125^{\frac{5}{3}}$ **15. a)** 1.2 m **b)** 2.0 m **16. a)** $2a$ **b)** $3ab^2$ **c)** $25a^2$ **d)** $-2ab^2$ **17. a)** x^{18} **b)** $x^3y^{\frac{1}{2}}$ **c)** $25x^3y^3$ **d)** $125x^6y^{\frac{3}{4}}$ **18. a)** 8 **b)** $\frac{2}{3}$

2.3 Evaluate Exponential Expressions Using a Scientific Calculator, pp. 54–55

1. a) 636.22 **b)** 5.66 **c)** 1.97 **d)** 7.07 **e)** 2.15 **f)** 21.03 **g)** 140.30 **h)** 0.02 **i)** 26.25 **j)** 0.51 **k)** 7.70 **l)** 10.39 **2. a)** 632.914 **b)** 0.011 **c)** 5.278 **d)** 677 916.924 **3. a)** 904.36 **b)** 4287.34 **c)** 944.05 **d)** 1834.76 **e)** 914.54 **f)** 257.25 **4. a)** 257.60 **b)** 1016.19 **c)** 8352.61 **d)** 1567.74 **e)** 820.24 **f)** 17 952.22 **5.** $720.06 **6.** It was 15.85 times noisier. **7. a)** $5186.41 **b)** $2035.41

8. a)

Note	C	D	E	F	G	A	B	C
Multiple of C	1	$(\sqrt[12]{2})^2$	$(\sqrt[12]{2})^4$	$(\sqrt[12]{2})^5$	$(\sqrt[12]{2})^7$	$(\sqrt[12]{2})^9$	$(\sqrt[12]{2})^{11}$	$(\sqrt[12]{2})^{12}$
Frequency (Hz)	264	296	333	352	396	444	498	528

b) Multiply the frequency by 2.

2.4 Solve Exponential Equations Using Common Bases, pp. 58–59

1. a) $x = 5$ **b)** $x = -4$ **c)** $x = -7$ **d)** $x = 4$ **e)** $x = 0.5$ **f)** $x = -3$ **2. a)** $x = 2$ **b)** $x = 3$ **c)** $x = 3$ **d)** $x = 4$ **e)** $x = 0$ **f)** $x = 5$ **g)** $x = 0$

h) $x = 1$ **i)** $x = 5$ **j)** $x = 4$ **k)** $x = -2$ **l)** $x = 6$ **3. a)** $x = 7$ **b)** $x = -5$

c) $x = -4$ **d)** $x = 6$ **e)** $x = 3$ **f)** $x = \dfrac{3}{2}$ **4. a)** $x = 4$ **b)** $x = 2$

c) $x = -2$ **5. a)** $x = 4$ **b)** $a = 6$ **c)** $x = 2$ **d)** $n = 4$ **e)** $x = \dfrac{3}{2}$

f) $x = 4$ **g)** $x = -1$ **h)** $x = -8$ **i)** $y = -2$ **j)** $x = -2$ **k)** $x = -\dfrac{1}{2}$

l) $x = -3$ **6. a)** $x = -\dfrac{3}{2}$ **b)** $x = -2$ **c)** $x = -\dfrac{3}{7}$ **d)** $x = \dfrac{5}{2}$ **e)** $x = -\dfrac{3}{2}$

f) $x = -2$ **7.** $x = 3.3$ **8. a)** $x = -\dfrac{3}{4}$ **b)** $q = 3$ **c)** $x = 1$

9. a) $x = 3$, $x = -1$ **b)** $x = 5$, $x = -3$ **c)** $x = 10$

Case Study Wrap-Up, p. 61

1. It is 10 000 times as intense. **2. a)** 100 dB

Review, pp. 62–63

1. a) 125 **b)** 1 **c)** $\dfrac{1}{16}$ **d)** -8 **e)** -1 **f)** 1 **2. a)** 3^9 **b)** $(-2)^8$ **c)** 5^1

d) 3^6 **e)** 6^{-6} **f)** 4^5 **3. a)** $5^2 = 25$ **b)** $4^0 = 1$ **c)** $6^{-1} = \dfrac{1}{6}$ **d)** $7^{-2} = \dfrac{1}{49}$

e) $3^4 = 81$ **f)** $6^0 = 1$ **4. a)** b^{-2} **b)** x^6 **c)** m^6 **d)** $2x^6$ **e)** $2x^4 y^{-6}$ **f)** $20b^3$

5. a) 7 **b)** 4 **c)** $\dfrac{1}{2}$ **d)** 216 **e)** 32 **6. a)** 6 **b)** $\dfrac{26}{9}$ **c)** 125 **d)** 2

7. a) 10 cm **b)** 20 cm **c)** 6 cm **8. a)** 883 883.48 **b)** 53.30 **c)** 0.02

d) 3.18 **e)** 0.23 **9. a)** 0.21 **b)** 2818.38 **c)** 222.86 **10. a)** 1322.67

b) 3234.65 **c)** 845.37 **11.** 2.68 cm **12. a)** $x = 3$ **b)** $k = 4$

c) $n = 2$ **d)** $a = -3$ **e)** $x = 2$ **f)** $y = \dfrac{2}{3}$ **g)** $y = 2$ **h)** $k = -\dfrac{1}{3}$ **i)** $t = \dfrac{3}{4}$

Practice Test, pp. 64–65

1. a) 1000 **b)** 1 **c)** -125 **d)** 1 **2. a)** $\dfrac{1}{16}$ **b)** $\dfrac{1}{16}$ **c)** $\dfrac{1}{125}$ **d)** $\dfrac{1}{7}$

3. a) $5^3 = 125$ **b)** $3^2 = 9$ **c)** $2^0 = 1$ **d)** $4^{-2} = \dfrac{1}{16}$ **4. a)** 7 **b)** 27 **c)** $\dfrac{1}{6}$

d) $\dfrac{1}{25}$ **e)** 32 **5. a)** a^3 **b)** $4x^2$ **c)** $x^6 y^9$ **d)** $27a^{-6}$ **6. a)** 199.53 **b)** 0.06

c) 0.29 **d)** 13.34 **7. a)** 4389.03 **b)** 3153.97 **c)** 1014.73

8. \$24 273.35 **9. a)** $x = 4$ **b)** $x = 4$ **c)** $x = 2$ **d)** $x = -3$ **e)** $x = -7$

f) $x = -\dfrac{5}{4}$ **10. a)** 12.0 cm **b)** 24 cm × 24 cm × 24 cm; 3456 cm^2

Chapter 3 – Sequences and Simple and Compound Interest

Get Ready, pp. 68–69

1. a) 9, 11 **b)** 16, 32 **c)** -7, -9 **d)** $\dfrac{1}{5}$, $\dfrac{1}{6}$ **2. a)** 23 **b)** 42 **c)** 35

d) 32 **3. a)** 243.33 **b)** 28 **c)** 1.16 **d)** 0.79 **e)** 0.92 **f)** 223.86

4. a) $n + 3$ **b)** $\dfrac{n}{2}$ **c)** $n - 8$ **d)** n^2 **e)** $2n - 1$ **f)** $\dfrac{n^2}{2}$ **5. a)** 0.34

b) 0.09 **c)** 0.008 **d)** 0.069 **e)** 0.1175 **f)** 0.0825 **6. a)** \$259.50

b) \$96.00 **c)** \$14.63 **d)** \$2600.00 **7. a)** $w = \dfrac{A}{l}$ **b)** $l = \dfrac{P}{2} - w$

c) $r = \dfrac{I}{Pt}$ **8. a)** $x = 11$ **b)** $m = -70$ **c)** $b = 45$ **d)** $m = -6$ **e)** $x = 3$

f) $y = -7$ **9. a)** 2.01 **b)** 1.05 **c)** 0.61 **d)** 0.93 **e)** 609.50 **f)** 320.84

3.1 Sequences, pp. 74–76

1. a) Add odd numbers: add 3, then 5, then 7, … ; 16, 25.
b) Subtract 4 from the previous term; -7, -11. **c)** Multiply the previous term by 2; 48, 96. **d)** Multiply the previous term by -1; 1, -1. **2. a)** $t_1 = 4$, $t_2 = 9$, $t_3 = 14$, $t_4 = 19$, $t_5 = 24$
b) $t_1 = 1$, $t_2 = 8$, $t_3 = 27$, $t_4 = 64$, $t_5 = 125$ **c)** $t_1 = 0$, $t_2 = 5$, $t_3 = 10$, $t_4 = 15$, $t_5 = 20$ **d)** $t_1 = 0$, $t_2 = \dfrac{1}{3}$, $t_3 = \dfrac{1}{2}$, $t_4 = \dfrac{3}{5}$, $t_5 = \dfrac{2}{3}$

3. a) Answers may vary, for example: 5, 11 **or** 4, 16.
b) Answers may vary, for example: 505, 1495 **or** 100, 10 000.
4. a) i) Answers may vary, for example: 11, 17. **ii)** Add 6 to the previous term. **b) i)** Answers may vary, for example: 9.5, 14, 18.5. **ii)** Add 4.5 to the previous term. **c) i)** Answers may vary, for example: 83, 163. **ii)** Add 80 to the previous term. **d) i)** Answers may vary, for example: 63, 123, 183 **or** 9, 27, 81. **ii)** Add 60 to the previous term **or** multiply the previous term by 3.
5. a) i) Multiply the term number by 2 and add 3.
ii) $t_n = 2n + 3$ **b) i)** Multiply the term number by 3. **ii)** $t_n = 3n$
c) i) Square the term number and add 1. **ii)** $t_n = n^2 + 1$
d) i) Divide 1 by the sum of the term number and 2.

ii) $t_n = \dfrac{1}{n + 2}$ **6. a)** $t_1 = 30$, $t_2 = 34$, $t_3 = 38$, $t_4 = 42$, $t_5 = 46$
b) $t_n = 4n + 26$ **c)** $t_n = 226$ **7. a)** \$12.50, \$16.00, \$19.50, \$23.00, … **b)** $t_n = 9 + 3.5n$ **c)** \$30 **d)** $n = 3$ **8. a)** 15 **b)** 21
c) $3n - 3$ **d)** 297 **9. a)** \$11.25/h, \$11.50/h, \$11.75/h, …
b) $11 + 0.25(n - 1)$ or $10.75 + 0.25n$ **c)** 23 months
12. -7, -12, -17 **13.** Answers will vary, for example:
$t_n = 8 + t_{n-1}$. **14. a)** 1, 1, 2, 3, 5, 8, 13, 21, 34, 55, 89, 144, 233, 377, 610 **b)** $t_1 = 1$, $t_2 = 1$; $t_n = t_{n-1} + t_{n-2}$ **c)** Answers may vary, for example: The terms are odd, odd, even, odd, odd, even, … ; the differences also form a Fibonacci sequence.
15. a) $t_n = 6n + 8$ **b)** $t_n = -6n + 29$ **c)** $t_n = 3n + 41$

3.2 Arithmetic Sequences and Simple Interest, pp. 81–83

1. a) Yes; common difference = 5. **b)** Yes; common difference = -11. **c)** No; $t_2 - t_1 = 4$, $t_3 - t_2 = 5$. **d)** No; $t_2 - t_1 = 5$, $t_3 - t_2 = 10$. **e)** Yes; common difference = $\dfrac{1}{3}$. **f)** No; $t_2 - t_1 = 3$, $t_3 - t_2 = -4$. **2. a) i)** $t_n = 6n - 3$ **ii)** $t_{12} = 69$ **b) i)** $t_n = 14 - 4n$ **ii)** $t_8 = -18$ **c) i)** $t_n = 9n - 29$ **ii)** $t_{25} = 196$ **3. a)** $t_n = 7 + 3(n - 1)$; $t_{15} = 49$ **b)** $t_n = 5 - 7(n - 1)$; $t_{15} = -93$ **c)** $t_n = 1 + 22(n - 1)$; $t_{15} = 309$ **d)** $t_n = -1 + 1.5(n - 1)$; $t_{15} = 20$ **e)** $t_n = 100 - 4.8(n - 1)$; $t_{15} = 32.8$ **f)** $t_n = 8.5n + 100$; $t_{15} = 227.50$ **4. a)** $t_1 = 5$, $t_2 = 2$, $t_3 = -1$, $t_4 = -4$, $t_5 = -7$; $a = 5$, $d = -3$ **b)** $t_1 = -11$, $t_2 = -9$, $t_3 = -7$, $t_4 = -5$, $t_5 = -3$; $a = -11$, $d = 2$ **c)** $t_1 = 1$, $t_2 = 9$, $t_3 = 17$, $t_4 = 25$, $t_5 = 33$; $a = 1$, $d = 8$ **5. a)** $t_n = 100 + \dfrac{n}{2}$ **b)** \$103.50

6. a) 1 pen = 4 panels; 2 pens = 7 panels; 3 pens = 10 panels
b) $t_n = 3n + 1$ **c)** 31 **d) i)** 22 **ii)** $t_n = 5n + 2$ **iii)** 52 **e)** A double row uses fewer panels, for example: To add two pens to a single row requires 6 panels, whereas to add 2 pens to a double row requires 5 panels.

7. Encke's Comet: **a)** 2003, 2006, 2009 **b)** $t_n = 1991 + 3n$; Faye's Comet: **a)** 2006, 2013, 2020 **b)** $t_n = 1978 + 7n$; Halley's Comet: **a)** 2062, 2138, 2214 **b)** $t_n = 1758 + 76n$
8. a) $t_n = 2300 + 200n$ **b)** $3300 **c)** $4100 **9. a)** $1050 **b)** $1200 **c)** $75 **10.** Answers may vary, for example: The amount owing after each period forms an arithmetic sequence, such as $107, $114, $121, … . **11.** Answers may vary, for example: No; if you know the first few terms and the common difference, it is easier to add the common difference to find the next few terms. If you need to find, for example, the 50th term, the formula is more efficient. **12. a)** $t_n = 1892 + 4n$ **b)** 33rd **c)** 52nd **d)** 21st
13. a) 100 **b)** 66 **c)** 42 **d)** 200

3.3 Geometric Sequences, pp. 88–90

1. a) 1, 4, 16, 64 **b)** 200, 100, 50, 25 **c)** 10, –30, 90, –270
d) 240, –120, 60, –30 **2. a)** Geometric; the common ratio is 4.
b) Arithmetic; the common difference is 4. **c)** Neither; there is no common difference or common ratio. **d)** Geometric; the common ratio is –3. **e)** Geometric; the common ratio is $\frac{1}{4}$.
f) Arithmetic; the common difference is –4.
3. a) i) $t_n = 3(6)^{n-1}$ **ii)** $t_{10} = 30\ 233\ 088$ **b) i)** $t_n = 10(-4)^{n-1}$
ii) $t_8 = -163\ 840$ **c) i)** $t_n = -20(0.5)^{n-1}$ **ii)** $t_{15} = -\dfrac{5}{4096}$ or
–0.001 22 **4. a)** $t_n = 7(2)^{n-1}$; $t_{12} = 14\ 336$ **b)** $t_n = 3(-2)^{n-1}$;
$t_{12} = -6144$ **c)** $t_n = (0.5)^{n-1}$; $t_{10} = 0.0020$ **d)** $t_n = -5(4)^{n-1}$;
$t_{12} = -20\ 971\ 520$ **e)** $t_n = 20\ 000\ 000(-0.1)^{n-1}$; $t_8 = -2$
f) $t_n = 1000(0.1)^{n-1}$; $t_7 = 0.001$ **5. a)** $t_1 = 8$, $t_2 = 24$, $t_3 = 72$,
$t_4 = 216$, $t_5 = 648$; $a = 8$, $r = 3$ **b)** $t_1 = 5120$, $t_2 = 2560$, $t_3 = 1280$,
$t_4 = 640$, $t_5 = 320$; $a = 5120$, $r = 0.5$ **6. a)** $t_n = 10(2)^n$
b) 10 485 760 **7. a)** 256 **b)** 508 **8. a)** $t_n = 512(0.5)^{n-1}$ **b)** 8
9. a) 64 **b)** 256 **c)** 510 **11.** 0.95 m **12. b)** spiral with square corners **d)** Part c) is a square; part a) is a geometric sequence and part c) is an arithmetic sequence. **13. a)** 2, 1, $\dfrac{1}{2}$, $\dfrac{1}{4}$, $\dfrac{1}{8}$, $\dfrac{1}{16}$, $\dfrac{1}{32}$, $\dfrac{1}{64}$, $\dfrac{1}{128}$, $\dfrac{1}{256}$, $\dfrac{1}{512}$, $\dfrac{1}{1024}$ **b)** 1.4, 2, 2.86, 4.08, 5.83, 8.33, 11.9, 17, 24.29 **14. a)** 24 **b)** 13 **15. a)** If he continues to only reach the halfway point each time, he will never finish the course. **b)** The distance remaining forms a geometric sequence (8, 4, 2, 1, … ; $r = 0.5$). The time required to complete each distance seems to be constant, but cannot be if the runner is running at a constant speed. Constant speed is a constant difference, which is arithmetic.

3.4 Compound Interest, pp. 96–98

1. a) 1082.86 **b)** 879.97 **c)** 5664.86 **d)** 1518.38 **2.** Answers may vary depending on the calculator, for example:
5000 $\times$ 1.0025 y^x 50 $=$ or 5000 $\times$ 1.0025 $\wedge$ 50 ENTER **3. a)** $P = 600$, $n = 20$, $i = 0.02$ **b)** $P = 2000$, $n = 24$,
$i = 0.0025$ **c)** $P = 750$, $n = 8$, $i = 0.1$ **d)** $P = 1000$, $n = 3$,
$i = 0.035$ **4. a)** $A = 500(1 + 0.005)^{24}$ **b)** $A = 2500(1 + 0.045)^{6}$
c) $A = 10\ 000(1 + 0.015)^{80}$ **d)** $A = 375(1 + 0.0025)^{120}$

5. a) $2431.01 **b)** $431.01 **6. a)** $5842.32 **b)** $3842.32
7. a) $3589.24 **b)** $589.24 **8. a)** 13 255 **b)** The formula $A = P(1 + i)^n$ can be used if A is the projected population, P is the initial population, i is the projected annual growth rate, and n is the number of years. **9.** $3987.86 **10.** $39 359.48
11. a)

	A	B	C
1	Compounding Period	Interest ($)	Amount ($)
2	0	0.00	2000.00
3	1	60.00	2060.00
4	2	61.80	2121.80
5	3	63.65	2185.45
6	4	65.56	2251.02

b) The amount is multiplied by 1.03 at the end of each compounding period. **13. a)** He should choose the interest rate of 10%, compounded quarterly, because he will pay less interest for the same principal. **b)** $589.59 **14.** $46.55 **15.** 5% simple interest because she will earn more interest for the same principal. **16. a)** $1645.64 **b)** $1712.13 **c)** $66.49 **d)** $362.13
17. a) Compare $t_n = ar^{n-1}$ to $A = P(1 + i)^n$: $t_n = A$, $a = P$, $r = 1 + i$, and $n - 1$ is represented by n. **b)** Divide the amount of the investment after n compounding periods by the amount of the investment after $n - 1$ compounding periods. **c)** $r = 1 + i$
19. $1895.97

3.5 Present Value, pp. 103–105

1. a) 256.05 **b)** 610.92 **c)** 624.60 **d)** 9411.19 **e)** 2207.95
f) 369.25 **2. a)** $417.82 **b)** $655.80 **3. a)** $1016.70 **b)** $1013.35
4. $6060.93 **5.** $4103.73 **6.** $202 670.19 **7.** $1254.03
8. $6000.00 **9. a)** 111 386 **b)** Use the formula $PV = A(1 + i)^{-n}$, substituting population for A, the growth rate for i, and the number of years for n. **12.** 6%, compounded semi-annually, because she will need to invest less money today for the same final amount. **13. a)** Investment A **b)** $59.02 **14.** $2062.62
15.

	A	B	C
1	Compounding Period	Interest ($)	Amount ($)
2	0	0.00	4439.86
3	1	88.80	4528.66
4	2	90.57	4619.23
5	3	92.38	4711.61
6	4	94.23	4805.85
7	5	96.12	4901.96
8	6	98.04	5000.00

16. a) i) 4 **ii)** 9 **b)** Substitute the first term (a), common ratio (r), and number of terms (n) into $t_n = ar^{n-1}$ to see if t_n equals the last term.

3.6 Linear and Exponential Growth, pp. 110–111

1. a) Answers will vary, for example: 2, 4, 6, 8, … ; 2, 5, 8, 11, … .
b) points in a straight line **2. a)** Answers will vary, for example: 2, 4, 8, 16, … ; 2, 6, 18, 54, … . **b)** points in a curved line
3. a)

Year	Value ($)
0	1000.00
1	1120.00
2	1254.40
3	1404.93
4	1573.52
5	1762.34
6	1973.82

b) There is a common ratio of 1.12. **c)** $t_n = 1000(1.12)^n$

d)
```
WINDOW
Xmin=0
Xmax=6
Xscl=1
Ymin=1000
Ymax=2000
Yscl=100
Xres=1
```
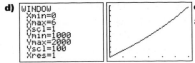

e) Exponential; there is a common ratio.

4. a)

Month	Amount Owing ($)
0	2000
1	2015
2	2030
3	2045
4	2060
5	2075
6	2090
7	2105
8	2120
9	2135
10	2150
11	2165
12	2180

b) There is a common difference of 15.
c) $t_n = 2000 + 15n$

d)
```
WINDOW
Xmin=0
Xmax=12
Xscl=1
Ymin=2000
Ymax=2200
Yscl=25
Xres=1
```

e) Linear; there is a common difference.

5. a)

Compounding Period	Value ($)
0	650.00
1	659.75
2	669.65
3	679.69
4	689.89
5	700.23
6	710.74
7	721.40
8	732.22

b) There is a common ratio of 1.015. **c)** $t_n = 650(1.015)^n$

d)
```
WINDOW
Xmin=0
Xmax=8
Xscl=1
Ymin=650
Ymax=740
Yscl=10
Xres=1
```

e) Exponential; there is a common ratio.

6. a)

Years	Height (cm)
0.5	21
1.0	23
1.5	28
2.0	31
2.5	34
3.0	38

b) There is neither an arithmetic nor a geometric relationship.
c) Not possible.

d)

e) Other; there is no common difference or common ratio.

7. a)

Week	Audience Share (%)
1	12
2	15
3	18
4	21
5	24

b) There is a common difference of 3.
c) $t_n = 9 + 3n$

d)
```
WINDOW
Xmin=1
Xmax=5
Xscl=1
Ymin=10
Ymax=25
Yscl=1
Xres=1
```

e) Linear; there is a common difference.

8. Linear; there is a common difference of 15. **9.** Exponential; there is a common ratio of 1.015. **11. a)** Exponential; the average common ratio is about 1.4 (between 1.2 and 1.64).

Review, pp. 114–115

1. a) Add 3 to the previous term; 13, 16. **b)** Divide the previous term by 2; 12, 6. **2. a)** $t_1 = 1$, $t_2 = 4$, $t_3 = 7$, $t_4 = 10$, $t_5 = 13$
b) $t_1 = 2$, $t_2 = 5$, $t_3 = 10$, $t_4 = 17$, $t_5 = 26$ **3.** $t_n = \dfrac{2}{n+2}$
4. a) i) There is a common difference of 4. **ii)** $t_n = 4n + 3$
iii) 67 **b) i)** There is a common difference of -7.
ii) $t_n = -7n + 11$ **iii)** $t_{16} = -101$ **5. a)** $t_1 = -2$, $t_2 = -7$, $t_3 = -12$,
$t_4 = -17$, $t_5 = -22$ **b)** $a = -2$, $d = -5$ **6. a)** $t_n = 9.60 + 0.25n$
b) $10.85/h **7. a) i)** There is a common ratio of 2.
ii) $t_n = 9(2)^{n-1}$ **iii)** $t_9 = 2304$ **b) i)** There is a common ratio of
$-\dfrac{1}{3}$. **ii)** $t_n = 13\,122\left(-\dfrac{1}{3}\right)^{n-1}$ **iii)** $t_9 = 2$ **8. a)** $t_1 = 5$, $t_2 = -15$,
$t_3 = 45$, $t_4 = -135$, $t_5 = 405$ **b)** $a = 5$, $r = -3$ **9. a)** $t_n = 41.2(2)^{n-1}$
b) 2636.8 Hz **10. a)** Geometric sequence; it has a common ratio of $1 + i$. **c)** Compound interest is calculated on principal plus interest earned so far, every compounding period. Simple interest is calculated on principal only.
11. a) $A = 800(1 + 0.02)^{12}$ **b)** $P = 800$, $i = 0.08 \div 4$, $n = 3 \times 4$
12. a) $4266.30 **b)** $1266.30 **13. a)** The final amount of the investment is $5000. The interest rate per compounding period is 6%. There are 10 compounding periods. **b)** Answers may vary depending on the calculator, for example: 5000 $\boxed{\times}$ 1.06
$\boxed{y^x}$ 10 $\boxed{+/-}$ $\boxed{=}$ **or** 5000 $\boxed{\times}$ 1.06 $\boxed{\wedge}$ $\boxed{(-)}$ 10 $\boxed{\text{ENTER}}$.
14. $1575.13; $PV = 2000(1 + 0.01)^{-24}$ **15.** $1562.40
16. a) Sequence:

Compounding Period	Amount ($)
0	650.00
1	666.25
2	682.91
3	699.98
4	717.48
5	735.42
6	753.80
7	772.65
8	791.96
9	811.76
10	832.05
11	852.86
12	874.18

Formula: $t_n = 650(1.025)^n$

Graph: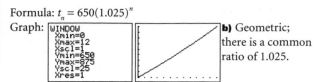

b) Geometric; there is a common ratio of 1.025.

17. Answers may vary, for example: an investment with simple interest.

Practice Test, pp. 116–117

1. a) i) Each term is 6 more than the previous term. **ii)** 22, 28 **iii)** The term value is 2 less than 6 times the term number. **b) i)** The base and the exponent of each term are both 1 more than the base and the exponent of the previous term. **ii)** $6^7, 7^8$ **iii)** The base of the term value is the term number plus 2. Its exponent is the term number plus 3. **c) i)** The next term is 7 less than the previous term. **ii)** −21, −28 **iii)** The term value is 14 more than −7 times the term number. **2. a)** Neither; there is no common difference or common ratio. **b)** Arithmetic; there is a common difference of 5. **c)** Geometric; there is a common ratio of $\frac{1}{10}$ or 0.1. **3. a)** $t_1 = \frac{1}{4}, t_2 = \frac{1}{5}, t_3 = \frac{1}{6}, t_4 = \frac{1}{7}, t_5 = \frac{1}{8}$
b) $t_1 = 2, t_2 = 6, t_3 = 18, t_4 = 54, t_5 = 162$ **c)** $t_1 = 5, t_2 = 12,$
$t_3 = 19, t_4 = 26, t_5 = 33$ **4. a)** $t_n = 4n - 6; t_{12} = 42$
b) $t_n = -4(-3)^{n-1}; t_{12} = 708\,588$ **c)** $t_n = 2187\left(\frac{1}{3}\right)^{n-1}; t_8 = 1$

5. a) $t_{50} = 203; t_n = 4n + 3$ **b)** $t_{21} = -6\,973\,568\,802;$
$t_n = -2(-3)^{n-1}$ **6. a)** Answers may vary, for example: 1, 4, 9, 16, … . **b)** There is no common difference or common ratio.
7. $3532.43 **8.** $6543.23; $1543.23 **10.** $7462.15 **11.** $819.54
12. a) arithmetic **b)** It would be geometric because, with compound interest, there is a common ratio, whereas with simple interest, there is a common difference. **c)** It would still be geometric. The common ratio would be less for monthly compounding but the number of compounding periods would be greater, resulting in a graph with a steeper curve.

Chapter 4 – The Effects of Compounding

Get Ready, pp. 120–121

1. a) 0.06 **b)** 0.12 **c)** 0.041 **d)** 0.055 **e)** 0.0675 **f)** 0.0575 **g)** 0.065
h) 0.0325 **2. a)** 0.005 **b)** 0.0475 **c)** 0.02 **d)** 0.0025 **e)** 0.05
f) 0.0225 **g)** 0.02125 **h)** 0.0075 **3. a)** $n = 8, i = 0.06$ **b)** $n = 16,$
$i = 0.03$ **4. a)** 600.29 **b)** 3571.83 **c)** 25 513.75 **5. a)** It calculates
$1000(1 + 0.12 \div 4)^{16}$, where 1000 is the principal, $0.12 \div 4$ is the interest rate per compounding period, and 16 is the number of quarterly compounding periods in 4 years.

b) Answers may vary slightly: scientific calculator:
8500 [×] [(] 1 [+] 0.06 [÷] 12 [)] [y^x] 24 [=]; graphing
calculator: 8500 [(] 1 [+] 0.06 [÷] 12 [)] [^] 24
[ENTER] **6. a)** $1500.00 at 6%, compounded semi-annually, for 4 years is $1900.16. **b)** $4730.96 at 8%, compounded quarterly, for 3 years is $6000.00. **7. b)** $1593.85; $561.65 **8. a)** $3886.62
b) $10 187.06 **9. a)** 3 years **b)** 2.5 years **c)** 1.5 years

4.1 Effect of Interest Rates, pp. 127–129

1. a) ii) $n = 8, i = 0.03$ **iii)** $1520.12 **b) ii)** $n = 20, i = 0.025$
iii) $1605.84 **c) ii)** $n = 24, i = 0.005$ **iii)** $9653.00
2. a) ii) $n = 24, i = 0.0175$ **iii)** $2308.03 **b) ii)** $n = 20, i = 0.04$
iii) $3993.39 **c) ii)** $n = 24, i = 0.0125$ **iii)** $11 875.15 **3.** $193.05
4. $8730.89 **5. a)** A **b)** $298.93 **6. a)** C **b)** $36.42 **7. a)** Susan
b) $47.30 **8.** $1565.30 **9. a) i)** $15 033.47 **ii)** $14 311.28
b) a difference of $722.19 **10. a)** $5037.90 **b)** $5338.67
11. Answers will vary, for example: Investing $1000.00 at 4%, compounded annually, for 8 years will result in a final amount of $1368.57; investing $1000.00 at 8%, compounded annually, for 4 years will result in a final amount of $1360.49; $1368.57 ≠ $1360.49. **13. b) i)** $10.19 **ii)** $20.09 **iii)** $30.37
14. a) $4181.94 **b)** $239.47 **15.** approximately $63 000
16. Answers will vary, for example: **a)** $1000 at 21.8%, compounded annually, for 5 years **b)** $1000 at 10%, compounded annually, for 10 years **c)** $1000 at 9%, compounded monthly, for 11 years

4.2 Effect of Compounding Frequency, pp. 135–137

1. a) i) annually, or once a year **iii)** $1319.40 **b) i)** semi-annually, or twice a year **iii)** $530.68 **c) i)** quarterly, or four times a year **iii)** $4528.90 **d) i)** monthly, or 12 times a year **iii)** $13 307.78
2. a) The one compounded quarterly because the compounding is more frequent. **b)** quarterly: $2971.89; semi-annually: $2960.49 **3.** Kara's investment; $6909.74
4. $2.54 **5.** $174.11 **6.** $62.35 **7. a)** One has more frequent compounding than the other but its interest rate is lower.
b) Kali: $26 532.98; Connor: $31 058.48 **8.** 9%, compounded semi-annually; $80.68 **9.** If you change more than one thing and the result is different, you will not know what change caused the difference. **10.** Answers will vary, for example: Determine which investment will have a greater final amount: Investment A: $1000 at 8%, compounded annually, for 5 years; Investment B: $1000 at 8%, compounded quarterly, for 5 years.
13. a) Answers may vary, for example: He will have 20% of his money available at any time if he needs it, 30% is available after 1 year and can be re-invested at a higher rate if interest rates go up, and 50% is locked in for 2 years at the best rate possible at the time. **b)** $5583.47 **14.** Answers will vary, for example: **a)** $5000 invested at 1%, compounded annually, for 10 years **b)** $5000 invested at 10%, compounded semi-annually, for 1 year

4.3 Find the Interest Rate, pp. 142–144

1. a) 7.57% **b)** 7.18% **c)** 14.72% **d)** 2.92% **e)** 5.71% **f)** 7.05% **g)** 8.70% **h)** 7.43% **2. a)** 4.64% **b)** The interest rate would be lower because monthly compounding is more frequent than annual compounding. **3. a)** 3.11% **b)** The interest rate would be higher because annual compounding is less frequent than semi-annual compounding. **4.** 7.20% **5.** 6.95% **6.** 8.85% **7. a) i)** 6.97% **ii)** 6.85% **iii)** 6.79% **iv)** 6.76% **b)** The rates become lower as the compounding frequency increases because the more frequent the compounding, the lower the interest rate required. **8. a)** Between 4% and 8%, because 4% resulted in a low final amount and 8% resulted in a high final amount. **c)** 5.92% **9. a) i)** higher than 2.64% **ii)** lower than 2.64% **b) i)** Annual compounding is less frequent, so, a higher interest rate would be required for the final amount. **ii)** Quarterly compounding is more frequent, so, a lower interest rate would be required for the final amount. **10. a) i)** 35.16% **ii)** 36.20% **iii)** 37.84% **iv)** 41.42% **b)** No. Interest rates of 35% to 42% are not available for savings alternatives. **c)** Krysta's goal is not realistic because interest rates of 23% to 26% for savings alternatives are not available. **d)** Answers will vary, for example: about $2800 at 5%. **11. a) i)** 9% **ii)** 14.4% **iii)** 18% **b) i)** $A = \$1992.56$; difference = $7.44 **ii)** $A = \$3006.35$; difference = $6.35 **iii)** $A = \$30\,335.55$; difference = $335.55 **c) i)** 9.05% **ii)** 14.35% **iii)** 17.45%

4.4 Find the Term, pp. 148–150

1. a) i) 5 years **ii)** 3 years, 6 months **iii)** 3 years, 3 months **iv)** 1 year, 4 months **b) i)** 7 **ii)** 7 **iii)** 21 **iv)** 73 **2. a)** 7 years **b)** 10 years **c)** 17 years **d)** 39 years **e)** 7 years **f)** 8 years **g)** 11 years, 7 months **h)** 8 years **3.** 3 years **4. a)** 4 years **b)** $8320 at 10.5%, compounded semi-annually, for 4 years is $12 528.53. **5.** 11 years **6.** 7 years **7.** 8 years, 9 months **8. a)** 8 years **b)** 12 years **c)** 15 years **9.** Yes; he will have $32 418.47. **10. a) i)** 7 years **ii)** 7 years **iii)** 7 years **b)** The term is exactly the same because you must round up to the next compounding period, and 6.87 years, semi-annually, and 6.8 years, quarterly, both round up to 7 years. **11. a)** between 8 and 9 compounding periods **c)** 5 years **12. a)** False. **b)** Semi-annual compounding is more frequent than annual, so, it would take less than 5 years for the same final amount. **13. a) i)** longer than 3.5 years **ii)** shorter than 3.5 years **b)** The more frequent the compounding, the less time is required for the same final amount. **14.** No; in 2 years she will only have $7613.47. **15.** Answers will vary, for example: If he takes the maximum term, 10 years, and the most frequent compounding, monthly, he will need an interest rate of 6.95%, which is realistic. **16.** If she invests $2000 at 10%, compounded annually, for 10 years, she will have $5187.48. If she invests $1500 for 9 years at the same rate, she will have $3536.92. If she invests $4000 for 5 years at the same rate, she will have $6442.04. That is $15 166.44 altogether.

17. a) Answers will vary, for example: $1000 at 10%, compounded semi-annually, for 16.5 years is $5000; $1000 at 5%, compounded semi-annually, for 32.5 years is $5000. **18. a) i)** 8 years **ii)** 9 years **iii)** 18 years **b) i)** $A = \$4287.18$; difference = $287.18 **ii)** $A = \$1012.91$; difference = $12.91 **iii)** $A = \$20\,471.00$; difference = $471.00 **c) i)** 8 years **ii)** 9 years **iii)** 17.5 years **19.** Answers may vary. For example, use the Rule of 115 (i.e., replace 72 with 115).

4.5 Savings and Investment Alternatives, pp. 157–159

1. a) $1826.91 **b)** $1537.95 **2. a)** GIC = $1276.28; C-Bond = $1269.74 **b)** The GIC is better if you want to earn more interest but the C-Bond is better if you need to be able to cash it at any time. **4.** Answers will vary, for example: Mixing high-risk, high-return stocks and low-risk, low-return stocks gives the overall portfolio a moderate return with moderate risk. **5. a) i)** lose money **ii)** break even **iii)** make a little money **iv)** make a lot of money **b)** In the short term, stock values go up and down quickly but over the long term the trend is up. **12. a)** Answers will vary, for example: No, because it will depend on factors other than the length of time you are investing for. **b)** your purpose for investing, how much risk you are comfortable with, your investment knowledge

Review, pp. 162–163

1. 8%: $2355.40; 7%: $2473.89 **2.** $51.28 **3.** the GIC at 6% by $151.87 **4. b)** The GIC compounded semi-annually because it has more frequent compounding. **c)** The GIC compounded annually results in a final amount of $2315.25. The GIC compounded semi-annually results in a final amount of $2319.39. **5. a)** It is difficult to predict because the GIC with more frequent compounding also has a lower interest rate. **b)** The GIC at 5% requires $148.31 less. **6. a)** The 2-year GIC will result in $19.78 more. **b)** Answers will vary, for example: The 2-year GIC earns more interest but it may be locked in. The 1-year GIC earns less interest but, after 1 year, could be invested at a higher interest rate if interest rates go up. **8. a)** annual: 9.58%; quarterly: 9.25% **b)** between 9.25% and 9.58% **9. a)** annual: higher; monthly: lower **b)** More frequent compounding requires a lower interest rate. **c)** annual: 9.2%; monthly: 8.83% **10. a)** annually: 6 years; quarterly: 5 years, 9 months **b)** between 5.75 years and 6 years **11.** 4 years, 3 months **12.** 10 years

Practice Test, pp. 164–165

1. a) 8% **b)** monthly **c)** The highest interest rate and most frequent compounding will result in the greatest final amount. **d)** $170.85 **2. a)** $4187.42 **b)** Less because the compounding is more frequent. **3.** Answers will vary, for example: Calculate the final amount of an investment with annual compounding and then, recalculate with semi-annual compounding.

4. Savings accounts usually have low interest rates but they are easily available and your money can be withdrawn at any time. **5. a)** Answers may vary, for example: financial institutions. **b)** type of interest, interest rate, compounding frequency, minimum investment, when interest is paid if simple, when it is cashable, where it is available **6. a)** Lower because monthly compounding is more frequent than semi-annual. **b)** 5.68% **7.** 7.26% **8.** 12 years; 15.5 years **9.** 7 years

Cumulative Review, Chapters 1–4, pp. 166–167

2. a)

Jena's Monthly Budget

	Current
Monthly Net Income	$477
Monthly Living Expenses:	
Transportation	$43
Entertainment	$217
Clothing	$100
Health/Personal	$54
Total Living Expenses	$414
Left Over For Savings	$63

b) 2 years, 8 months **3. a)** 9 months **b)** $30 **4. a)** $5000 **b)** 11% **5. a)** $5^5 = 3125$ **b)** $2^{10} = 1024$ **c)** $7^7 = 823\ 543$ **d)** $10^{-3} = 0.001$ **6. a)** b^{11} **b)** $\dfrac{a^3}{72}$ **c)** x **7. a)** 10 **b)** 10 **c)** $\dfrac{1}{2}$ **d)** 625 **e)** $\dfrac{1}{64}$ **f)** 99.85 **g)** $740\dfrac{1}{3}$ **8. a)** $x = 4$ **b)** $x = -8$ **c)** $x = -3$ **d)** $x = 2$ **9. a) i)** Add 5 to the previous term; 28, 33. **ii)** Arithmetic; there is a common difference of 5. **iii)** The term value is 8 more than the product of the term number and 5. **iv)** $t_n = 8 + 5n$; $t_7 = 43$ **b) i)** Multiply the previous term by -3; 108, -324. **ii)** Geometric; there is a common ratio of -3. **iii)** The term value is -3 to the exponent of 1 less than the term number, all multiplied by -4. **iv)** $t_n = -4(-3)^{n-1}$; $t_7 = -2916$ **c) i)** Divide the previous term by 5; 2500, 500. **ii)** Geometric; there is a common ratio of $\dfrac{1}{5}$. **iii)** The term value is $\dfrac{1}{5}$ to the exponent of 1 less than the term number, all multiplied by 312 500. **iv)** $t_n = 312\ 500\left(\dfrac{1}{5}\right)^{n-1}$; $t_7 = 20$ **10. a)** $2(2)^{n-1}$ or 2^n **b)** 1 048 576 **11.** $3720.47 **12. a)** $18 438.83; $3438.83 is interest. **b)** Exponential growth; there is a common ratio of 1.035 between each 6-month period. **c)** Even though the final amount would be the same, the growth would be linear; there would be a common difference of $573 between each 6-month period. **13. a)** GIC B; it has more frequent compounding at the same interest rate. **b)** GIC B has a final amount that is $0.39 higher for the same principal. **c)** GIC B requires a principal that is $1.60 higher for the same final amount. **15. a)** 14 years **b)** 14.11%

Chapter 5 – Series and Annuities

Get Ready, pp. 170–171

1. a) Arithmetic; there is a common difference of 3. **b)** Arithmetic; there is a common difference of -5. **c)** Geometric; there is a common ratio of 2. **d)** Geometric; there is a common ratio of -3. **e)** Neither; there is neither a common difference nor a common ratio. **f)** Neither; there is neither a common difference nor a common ratio. **2. a)** $a = 8$, $r = 3$; $t_1 = 8$, $t_2 = 24$, $t_3 = 72$, $t_4 = 216$, $t_5 = 648$ **b)** $a = -5$, $r = -2$; $t_1 = -5$, $t_2 = 10$, $t_3 = -20$, $t_4 = 40$, $t_5 = -80$ **c)** $a = 5120$, $r = \dfrac{1}{2}$; $t_1 = 5120$, $t_2 = 2560$, $t_3 = 1280$, $t_4 = 640$, $t_5 = 320$

3. a) $5(n + 2)$ **b)** $3(2n + 1)$ **c)** $4(2n + 3)$ **4. a)** 93 **b)** -10 **c)** 6561 **d)** 2560 **e)** 624 992 **f)** -3.75 **g)** 318.5 **h)** 154.76 **i)** 0.63 **j)** 86.13 **k)** 0.37 **l)** 487.73 **5. a)** $n = 24$, $i = 0.005$ **b)** $n = 20$, $i = 0.01$ **c)** $n = 6$, $i = 0.015$ **d)** $n = 6$, $i = 0.069$ **6. a)** $365.70 **b)** $1195.62 **c)** $612.63 **d)** $3257.79 **7. a)** $1224.45 **b)** $454.28 **c)** $434.70 **d)** $1487.11

5.1 Arithmetic Series, pp. 176–178

1. a) Arithmetic; there is a common difference of 5. **b)** Neither; there is neither a common difference nor a common ratio. **c)** Arithmetic; there is a common difference of 2. **d)** Geometric; there is a common ratio of 2. **e)** Arithmetic; there is a common difference of -7. **f)** Arithmetic; there is a common difference of -5. **2. a)** $S_n = n^2$; $S_{10} = 100$ **b)** $S_n = 1.5n^2 + 3.5n$; $S_6 = 75$ **c)** $S_n = -2.5n^2 + 12.5n$; $S_{20} = -750$ **d)** $S_n = -n^2 - 2n$; $S_9 = -99$ **e)** $S_n = 0.8n^2 + 3.3n$; $S_3 = 17.1$ **f)** $S_n = -2.75n^2 + 102.75n$; $S_{40} = -290$ **3. a)** $S_n = -5n^2 + n$; $S_{12} = -708$ **b)** $S_n = 1.2n^2 + 4.8n$; $S_{12} = 230.4$ **c)** $S_n = -9n^2 + 18n$; $S_{12} = -1080$ **d)** $S_n = 1.5n^2 + 0.5n$; $S_{12} = 222$ **e)** $S_n = -3.5n^2 + 0.5n$; $S_{12} = -498$

4. a) $S_n = -2n^2 + 102n$ **b)** 1188 cans **5. a)** $S_n = n^2 + 19n$ **b)** 182 seats **c)** 372 seats **d)** $46 500 **6.** $350 per week with a $50 raise each week is better because you would earn $60 more in 8 weeks. **7.** 17 years **8.** $280 **10.** 3912 stitches

11. a) $S_n = \dfrac{n}{2}(1 + n)$ **b)** 5050 **12. a)** Answers will vary, for example: $6 + 13 + 20 + \ldots + 69$. **c)** Yes; any series for which the values of a and d make the following equation true: $375 = 5(2a + 9d)$. **13. a)** The possible points in order are 10, 15, 20, … , 60, so, the maximum number of points is $S_{11} = \dfrac{11}{2}[2(10) + (11 - 1)5]$. **b)** 385

5.2 Geometric Series, pp. 183–185

1. a) Arithmetic; there is a common difference of 2. **b)** Geometric; there is a common ratio of 2. **c)** Geometric; there is a common ratio of $\dfrac{1}{2}$. **d)** Neither; there is neither a common difference nor a common ratio. **e)** Geometric; there is a common ratio of -4. **f)** Arithmetic; there is a common difference of -5.

2. a) $S_n = \frac{3}{4}(5^n - 1)$; $S_8 = 292\ 968$ **b)** $S_n = -2000\left[\left(\frac{1}{2}\right)^n - 1\right]$;

$S_{10} = \frac{127\ 875}{64}$ **c)** $S_n = 5000(1.02^n - 1)$; $S_{10} = 1094.9721$

d) $S_n = 0.8[(-4)^n - 1]$; $S_9 = -209\ 716$

e) $S_n = -\frac{5}{2}[(-3)^n - 1]$; $S_{12} = -1\ 328\ 600$

f) $S_n = \dfrac{15\ 625\left[\left(-\frac{1}{5}\right)^n - 1\right]}{-1.2}$; $S_6 = 13\ 020$ **3. a)** $S_n = 5^n - 1$;

$S_8 = 390\ 624$ **b)** $S_n = 640\left[\left(\frac{1}{2}\right)^n - 1\right]$; $S_8 = -637.5$

c) $S_n = 10\ 000(1.05^n - 1)$; $S_8 = 4774.55$ **4.** 255 matches
5. a) i) 2046 pages **ii)** 65 534 pages **b)** Geometric series grow
exponentially, which means very quickly. **6.** 508 mg
7. 16.3 km **9.** 14 m **10.** 15 stages **11.** If there are 28 days in
the month, the friend should choose prize A. If there are 29 or
more days in the month, the friend should choose prize B.
12. a) He probably thought it was an arithmetic series rather
than a geometric series, which grows very quickly because
growth is exponential. **b)** 1.84×10^{19}
13. a) $S_n = \dfrac{10^n - 1}{9}$ **b)** 1 111 111 111 **14.** y^{127}

15. a) Answers will vary, for example: $3 + 6 + 12 + \ldots + 1536$.
c) Yes; any series for which the values of a and r make the

following equation true: $3069 = \dfrac{a(r^{10} - 1)}{r - 1}$

5.3 Future Value of an Ordinary Annuity, pp. 192–193

1. a) ii) $PMT = 300$, $i = 0.005$, $n = 12$ **iii)** $\$3700.67$
b) ii) $PMT = 5000$, $i = 0.058$, $n = 10$ **iii)** $\$65\ 288.24$
c) ii) $PMT = 1500$, $i = 0.023$, $n = 8$ **iii)** $\$13\ 011.74$
d) ii) $PMT = 650$, $i = 0.01$, $n = 20$ **iii)** $\$14\ 312.35$ **2. a)** $\$19\ 794.94$
b) $\$1596.93$ **c)** $\$24\ 991.26$ **3. a)** $\$2470.28$ **b)** $\$70.28$
4. a) $\$44\ 401.92$ **b)** $\$4401.92$ **5. a)** $\$30\ 905.65$ **b)** $\$12\ 905.65$
6. $\$251\ 282.84$ **7. a)** Ms. Wong: $\$125\ 000$; Ms. Ellis: $\$122\ 500$
b) Ms. Wong: $\$238\ 635.49$; Ms. Ellis: $\$496\ 066.66$ **c)** Ms. Ellis
invested $\$2500$ less; however, she invested her money for almost
double the amount of time. **d)** You should start investing at a
young age in order to gain more interest. **8. a)** Jeremy: $\$2470.28$;
Mohsin: $\$2463.95$ **b)** Jeremy's interest is compounded monthly,
while Mohsin's interest is compounded quarterly. More frequent
compounding results in a greater future value for the same
principal. **9. a)** $\$7524.11$ **b)** $\$9405.14$ **c)** $\$7867.22$ **d)** Answers
may vary, for example: deposit $\$305.07$ at the end of every month
for 3 years at 6%, compounded monthly. **12.** Answers may vary,
for example: payments of $\$1000$ at the end of each year for 5 years
at 2%, compounded annually. **13.** Answers will vary, for
example: payments of $\$1000$ at the end of each year for 10 years at
5%, compounded annually.

5.4 Present Value of an Ordinary Annuity, pp. 200–201

1. a) ii) $PMT = 300$, $i = 0.005$, $n = 12$ **iii)** $\$3485.68$
b) ii) $PMT = 5000$, $i = 0.058$, $n = 10$ **iii)** $\$37\ 151.66$
c) ii) $PMT = 1500$, $i = 0.023$, $n = 8$ **iii)** $\$10\ 847.51$
d) ii) $PMT = 650$, $i = 0.01$, $n = 20$ **iii)** $\$11\ 729.61$
2. a) $\$35\ 117.91$ **b)** $\$12\ 019.45$ **c)** $\$9861.30$ **3.** $\$72\ 366.99$
4. $\$3314.63$ **5.** $\$19\ 000.12$ **6.** $\$55\ 092.54$ **7.** $\$2\ 421\ 240.33$
8. a) $\$1170.59$ **b)** Answers will vary, for example: No, because
the client may not have $\$1170.59$ to pay in a lump sum.
9. a) $\$6289.36$ **b)** She might not have enough money to pay the
lump sum right now. **c)** She can earn interest on the money she
saves, and she will not have to pay interest. **11.** Answers may
vary, for example: Payments of $\$1000$ at the end of each month
for 1 year at 3%, compounded monthly. **12.** Answers may
vary, for example: payments of $\$1500$ at the end of each year
for 10 years at 4%, compounded annually.

5.5 Payment of an Ordinary Annuity, pp. 207–209

1. a) ii) $PV = 1000$, $i = 0.0025$, $n = 12$ **iii)** $\$84.69$
b) ii) $FV = 5000$, $i = 0.015$, $n = 12$ **iii)** $\$383.40$
c) ii) $FV = 10\ 000$, $i = 0.035$, $n = 10$ **iii)** $\$852.41$
d) ii) $PV = 2500$, $i = 0.028$, $n = 2$ **iii)** $\$1302.74$ **2.** $\$157.70$
3. $\$86.07$ **4.** $\$485.77$ **5.** $\$7443.14$ **6.** $\$802.43$ **7.** $\$3513.13$
8. $\$682.55$ **9. a) i)** $\$317.54$ **ii)** $\$246.11$ **iii)** $\$193.78$ **b)** The term
with the lowest monthly payment will take the longest time to
pay off. So, you end up paying the most interest.
10. a) i) $\$120.23$ **ii)** $\$92.03$ **iii)** $\$71.22$ **b) i)** Answers may vary,
for example: Sarah has a high enough salary for the higher
monthly payments. **ii)** Answers may vary, for example: Sarah
feels that her salary is too low for the 5-year and the 7-year
term payments. **11.** $\$79.86$ **13.** $\$3320.35$

Review, pp. 212–213

1. a) $S_n = 2n^2 + n$; $S_{12} = 300$ **b)** $S_n = -10n^2 + 110n$; $S_{25} = -3500$
c) $S_n = -5n^2 + 3n$; $S_{20} = -1940$ **d)** $S_n = 10n^2 - 110n$; $S_{10} = -100$
2. a) 21 km; 24.5 km; 28 km **b)** $S_n = 1.75n^2 + 19.25n$ **c)** 266 km
3. a) $S_n = 6(2^n - 1)$; $S_8 = 1530$ **b)** $S_n = 781.25 - 781.25(0.2)^n$;
$S_{10} = 781.249\ 92$ **c)** $S_n = -[(-2)^n - 1]$; $S_9 = 513$

d) $S_n = -\dfrac{1000}{1.1}[(-0.1)^n - 1]$; $S_7 = 909.091$ **4. a)** $S_n = \dfrac{3^{n+1} - 3}{2}$

b) 3279 members **5. a) ii)** $PMT = 200$, $i = 0.0125$, $n = 12$
iii) $\$2572.07$ **b) ii)** $PMT = 100$, $i = 0.005$, $n = 12$ **iii)** $\$1233.56$
c) ii) $PMT = 2000$, $i = 0.015$, $n = 16$ **iii)** $\$35\ 864.74$ **6.** Yes; the
future value of his investment is $\$21\ 634.86$. **7. a)** $\$2258.93$
b) $\$13\ 089.01$ **8.** $\$155\ 891.62$ **9.** $\$1654.89$ **10. a)** $FV = 8000$;
$i = 0.03$, $n = 12$ **11.** $\$1298.89$ **12.** $\$407.16$

Practice Test, pp. 214–215

1. a) i) Arithmetic; there is a common difference of 3.
ii) $S_n = 1.5n^2 + 4.5n$ **iii)** $S_{16} = 456$ **b) i)** Geometric; there is a
common ratio of 2. **ii)** $S_n = 7(2)^n - 7$ **iii)** $S_{10} = 7161$

c) i) Geometric; there is a common ratio of $\frac{1}{2}$.

ii) $S_n = 1536 - 1536\left(\frac{1}{2}\right)^n$ **iii)** $S_8 = 1530$ **d) i)** Arithmetic; there is a common difference of -4. **ii)** $S_n = -2n^2 + 7n$ **iii)** $S_{14} = -294$
2. $8730 **3.** 63 matches **4. a)** $19 394.01 **b)** $1394.01
5. $188 562.70 **6.** $1954.69 **7.** $1288.74 **8.** $319.18
9. a) $51 089.32 **b)** $134 805.11 **c)** No; the future value of an annuity shows exponential growth. **10.** Option A results in $20 973.27 more in 30 years.

Chapter 6 – Exponential Growth

Get Ready, pp. 218–219

1. a) 7 **b)** 1 **c)** -7 **d)** 21 **e)** 48 **f)** -32 **2. a)** -1 **b)** -11 **c)** 9 **d)** 9
e) 30 **f)** 19 **3. a)** slope = 2, y-intercept = 5 **b)** slope = -3, y-intercept = 4 **c)** slope = -0.2, y-intercept = 0 **d)** slope = 0, y-intercept = 4 **e)** slope = -2, y-intercept = 6 **f)** slope = $\frac{3}{2}$, y-intercept = -3

4. a) i) $y = 2x - 5$

x	y	First Differences
-2	-9	
-1	-7	2
0	-5	2
1	-3	2
2	-1	2

ii) $y = -3x + 2$

x	y	First Differences
-2	8	
-1	5	-3
0	2	-3
1	-1	-3
2	-4	-3

b) Each equation represents a straight line. **5.** increasing functions: $y = 2x + 5$, $3x - 2y = 6$; decreasing functions: $y = -3x + 4$, $y = -0.2x$, $2x + y = 6$ **6. a)** x-intercept = 5, y-intercept = 5 **b)** x-intercept = -7, y-intercept = 7 **c)** x-intercept = 3, y-intercept = -5 **7. a)** negative **b)** positive **c)** 0 **d)** not defined **8. a)** $y = 0$ **b)** $x = 0$ **9. a)** Not quadratic; when expressed in the form $y = ax^2 + bx + c$, $a = 0$. **b)** Quadratic; can be expressed in the form $y = ax^2 + bx + c$, where a, b, $c \in R$ and $a \neq 0$. **c)** Quadratic; can be expressed in the form $y = ax^2 + bx + c$, where a, b, $c \in R$ and $a \neq 0$.
10. a) opens upward; vertex = (0, 0); domain: $x \in R$; range: $y \leq 0$ **b)** opens downward; vertex = (0, 5); domain: $x \in R$; range: $y \leq 5$ **c)** opens downward; vertex = $(-2, -1)$; domain: $x \in R$; range: $y \leq -1$
11. a) $y = x^2 - 4$ **b)** $y = (x + 5)^2 - 3$

6.1 Exponential Functions, pp. 223–225

1. a)

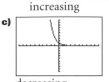

increasing

b)

increasing

c)

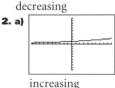

decreasing

d)

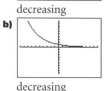

decreasing

2. a)

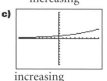

increasing

b)

decreasing

c)

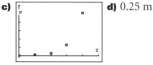

increasing

3. a)

Function	Domain	Range	y-intercept
$y = 4^x$	$x \in R$	$y > 0$	1
$y = \left(\frac{1}{4}\right)^x$	$x \in R$	$y > 0$	1

b) $y = 4^x$ is increasing; $y = \left(\frac{1}{4}\right)^x$ is decreasing. **4. a)** $y = 5.2^x$
b) $y = 3(1.5)^x$ **5. a)** $y = 0.2^x$ **b)** $y = 120(0.7)^x$ **6. b)** $y = 4^x$
c)

d) 0.25 m

7. 15.625 m **8.** 11 200 years **9. a)** 6400 years **b)** 12 800 years
10. $y = 1.05^x$ represents faster growth; explanations may vary.
12. a)

Time (min)	Number of Divisions	Number of Bacteria
0	0	1
15	1	2
30	2	4
45	3	8
60	4	16
75	5	32
90	6	64
105	7	128
120	8	256
135	9	512
150	10	1024
165	11	2048
180	12	4096

b)

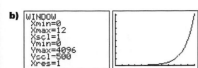

c) $y = 2^n$ **d)** 20 divisions have occurred; 300 min have elapsed.

13. 15 h

6.2 Sketch Graphs of Exponential Functions Without Technology, pp. 228–230

1. a) domain: $x \in R$; range: $y \in R$ **b)** domain: $x \in R$; range: $y \geq 0$ **c)** domain: $x \in R$; range: $y > 0$; asymptote: $y = 0$
d) domain: $x \in R$; range: $y > 0$; asymptote: $y = 0$

2. a)

x	y
-3	$\frac{1}{27}$
-2	$\frac{1}{9}$
-1	$\frac{1}{3}$
0	1
1	3
2	9
3	27

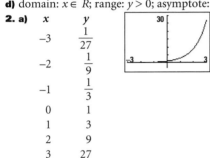

y-intercept: 1; asymptote: $y = 0$; domain: $x \in R$; range: $y > 0$

b)

x	y
-3	$\frac{1}{125}$
-2	$\frac{1}{25}$
-1	$\frac{1}{5}$
0	1
1	5
2	25
3	125

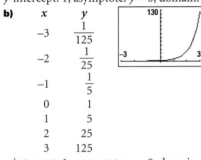

y-intercept: 1; asymptote: $y = 0$; domain: $x \in R$; range: $y > 0$

c)

x	y
-3	8
-2	4
-1	2
0	1
1	$\frac{1}{2}$
2	$\frac{1}{4}$
3	$\frac{1}{8}$

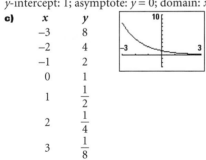

y-intercept: 1; asymptote: $y = 0$; domain: $x \in R$; range: $y > 0$

d)

x	y
-3	27
-2	9
-1	3
0	1
1	$\frac{1}{3}$
2	$\frac{1}{9}$
3	$\frac{1}{27}$

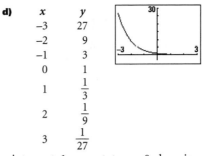

y-intercept: 1; asymptote: $y = 0$; domain: $x \in R$; range: $y > 0$

3. a)

x	$y = 5^x$	$y = \left(\frac{1}{5}\right)^x$
-3	$\frac{1}{125}$	125
-2	$\frac{1}{25}$	25
-1	$\frac{1}{5}$	5
0	1	1
1	5	$\frac{1}{5}$
2	25	$\frac{1}{25}$
3	125	$\frac{1}{125}$

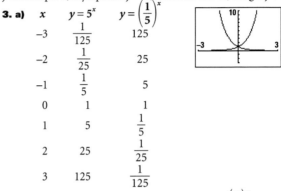

b)

	$y = 5^x$	$y = \left(\frac{1}{5}\right)^x$
y-intercept	1	1
domain	$x \in R$	$x \in R$
range	$y > 0$	$y > 0$
equation of asymptote	$y = 0$	$y = 0$

c) $y = 5^x$ is an increasing function, while $y = \left(\frac{1}{5}\right)^x$ is a

decreasing function. The graphs are reflections of each other in the y-axis.

4. a)

x	$y = \left(\frac{5}{3}\right)^x$	$y = \left(\frac{3}{5}\right)^x$
-3	$\frac{27}{125}$	$\frac{125}{27}$
-2	$\frac{9}{25}$	$\frac{25}{9}$
-1	$\frac{3}{5}$	$\frac{5}{3}$
0	1	1
1	$\frac{5}{3}$	$\frac{3}{5}$
2	$\frac{25}{9}$	$\frac{9}{25}$
3	$\frac{125}{27}$	$\frac{27}{125}$

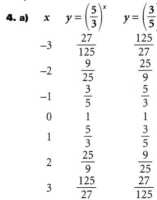

b)

	$y=\left(\dfrac{5}{3}\right)^x$	$y=\left(\dfrac{3}{5}\right)^x$
y-intercept	1	1
domain	$x \in R$	$x \in R$
range	$y > 0$	$y > 0$
equation of asymptote	$y = 0$	$y = 0$

c) $y=\left(\dfrac{5}{3}\right)^x$ is an increasing function, while $y=\left(\dfrac{3}{5}\right)^x$ is a

decreasing function. The graphs are reflections of each other in the y-axis.

5. a) 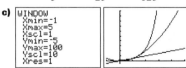 **b)** No. **c)** Answers may vary, but should be near 28°C.

6. a) $x \geq 0$; explanations may vary.

b)

x	y
0	500.00
1	600.00
2	720.00
3	864.00
4	1036.80
5	1244.16

c)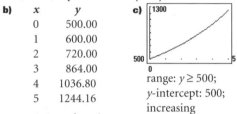

range: $y \geq 500$;
y-intercept: 500;
increasing

7. a) $x \geq 0$; explanations may vary.

b)

x	y
0	80 000.00
1	48 000.00
2	28 800.00
3	17 280.00
4	10 368.00
5	6 220.80

c)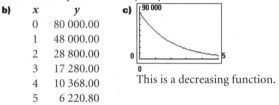

This is a decreasing function.

d) range: $0 \leq y \leq 80\ 000$; realistic ranges and explanations may vary.

6.3 Compare Rates of Change, pp. 234–237

1. a) linear **b)** exponential **c)** linear **d)** quadratic
2. a) quadratic **b)** exponential **c)** linear

3. a)

x	$y = 5x$	$y = 5x^2$	$y = 5^x$
0	0	0	1
1	5	5	5
2	10	20	25
3	15	45	125
4	20	80	625
5	25	125	3125

c)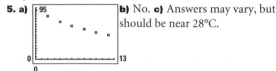

d) slowest: $y = 5x$; fastest: $y = 5^x$

4. a) $y = 4x$

x	y	First Differences
0	0	
1	4	4
2	8	4
3	12	4
4	16	4
5	20	4

$y = 4x^2$

x	y	First Differences
0	0	
1	4	4
2	16	12
3	36	20
4	64	28
5	100	36

$y = 4^x$

x	y	First Differences
0	1	
1	4	3
2	16	12
3	64	48
4	256	192
5	1024	768

$y = 4x$ is linear; $y = 4x^2$ is quadratic; $y = 4^x$ is exponential.
5. a) Exponential; first differences form a geometric sequence.
b) Quadratic; first differences form an arithmetic sequence.
c) Linear; first differences are constant.

6. a)

Time, t (h)	Cost to Rent, C ($)	
	Rent-All	U-dig
1	525	55
2	550	75
3	575	175
4	600	675
5	625	3175

b) Rent-All would be cheaper for $t \geq 4$; U-dig would be cheaper for $t \leq 3$. **7.** You are likely to win more money in the exponent game. **8. a)** $y = \dfrac{1}{2}x$ **b)** $y = \dfrac{1}{2}x^2$; increasing when $x > 0$; decreasing when $x < 0$. **c)** $y = \left(\dfrac{1}{2}\right)^x$

d)

x	$y = \dfrac{1}{2}x$	$y = \dfrac{1}{2}x^2$	$y = \left(\dfrac{1}{2}\right)^x$
x-intercept	0	0	none
y-intercept	0	0	1

9. a) $y = \dfrac{1}{4}x$ is linear; $y = \dfrac{1}{4}x^2$ is quadratic; $y = \left(\dfrac{1}{4}\right)^x$ is exponential.

b) $y = \dfrac{1}{4}x$

x	y	First Differences
-3	$-\dfrac{3}{4}$	
-2	$-\dfrac{1}{2}$	$\dfrac{1}{4}$
-1	$-\dfrac{1}{4}$	$\dfrac{1}{4}$
0	0	$\dfrac{1}{4}$
1	$\dfrac{1}{4}$	$\dfrac{1}{4}$
2	$\dfrac{1}{2}$	$\dfrac{1}{4}$
3	$\dfrac{3}{4}$	$\dfrac{1}{4}$

$y = \dfrac{1}{4}x^2$

x	y	First Differences
-3	$\dfrac{9}{4}$	
-2	1	$-\dfrac{5}{4}$
-1	$\dfrac{1}{4}$	$-\dfrac{3}{4}$
0	0	$-\dfrac{1}{4}$
1	$\dfrac{1}{4}$	$\dfrac{1}{4}$
2	1	$\dfrac{3}{4}$
3	$\dfrac{9}{4}$	$\dfrac{5}{4}$

$y = \left(\dfrac{1}{4}\right)^x$

x	y	First Differences
-3	64	
-2	16	-48
-1	4	-12
0	1	-3
1	$\dfrac{1}{4}$	$-\dfrac{3}{4}$
2	$\dfrac{1}{16}$	$-\dfrac{3}{16}$
3	$\dfrac{1}{64}$	$-\dfrac{3}{64}$

c) For $y = \dfrac{1}{4}x$, the first differences are constant, so the growth is linear. For $y = \dfrac{1}{4}x^2$, the first differences form an arithmetic sequence, so the growth is quadratic. For $y = \left(\dfrac{1}{4}\right)^x$, the first differences form a geometric sequence, so the growth is exponential.

10. a)
```
WINDOW
Xmin=1881
Xmax=2006
Xscl=10
Ymin=0
Ymax=35
Yscl=5
Xres=1
```

c) and d)

Year	Population	First Differences	Increase (%)
1891	4.8		
1901	5.4	0.6	12.5
1911	7.2	1.8	33.3
1921	8.8	1.6	22.2
1931	10.4	1.6	18.2
1941	11.5	1.1	10.6
1951	14.0	2.5	21.7
1961	18.2	4.2	30.0
1971	21.6	3.4	18.7
1981	24.0	2.4	11.1
1991	27.1	3.1	12.9

Average percent increase: 19.1% **e)** $y = 4.8(1.191)^x$, where y represents the population and x is the number of 10-year periods after 1891.

f)

Function Values	Actual Values
4.8	4.8
5.7	5.4
6.8	7.2
8.1	8.8
9.7	10.4
11.5	11.5
13.7	14.0
16.3	18.2
19.4	21.6
23.1	24.0
27.6	27.1

11. a)
```
WINDOW
Xmin=0
Xmax=7
Xscl=1
Ymin=1800
Ymax=2000
Yscl=20
Xres=1
```

b) No. **c)** The first differences indicate that the growth is not exponential, quadratic, or linear.

Population (in billions)	Year	First Differences
1	1804	
2	1927	123
3	1960	33
4	1974	14
5	1987	13
6	1999	12

6.4 Applications of Exponential Functions, pp. 241–243

1. In parts a) to c), n is the number of compounding periods.
a) $A = 1000(1.03)^n$; $1194.05 **b)** $A = 4500(1.01125)^n$; $5628.38
c) $A = 250\left(1 + \dfrac{0.05}{12}\right)^n$; $271.68

2.

Year	a) Mountain Bike ($)	b) 1-year College Tuition ($)
0	600.00	2417.00
1	619.20	2494.34
2	639.01	2574.16
3	659.46	2656.54
4	680.57	2741.55
5	702.34	2829.27

3. $P = 5\,917\,000(0.993)^n$ **4. a)** $A = 11\,514\,000(1.011)^n$, where P is the projected population and n is the number of years.
b) 2010: 12 986 405; 2020: 14 487 735

5.

Bird Type	a) Function	b) Number in 5 years
Loon	$F = I(1.033)^n$	1176
Canada goose	$F = I(1.511)^n$	7876
Red-headed woodpecker	$F = I(0.947)^n$	762
Red-winged blackbird	$F = I(0.985)^n$	927
Black-capped chickadee	$F = I(1.025)^n$	1131

6. a) $A = 3200(0.7)^n$ **b)** \$1568 **c)** \$537.82 **7. a)** 48 units
b) 6 units **c)** $\frac{3}{32}$ units **8. a)** 0.9 units **b)** 0.225 units
c) 0.014 062 5 units **9. a)** $A = 541\,000(0.992)^n$, where A is the projected population and n is the number of years since 1999.
b) 439 037 **10.** 2002 **11. a)** \$12 517.96 **b)** \$12 548.23
12. a) 0.65% **b)** $A = 408\,000(1.0065)^n$, where A is the projected population and n is the number of years since 1995. **c)** 479 739
13. a) \$58 381.16 **b)** \$56 697.08 **c)** It is less by \$1684.08.

Case Study Wrap-Up, p. 245

1. 1 333 333 **2.** $1\,333\,333(0.97)^{n-1} - 1\,333\,333(0.97)^n = 38\,800$ or $0.97(40\,000) = 38\,800$ **3.** 23 years

Review, pp. 246–247

1. a) 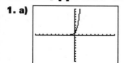 **b)**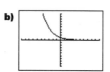

increasing; y-intercept = 1   decreasing; y-intercept = 1
c) decreasing; y-intercept = 1

2. a) $y = 10^x$: domain: $x \in R$; range: $y > 0$; y-intercept = 1
$y = \left(\frac{1}{10}\right)^x$: domain: $x \in R$; range: $y > 0$; y-intercept = 1
b) $y = 10^x$ is increasing; $y = \left(\frac{1}{10}\right)^x$ is decreasing. **3.** 16 800 years
4. a) domain: $x \in R$; range: $y \in R$ **b)** domain: $x \in R$; range: $y > 0$; asymptote: $y = 0$ **c)** domain: $x \in R$; range: $y \leq 0$
d) domain: $x \in R$; range: $y > 0$; asymptote: $y = 0$ **5. a)** $y = 3^x$: domain: $x \in R$; range: $y > 0$; y-intercept: 1; asymptote: $y = 0$;
$y = \left(\frac{1}{3}\right)^x$: domain: $x \in R$; range: $y > 0$; y-intercept: 1; asymptote: $y = 0$ **b)** One is the reflection in the y-axis of the other.
6. a)

$y = 4x$

x	y	First Differences	
0	0		
1	4	4	First differences are
2	8	4	constant; the function
3	12	4	is linear.
4	16	4	
5	20	4	

b)

$y = 4x^2$

x	y	First Differences	
0	0		
1	4	4	First differences form
2	16	12	an arithmetic sequence;
3	36	20	the function is quadratic.
4	64	28	
5	100	36	

c)

$y = 4^x$

x	y	First Differences	
0	1		
1	4	3	First differences form
2	16	12	a geometric sequence;
3	64	48	the function is
4	256	192	exponential.
5	1024	768	

7. a)

x	$y = \frac{1}{4}x$	$y = \frac{1}{4}x^2$	$y = \left(\frac{1}{4}\right)^x$
-8	-2	16	65 536
-4	-1	4	256
-1	$-\frac{1}{4}$	$\frac{1}{4}$	4
0	0	0	1
1	$\frac{1}{4}$	$\frac{1}{4}$	$\frac{1}{4}$
4	1	4	$\frac{1}{256}$
8	2	16	$\frac{1}{65\,536}$

```
WINDOW
Xmin=-8
Xmax=8
Xscl=2
Ymin=-5
Ymax=5
Yscl=1
Xres=1
```

```
WINDOW
Xmin=-10
Xmax=10
Xscl=2
Ymin=-2
Ymax=20
Yscl=2
Xres=1
```

```
WINDOW
Xmin=-10
Xmax=10
Xscl=2
Ymin=-20
Ymax=500
Yscl=50
Xres=1
```

b) $y = \frac{1}{4}x$ is always increasing; $y = \left(\frac{1}{4}\right)^x$ is always decreasing.
c) $y = \frac{1}{4}x^2$ both increases and decreases. It increases when $x > 0$. It decreases when $x < 0$. **d)** $y = \frac{1}{4}x$: x-intercept = 0; y-intercept = 0; $y = \frac{1}{4}x^2$: x-intercept = 0; y-intercept = 0;
$y = \left(\frac{1}{4}\right)^x$: no x-intercept; y-intercept = 1 **8. a)** $y = 32\,600(0.7)^n$, where y is the depreciated value and n is the number of years.
b) \$7827.26 **9. a)** $y = 870(0.95)^n$, where y is the projected population and n is the number of years. **b)** 673 **c)** 5 years

Practice Test, pp. 248–249

1. a) increasing; y-intercept $= 1$; domain: $x \in R$; range: $y > 0$; equation of asymptote: $y = 0$ **b)** decreasing; y-intercept $= 1$; domain: $x \in R$; range: $y > 0$; equation of asymptote: $y = 0$
2. a) 20 **b)** 160 **c)** 1.4×10^{15}
3. a)

x	y
-2	$\dfrac{1}{16}$
-1	$\dfrac{1}{4}$
0	1
1	4
2	16

b)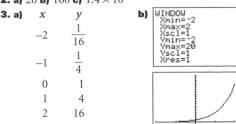

```
WINDOW
Xmin=-2
Xmax=2
Xscl=1
Ymin=-2
Ymax=20
Yscl=1
Xres=1
```

c) y-intercept $= 1$; equation of asymptote: $y = 0$

4. a)

x	y	First Differences
0	0	
1	3	3
2	6	3
3	9	3
4	12	3
5	15	3

First differences are constant; the function is linear.

b)

x	y	First Differences
0	0	
1	3	3
2	12	9
3	27	15
4	48	21
5	75	27

First differences form an arithmetic sequence; the function is quadratic.

c)

x	y	First Differences
0	1	
1	3	2
2	9	6
3	27	18
4	81	54
5	243	162

First differences form a geometric sequence; the function is exponential.
5. a) $y = 25(1.08)^x$ is increasing more quickly; explanations may vary. **b)** $y = 18(0.06)^x$ is decreasing more quickly; explanations may vary. **6. a)** domain: $x \in R$; range: $y > 0$; equation of asymptote: $y = 0$ **b)** domain: $x \in R$; range: $y > 0$; equation of asymptote: $y = 0$ **7. a)** $y = 1.29(1.032)^n$, where y is the projected cost and n is the number of years; $1.77. **b)** $y = 29.99(1.032)^n$, where y is the projected cost and n is the number of years; $41.09. **8. a)** $y = 1150(1.05)^n$, where y is the projected population and n is the number of years. **b)** 1268 **c)** 7 years

Chapter 7 – Vehicle Costs

Get Ready, pp. 252–253

1. a) 402 **b)** 8294.4 **c)** 27.2 **d)** 6 **2. a)** 5.97 **b)** 1593.43 **c)** 2136.2
3. a) 0.15 **b)** 4.48 **c)** 47.06 **4. a)** $1350 **b)** $609 **c)** $632
d) $1500 **e)** $3.75 **f)** $1780 **5. a)** $11 280 **b)** $2300 **6. a)** 10%
b) 20% **c)** 50% **d)** 20% **7. a)** 3692.7 **b)** 20 448.42 **c)** 2772.01
8. a) $45.27 **b)** $30.76 **c)** $63.38 **9. a)** $6210 **b)** $10 235
c) $37 375 **d)** $8625 **10.** 25% **11.** $247.23 **12. a)** $8162.93
b) $16 227.37 **c)** $8615.13 **13. a)** $20 985 **b)** $28 868.35
14. a) $2823 **b)** $13 253

7.1 Investigate Buying a New Vehicle, pp. 260–261

1. $20 688.50 **2.** $41 695 **3.** $23 870.23 **4.** $51 850
5. $20 925 **6. b)** $25 869.25 **7.** $15 570.50 **11. a)** $646.88

7.2 Compare Buying a New Versus a Used Vehicle, pp. 267–269

1. 9% **2.** $55 900 **3.** 10.1% **4.** 11.6% **5.** $9857.14
6. $22 074.25 **7. a)** $7175 **b)** $8036

7.3 Fixed and Variable Operating Costs, pp. 274–276

1. $54.15 **2.** $1.04 **3.** $259
4.

	A	B	C	D	E	F
1	Qty.	Description	Each	Parts	Labour	Total
2	2	Front Brake Rotors	108.90	217.80		217.80
3	1	Set Front Brake Pads	72.95	72.95	110.00	182.95
4	1	Set Rear Brake Pads	72.95	72.95	135.00	207.95
5	1	Shim Kit Req'd			38.00	38.00
6	1	Service Sliders Req'd			20.00	20.00
7						
8	Subtotal					666.70
9	GST @ 7%					46.67
10	PST @ 8%					53.34
11	TOTAL					766.71

5. $575 **6. a)** 4.7 L/100 km **b)** 7.05 L/100 km

7.4 Buying Versus Leasing, pp. 280–281

1. $3231.35 **2.** $923.30 **3.** $14 860.44 **4.** $399.06 **5.** $184
6. Yes. **7.** $4694.70; $342.70 **8. a)** $20 800 **b)** $24 546.75
c) $606.86 **d)** $24 846.96 **9. a)** $18 756 **b)** $466.74 **c)** $27 403.52

Review, pp. 284–285

1. Yes. **2.** $17 825 **3.** $8491.50 **5.** $2624 **6. a)** 710 km; 36 920 km **b)** $2050 **7.** $2797.25 **8.** $362.85

Practice Test, pp. 286–287

1. $62 583 **2. a)** $5628 **b)** 23% **3.** $327.50 **4. a)** A **b)** B **c)** B
d) A **e)** B **f)** A **g)** A **h)** B **5.** $3138.20 **6.** $313.64

Chapter 8 – Consumer Spending

Get Ready, pp. 290–291

1. a) 0.24 **b)** 0.02 **c)** 0.025 **d)** 0.055 **e)** 1 **f)** 1.25 **g)** 0.032
h) 0.006 **2. a)** $80 **b)** $13 **c)** $5 **d)** $525 **e)** $5.75 **f)** $308
3. a) $75 **b)** $70 **c)** $20 **d)** $46.39 **e)** $82.50 **f)** $29.59 **g)** $41.43
h) $434.20 **4. a)** $2.80; $30.80 **b)** $30; $130 **c)** $9; $66 **d)** $6.25;
$118.75 **e)** $17; $217 **f)** $15.05; $83.95 **g)** $125; $375 **h)** $21.50;
$64.49 **5. a)** 28 days **b)** 21 days **c)** 42 days **d)** 38 days
e) 39 days **f)** 43 days **7. a)** $1191.02 **b)** $538.64 **c)** $811.82
d) $6092.01 **8. a)** 30 points **b)** 12 points **c)** 600 points
d) 240 points

8.1 Manage Your Retail Dollar, pp. 296–300

1. a) $24.95 **b)** $11.87 **c)** $40.10 **d)** $22.50 **e)** $16.50
2. a) $62.50 **b)** $16.25 **c)** $8.75 **d)** $13.23 **3. a)** 36.9% **b)** 7.0%
c) 6.5% **d)** 12.0% **5.** The catalogue is better for James; it will
cost $196.98 to buy the shoes at the store, and only $196.56 to
buy the shoes from the catalogue. **10. a) i)** 180 points
ii) 360 points **iii)** 1200 points **b)** 165 months; explanations may
vary. **16. a) i)** 155 **ii)** 780 **b) i)** 1 **ii)** 2 **iii)** 4 **c) i)** $0.50 **ii)** $0.25
iii) $0.20 **d) i)** $1 **ii)** $5 **iii)** $25 **iv)** $125

8.2 Manage Debit and Credit Cards, pp. 306–308

1. i) a) 52 **b)** 50 **c)** 47 **d)** 42 **e)** 41 **f)** 35 **g)** 27 **h)** 25 **ii) a)** $1.03
b) $4.92 **c)** $2.90 **d)** $7.23 **e)** $5.05 **f)** $1.32 **g)** $0.46 **h)** $0.49
iii) $23.40 **iv)** $40.47 **2. a)** $883.66 **b)** $4116.34 **c)** $0
d) Interest is calculated on the balance of $483.66. Simple
interest is charged from the posting date until the due date.
Then, the interest is compounded monthly until the balance is
paid off entirely. **3. a)** $2869.04 **b)** $1130.96 **c)** Interest would
be calculated on the balance of $2369.04. Simple interest is
charged from the posting date until the due date. Then, the
interest is compounded monthly until the balance is paid off
entirely. **4.** $27.89 **5.** $16.24 **7. a)** 58.1% **b)** The bank loan
would be the best option. Jason would only pay $187.52 in
interest with the bank loan instead of $629 with the monthly
payments or $391.04 with the credit card. **8. a)** 9.3% **b)** The
24 monthly payments of $85 would be Niki's best option. She
would only pay $181 in interest with the monthly payments
instead of $721 with the credit card or $321.40 with the bank
loan. **9. a)** $3.01 **b)** $18.44 **10.** Assuming that Caitlin's credit
card has an unpaid balance, 1 month: $1887.66; 2 months:
$1916.76

8.3 Foreign Exchange, pp. 313–315

1. a) i) $63.24 U.S. **ii)** $1.5813 Cdn per U.S. dollar
b) i) $6477.50 Jamaican **ii)** $0.0386 Cdn per Jamaican dollar
c) i) 24 070 rupees **ii)** $0.0415 Cdn per Pakistani rupee
d) i) 855 919.80 lire **ii)** $0.0007 Cdn per Italian lira
e) i) $2156.80 Singaporean **ii)** $0.9273 Cdn per Singaporean
dollar **f) i)** 89 887.64 bolivar **ii)** $0.0022 Cdn per Venezuelan

bolivar **g) i)** 3223.75 krona **ii)** $0.1551 Cdn per Swedish krona
2. a) i) $3809.25 Cdn **ii)** $0.6563 U.S. per Canadian dollar
b) i) $2499 Cdn **ii)** 6.0024 pesos per Canadian dollar
c) i) $645.84 Cdn **ii)** $1.2387 Barbadian per Canadian dollar
d) i) $67.41 Cdn **ii)** 5.1921 francs per Canadian dollar
e) i) $203.10 Cdn **ii)** 2.4618 riyals per Canadian dollar
f) i) $305.88 Cdn **ii)** $0.6539 Bermudan per Canadian dollar
g) i) $622.05 Cdn **ii)** 1.2057 reals per Canadian dollar
3. a) $25 **b)** $36 **c)** $45.37 **d)** $41.10 **4. a)** $794.01 per week
b) The Seattle hotel is more expensive by $136.01 Cdn per week
or $19.43 Cdn per night. **5. a)** $238.15 **b)** Barbados **6.** Anna
would receive $18.32 U.S. more at her bank. **7.** $10.64 Cdn
8. $46.20 Cdn **9. a) i)** $86 Cdn **ii)** $172 Cdn **10. a)** $801.76
b) $40.09 **c)** PST: $64.14; GST: $56.12 **d)** $962.11
11. a) $1939.85 **b)** $96.99 **c)** $116.39 **d)** PST: $155.19;
GST: $142.58 **e)** $2451.00 **13.** $748.16 **14.** $955.70

Career Profile, p. 316

1. $226.95 Cdn **2.** $1425.60 H.K. **3.** $140.39 Cdn
4. $116.28 Cdn

Review, pp. 318–319

2. 32.6% **4.** $44.85 **5. a)** 1 111 110 **6.** interest from previous
bill; fees for using the card (usually yearly); cash advances
(money taken out of a bank machine); purchases from previous
bills for which interest is being charged; new purchases for
which interest is not yet being charged (if you do not carry a
balance) **7.** $6.34 **8. a)** $1111.01 **b)** $2388.99 **c)** $0 **d)** Interest
is calculated on the balance of $611.01. Simple interest is
charged from the posting date until the due date. Then, the
interest is compounded monthly until the balance is paid off
entirely. **10. a)** $895.38 **b)** $1313.30 **11. a)** 16 118.50 pesos
b) 56 140.40 yen **12.** $33.86 Cdn **13. a)** $729.21
b) $69.27 Cdn **c)** PST: $57.12 Cdn; GST: $51.04 Cdn
d) $906.64 Cdn

Practice Test, pp. 320–321

1. 22.7% **2.** $3.13 **3.** $5.38 **4. a)** $302.48 **b)** 181 065.50
drachma **7. a)** $845.12 **b)** $4154.88 **c)** Interest is calculated on
the balance of $545.12. Simple interest is charged from the
posting date until the due date. Then, the interest is
compounded monthly until the balance is paid off entirely.
8. They spent an extra $21.50. **9. a)** cost of books: $369.25;
shipping: $15.02; handling: $7.39; GST: $27.42; money order:
$4.00 **b)** $423.08 **10. a)** $46.20

Cumulative Review, Chapters 5–8, pp. 322–323

1. a) arithmetic; $S_{12} = 276$ **b)** geometric; $S_7 = 1093$
c) geometric; $S_6 = -42$ **d)** arithmetic; $S_8 = 180$ **e)** arithmetic;
$S_{10} = 20$ **f)** arithmetic; $S_{15} = -165$ **2.** $170 250 **3. a)** $32 458.70
b) $3658.70 **4. a)** $13 403.83 **b)** $3096.17

5. a) 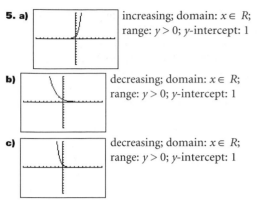 increasing; domain: $x \in R$; range: $y > 0$; y-intercept: 1

b) decreasing; domain: $x \in R$; range: $y > 0$; y-intercept: 1

c) decreasing; domain: $x \in R$; range: $y > 0$; y-intercept: 1

6. a) $y = 3500(0.7)^n$, where y is the depreciated value and n is the number of years. **b)** $1200.50 **7. a)** $y = 650(1.08)^n$, where y is the projected population and n is the number of years. **b)** 819 students **c)** 6 years **8. a)** 400 km **b)** $29 **9. a)** $250 **b)** She will have to finance $16 315.50. Her monthly payments will be $353.97. **c)** $3885.35 **10. a)** $770.72 **b)** $1729.28 **c)** $0 **d)** Interest is calculated on the balance of $370.72. Simple interest is charged from the posting date until the due date. Then, the interest is compounded monthly until the balance is paid off entirely. **12.** $2142.30

Chapter 9 – Accommodation Costs
Answers obtained using tables may differ slightly from those found using the **TVM Solver**.

Get Ready, pp. 326–327
1. a) 43% **b)** 70% **c)** 0.8% **d)** 1.75% **e)** 2.5% **f)** 6% **2. a)** 0.065 **b)** 0.0125 **c)** 0.005 **d)** 0.12 **e)** 0.0275 **f)** 0.0025 **3. a)** $1560 **b)** $12 800 **c)** $34 600 **d)** $1387.50 **e)** $330 **f)** $112.50 **4. a)** 14.4% **b)** 58.2% **c)** 195.3% **d)** 25% **e)** 11.9% **f)** 161.1% **5. a)** 20.8% **b)** 35.8% **c)** 28.2% **d)** 68.4% **e)** 15.2% **f)** 16.9% **6. a)** 1.25 years **b)** 12 years **c)** 6.25 years **d)** 0.5 years **e)** 1.5 years **f)** 21.75 years **7. a)** 180 months **b)** 240 months **c)** 300 months **8. a)** 38 days **b)** 38 days **c)** 30 days **d)** 25 days **e)** 19 days **f)** 43 days **9. a)** 1.009 759 **b)** 1.012 126 **c)** 1.024 114 **d)** 1.002 497 **e)** 1.001 786 **f)** 1.012 423 **10. a)** 6% **b)** 3% **c)** 1% **d)** 0.032 877% **11. a)** 3.25% **b)** 1.625% **c)** 0.541 667% **d)** 0.017 808% **12. a)** $820 **b)** 23.4%

9.1 Accommodation Options, pp. 330–332
5. a) $841.67 **b)** $1145 **c)** $1672.08 **d)** $1316.67 **7. a)** year 1: $688.50; year 2: $702.27 **b)** year 1: $1239.30; year 2: $1264.09 **c)** year 1: $999.60; year 2: $1019.59 **8. a)** $1950 **b)** $1191.67 **9.** Heather should choose the first apartment, which costs $760 per month and includes free laundry facilities. For the second apartment, she would spend $36.83/month on laundry, bringing the total monthly cost up to $761.83.

11. a) Option A: $1210; Option B: $1500; Option C: $1400 **b)** $403.33 **c)** $1125 **d) i)** Campus residence is the cheapest.

9.2 Costs of Buying: Introduction to Mortgages, pp. 337–340
2. a) CMHC **b)** broker **c)** mortgage **d)** semi-monthly **e)** interest **f)** home-inspection **g)** land-transfer tax **h)** bi-weekly **i)** amortization **j)** principal; Message: Home is where the heart is.
3.

	Monthly Payment	Weekly	Accelerated Weekly	Semi-monthly	Bi-weekly	Accelerated Bi-weekly
a)	$968.42	$223.48	$242.11	$484.21	$446.96	$484.21
b)	$843.15	$194.57	$210.79	$421.58	$389.15	$421.58
c)	$1248.89	$288.21	$312.22	$624.45	$576.41	$624.45

4. a) $13 440 **b)** $12 441 **c)** $16 334.24 **5. a)** $987 **b)** $987 **c)** $987 **6. a)** $6780 **b)** $33 900 **7. a)** $926.70 **b)** $23 167.50 **c)** $69 502.50 **d)** $25 619.20 **8.** $18.87 **9.** $556 **10. a)** $420.25 **b)** $210.13 **c)** $387.92 **11. a)** $213.04 **b) i)** $201.12 **ii)** $11.92 **12. a)** based on selling price: $6325; based on offer: $6100 **b)** $225 **13. a)** bi-weekly payments: $13 312/year; accelerated weekly payments: $11 908/year **b)** The accelerated weekly payment option is $1404 less per year. **14. a)** $135 000 **b)** $1350 **c)** $18 350 **d)** $4850 **15. a)** $4475; $3188.44 **b)** $75 000; $562.50 **c)** $2797.50
16. a)

Family	Cash Available to Buy Home	Closing Costs	Amount Available for Down Payment	Approximate Value of Home if Down Payment Is 5%	25%
Estey	$36 500	$4 750	$31 750	$635 000	$127 000
Chu	$25 000	$4 750	$20 250	$405 000	$81 000
Lloyd	$14 000	$4 750	$9 250	$185 000	$37 000

17. a) $335 800 **b) i)** $11 962.88 **ii)** $7555.50 **iii)** $3358 **18. a)** $8580 **b)** $147 420
19.

```
WINDOW
Xmin=0
Xmax=300000
Xscl=50000
Ymin=0
Ymax=4500
Yscl=250
Xres=1
```

9.3 Mortgage Interest, pp. 346–348
1. a) 0.736% **b)** 0.856% **c)** 0.595% **d)** 1.134% **2. a)** 0.006 154 52 **b)** 0.025 304 83 **c)** 0.001 174 19 **d)** 0.002 702 41 **e)** 0.022 252 42 **f)** 0.001 273 97 **3. a)** 0.005 344 74; $253.88 **b)** 0.024 695 08; $716.16 **c)** 0.000 247 77; $28.31 **d)** Equivalent Interest Rate: 0.002 349 06; Interest Owing: $363.44 **4. a) i)** monthly: $633.26; semi-annually: $625.31 **ii)** monthly: $30 576.03; semi-annually: $29 962.94 **b)** $613.09 **5. a)** $1241.90 **b)** $118 732.59 **6.** $444.39 **7. a)** 7 days; $120.33 **b)** 7 days; $279.46 **c)** 11 days; $343.61 **d)** 29 days; $1208.23 **9. a) i)** $1289.38 **ii)** $2129.45 **10.** Yes. **11. a)** 38 days **b)** 0.007 441 91 **c)** $1214.63 **12. a)** Estey: $147 156.59; Chu: $90 582.18; Lloyd: $97 005.19 **b)** Estey: $178 906.59; Chu: $110 832.18; Lloyd: $106 255.19

9.4 Mortgage Amortization Tables, pp. 358–360

1. a) 7.315 55 **b)** 6.547 42 **c)** 7.986 03 **3. a)** $918.83 **b)** $823.31 **c)** $491.24 **4. a)** Monthly Payment: $1209.40; To copy down the column using Microsoft® Excel®, highlight cells B10 to B14 and use **Fill Down. b)** The formula is =$C$5*E9 or +$C$5*E9. It will be located in cell C10. **c)** The formula is =B10–C10 or +B10–C10. It will be located in cell D10. **d)** The formula is =E9–D10 or +E9–D10. It will be located in cell E10. **e)** To copy the formula in cell C10 down the column using Microsoft® Excel®, highlight cells C10 to C14 and use **Fill Down.** To copy the formula in cell D10 down the column, highlight cells D10 to D14 and use **Fill Down.** To copy the formula in cell E10 down the column, highlight cells E10 to E14 and use **Fill Down. 5. a)** $556.75 **b)** $556.75 **c)** $562.72; by changing **C/Y** to 12, interest is compounded monthly instead of semi-annually. **d)** The answer in parts a) and b) is correct in Canada because Canadian mortgages are compounded semi-annually, not monthly. **6. a)** The mortgage with the 15-year amortization period will have the greatest monthly payment; the same amount of money has to be paid in a shorter amount of time. **b)** 15-year amortization: $51 412.66; 20-year amortization: $53 626.65; 25-year amortization: $54 794.20 **7.** interest: $5801.14; principal: $2045.78; balance owing: $82 954.22 **8. a)** $752.68 **b)** interest: $14 831.12; principal: $3233.20 **c)** $79 966.80 **9. a)** $121 500 **b)** $1107.31 **c)** $114 447.06 **d)** $59 385.66 **e)** $930.94 **f)** $41 050.88 **g)** For the second 5-year term, there is a lower interest rate and a smaller balance owing. **10.** The penalty is $2721.61; explanations may vary. **11. a)** $5475 **b)** $3900.94 **c)** $107 925.94 **d)** $929.27 **e)** $89 939.33 **f)** $170 857.57 **g)** $40 424.41 **12. a)** Estey: $120 346.32; Lloyd: $102 997.80 **b)** Estey: $2797.57; Lloyd: $2086.10 **13.** $179 913.44

9.5 Compare Your Mortgage Options, pp. 365–368

1. a) 25 years **b)** 15 years **c)** 17 years **d)** 20.15 years **e)** 17.5 years **f)** 21.63 years **2. a)** $442.01; $102.00 **b)** $946.07; $236.52 **c)** $1360.42; $680.21 **d)** $691.37; $319.09 **e)** $1888.48; $944.24 **3. a)** PMT: –707.15; P/Y: 12 **b)** N: 1137.41; P/Y: 52 **c)** PV: 164 465.24; Payment Frequency: semi-monthly **d)** PMT: –338.12; P/Y: 52 **e)** PMT: 1265.85; Payment Frequency: monthly **4. a)** monthly payment: $947.24; interest paid: $177 477.73 **b)** monthly payment: $883.45; interest paid: $158 336.99 **c)** $19 140.74 **6. a)** monthly: $710.73; semi-monthly: $355.37 **b)** monthly: $170 576.30; semi-monthly: $170 113.71 **c)** monthly: 20 years; semi-monthly: 19.96 years **d)** Semi-monthly; explanations may vary. **7. a)** monthly: $584.43; semi-monthly: $292.22; bi-weekly: $269.74 **b)** monthly: $101 852.37; semi-monthly: $100 826.99; bi-weekly: $100 752.05 **c)** Bi-weekly; explanations may vary.

8. a) $134.34; $268.68 **b)** $73 181.01; $73 500.57 **c)** Weekly; explanations may vary. **9. a)** $115 500 **b)** $31 425.57; $111 400.41 **10. a)** 1st year: $568.95; 2nd year: $597.40; 3rd, 4th, and 5th years: $625.85 **b)** total interest paid: $26 550.35 **c)** $26 213.20 **11. a)** $1063.50; $955.47; $900.01 **b)** $92 674.91; $130 557.91; $171 246.17 **12. a)** $103 504.57 **b)** $117 300.79 **c)** $126 291.53 **13. a)** $1280.30 **b)** $164 775.48 **c)** 25 years, 10 months **14.** Option A: interest rate = 13.78%, total interest paid = $188 000.24; Option B: interest rate = 15.83%, total interest paid = $289 999.54 **15. a)** $1062.27; $951.66; $894.49 **b)** $91 208.50; $128 401.74; $168 343.30 **c)** 6.4% **d)** 23.7% **e)** The 15- to 20-year amortization period change gives you more interest savings compared to payment increase. **17.** Option A; explanations may vary.

9.6 Make Accommodation Decisions, pp. 375–377

1. a) $9120/year **b)** $1008/month **c)** $179.20/week **2. a)** No. **b)** No. **3. a)** $945.17 **b)** $604.30 **c)** $1253.58 **d)** $675.18 **4. a)** $841.67 **b)** $1677.08 **c)** $1316.67 **8. a)** $23 905.82 **b)** none **9. a)** $1436.15 **b)** $71 866.94 **c)** $60 133.06 **10. a)** $2550 **b)** $1577.92 **c)** $3944.80 **11. a)** $24 000 **13.** $3773.91

Career Profile, p. 378

4. Annual sales must be $1 440 000, assuming the realtor's commission rate is 5%, and half of the commission goes toward expenses and real estate fees.

Case Study Wrap-Up, p. 379

1. Estey: $62 306.11; Chu: $20 250; Lloyd: $18 766.10

Review, pp. 380–381

2. Apartment A: $1290; Apartment B: $1230 **3. a)** $388.65 **b)** $421.04 **c)** $210.52 **d)** $842.14 **4. a)** $9460; $11 681 **b)** $2128.50; $87 268.50 **5. a)** 0.007 363 12 **b)** 0.003 291 76 **6. a)** $1768.26 **b)** $1800.31 **c)** $384.60 **7. a)** B4 **b)** C4 **c)** D4 **d)** E4 **8. a)** 20 years: $819.98; 25 years: $772.38 **b)** 20 years: $112 042.25; 25 years: $146 963.05 **c)** 6.2% **d)** 23.8%

9.

	Payment	Time Required to Pay Off Mortgage	Total Interest
a) monthly	$673.77	25 years	$132 130.97
b) semi-monthly	$336.89	24.7 years	$129 872.44
c) bi-weekly	$310.97	24.7 years	$129 716.96

10. They should choose the 20-year amortization period. If they choose the 15-year amortization period, they will not be able to afford the monthly payments. They can afford the payments on the 20-year and 25-year amortization periods, however, they will pay more interest with the 25-year amortization period than with the 20-year amortization period. **11. a)** $1539.50/month **b)** $1538.83/month **c)** $178 720.16

Practice Test, pp. 382–383

2. $1069 **3. a)** CHMC **b)** term; amortization period
c) interest; principal **4.** $885.06 **5. a)** $603.92; $596.52
b) $106 176.22; $103 958.73 **c)** $6340.22; $6229.95 **d)** monthly
payment: $7.40; interest paid: $2217.49; interest paid in 1 year:
$110.27 **6. a)** $565.86 **b)** $27 457.41 **c)** $70 855.81
7. a) 7.632 14 **b)** $522.04 **c)** 0.006 558 20 **d)** interest portion:
$448.58; principal portion: $73.46 **8. a)** Joe: $1015.90; Rehan:
$956.93 **b)** Joe pays $43 263.96 less interest. **9. a)** $79 726.37
b) They could choose a longer amortization period.
10. Option B will save more interest, since interest on a
Canadian mortgage is compounded semi-annually.
11. a) $236 957.46 **b)** $278 773.48

Chapter 10 – Personal Financial Decisions

10.4 Finance Your Future: A Case Study, pp. 394–399

30. b) $16 923.77

Cumulative Review, Chapters 1–10, pp. 400–403

1. a) $550 **c)** 7 months, assuming he continues to save $550
each month. **2.** 8.5% **3. a)** $\frac{1}{27}$ **b)** 1 **c)** $\frac{1}{5}$ **d)** 8 **e)** −8

4. a) $x = 4$ **b)** $x = \frac{3}{2}$ **c)** $x = -\frac{3}{5}$ **d)** $x = -\frac{1}{2}$ **5. a)** arithmetic; 18,
22 **b)** neither **c)** geometric; 32, 16 **6. a)** $t_n = 1.5 + 0.5n$
b) 6.5 km **c)** 135 km **7. a)** $3860.76 **b)** $1060.76 **8.** $1201.59
9. He should choose option B. In two years, option A will be
worth $4200, option B will be worth $4213.90, and option C
will be worth $4187.45. **10. a)** 5.5 years **b)** 9.5 years
11. a) i) arithmetic **ii)** $S_n = 3n^2 + 3n$ **iii)** $S_{12} = 468$
b) i) geometric **ii)** $S_n = 3(2^n - 1)$ **iii)** $S_{10} = 3069$ **c) i)** arithmetic
ii) $S_n = 7.5n - 1.5n^2$ **iii)** $S_{15} = -225$ **12.** 2618.15 **13.** $203.38
14.

```
WINDOW
Xmin=-4
Xmax=4
Xscl=1
Ymin=-1
Ymax=30
Yscl=5
Xres=1
```

a)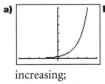
increasing;
y-intercept: 1

b)
decreasing;
y-intercept: 1

c)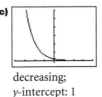
decreasing;
y-intercept: 1

15. a) domain: $x \in R$; range: $y > 0$; asymptote: $y = 0$
b) domain: $x \in R$; range: $y \geq 0$; asymptote: none **c)** domain:
$x \in R$; range: $y \in R$; asymptote: none **16.** year 1: $0.752/L;
year 2: $0.776/L; year 3: $0.801/L; year 4: $0.827/L; year 5:
$0.853/L **17. a)** 400; 1600; 409 600 **b)** 100 min
18. a) $P = 4\,680\,000(1.021)^n$, where P is the projected
population and n is the number of years after 1999.
b) 7 240 798 people **c)** Answers may vary, for example: The
growth rate might fluctuate. **19. a)** $P = 541\,000(0.992)^n$, where
P is the projected population and n is the number of years.
b) 475 756 **c)** 2009 **20. a)** $23 557.75 **b)** $388.63 **21.** $4567.10
24. a) $454.55 **b)** $1545.45 **c)** $0 **d)** Interest is calculated on the
balance of $254.55. Simple interest is charged from the posting
date until the due date. Then, the interest is compounded
monthly until the balance is paid off entirely. **25.** $196.16
27. a) option A: $768.13; option B: $818.19 **b)** option A:
$103 486.59; option B: $103 649.51 **c)** Answers may vary, for
example: She might choose option B because in 1 year she may
be able to negotiate a mortgage with a lower interest rate
without paying a penalty.

GLOSSARY

A

accelerated bi-weekly payments Payments for which the monthly mortgage payment is halved and this amount is paid once every 2 weeks. In this way, $26 \times \frac{1}{2}$ or 13 full monthly payments are made in 1 year.

accelerated weekly payments Payments for which the monthly mortgage payment is divided by 4 and this amount is paid each week. In this way, $52 \times \frac{1}{4}$ or 13 full monthly payments are made in 1 year.

aggressive investment An investment with a high potential rate of return but also with high risk.

algebraic expression An expression that includes at least one variable.

$3t$, $A(1 + i)$, and 2^x are algebraic expressions.

amortization period The period of time it takes for a mortgage to be fully repaid with regular equal payments.

amortization table A table that shows the part of each mortgage payment that is interest and principal, and the principal remaining.

amortize To set money aside regularly to pay off a debt.

annuity A series of equal payments made at equal intervals of time for a certain term (see ordinary annuity).

application The use of mathematics to solve real-world problems.

application fee A fee charged by some lenders to process a mortgage application.

arithmetic sequence A sequence that has a common difference between consecutive terms.

1, 4, 7, 10, … is an arithmetic sequence.

arithmetic series The sum of the terms of an arithmetic sequence.

asset Anything owned by an individual, family, or business.

asymptote A line that a curve approaches more and more closely, but never crosses or touches.

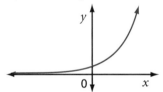

The x-axis is an asymptote.

B

base In a power, the number that is repeatedly multiplied.

In 3^4 the base is 3 because $3^4 = 3 \times 3 \times 3 \times 3$.

bi-weekly Every 2 weeks.

blue chip A well-established, well-managed, large company. Common stocks or shares from these companies are called blue-chip stocks.

broker A person who, for a fee, negotiates with a buyer and a seller. A stockbroker handles the sale of stocks.

budget A record of money earned (income) and spent (expenses) for a certain period of time. In a balanced budget, total expenses equal total income.

Canada Deposit Insurance Corporation (CDIC)
A federal crown corporation that offers deposit insurance of up to $60 000 per person per institution in case the institution goes bankrupt.

closed mortgage A mortgage for which only the regular specified payments may be made for the agreed term. If you want to make early extra payments, or pay the mortgage off early, a penalty is charged.

closing costs The extra costs that must be paid to buy a home. They include land-transfer tax, legal fees, and GST.

CMHC (Canada Mortgage and Housing Corporation) fee The fee paid when a person qualifies for a mortgage amount greater than or equal to 65% of the home price. The fee varies depending on the amount of the loan.

collateral Property pledged as security for a loan.

commission In investments, the money earned for the sale of financial products.

common difference The difference between consecutive terms of an arithmetic sequence.

    For 2, 5, 8, 11, … , the common difference is 3.

common ratio The ratio of consecutive terms of a geometric sequence.

    For 2, 6, 18, 54, … , the common ratio is 3.

compound interest Interest that is calculated at regular compounding periods, and then, added to the principal for the next compounding period.

compounding period Each period of time for which compound interest is earned or charged in an investment or loan.

conservative For investments, low risk; for investors, uncomfortable with risk.

consolidate debts To combine debts into one debt, usually at a lower overall interest rate.

constant rate of change A linear relationship between two variables where equal intervals of the first variable correspond to equal intervals of the second variable. For example, if gasoline costs $0.80/L, then, 1 L costs $0.80, 2 L cost $1.60, and so on.

consumer debt Loans taken out to finance purchases, such as car and furniture loans.

cross-product rule If $\dfrac{a}{b} = \dfrac{c}{d}$, then $ad = bc$.

decreasing function A function for which the first differences decrease.

deferred annuity An annuity for which the first payment is delayed until some time in the future.

depreciation The amount by which the value of an item decreases in value.

discount A deduction from the amount or cost, often expressed as a percent.

discretionary expense Money that is spent on things that improve quality of life, such as savings. Non-discretionary expenses are necessary expenses, such as shelter.

diversify To decrease the risk of investing by investing in a variety of investments.

dividend A portion of a company's profit paid to each investor. It is taxed at a lower rate than interest income from investments.

domain of a relation The set of numbers for which a relation is defined. The set of all first coordinates of the ordered pairs in a relation.

down payment The amount paid in cash at the time of purchase, with the rest of the cost financed.

education fund Money set aside for future education costs. A registered education savings fund (RESP) is registered with the federal government and allows income tax on earnings to be deferred until a later time. An RESP has conditions attached.

emergency fund Money that is set aside to deal with expenses such as unexpected repairs on a car or home. It is usually placed in a savings alternative with quick access and no withdrawal penalties.

equation A mathematical sentence formed by two equivalent expressions.

$5x - 3 = 2x + 6$ is an equation.

equity The difference between the value of an asset, such as a house, and the amount owed on the asset.

equivalent algebraic expressions Expressions that are equal for all values of the variable.

$7t + 3t$ and $10t$ are equivalent algebraic expressions.

equivalent equations Equations that have the same solution.

estate The assets of a deceased person.

expenses Spending or payment of money during a specific time period.

exponent A raised number in a power that indicates repeated multiplication of the base.

In $(1 + i)^3$, which means $(1 + i)(1 + i)(1 + i)$, the 3 is the exponent.

exponential equation An equation that has a variable in an exponent.

$3^x = 81$ is an exponential equation.

exponential form A shorthand method for writing repeated multiplication.

4^3 is the exponential form for $4 \times 4 \times 4$ or 64.

exponential function A relation of the form $y = ab^x$, where $a \neq 0$, $b > 0$, and $b \neq 1$.

$y = 500(1.03)^x$ is an exponential function.

exponential growth Non-linear growth represented by an exponential equation and a graph with an upward curve. Geometric sequences and compound interest show exponential growth.

expression A mathematical phrase made up of numbers and/or variables.

$3(100 + 0.01)^5$, $2x$, and $P(1 + i)^n$ are expressions.

financial plan A logical series of steps that help in reaching financial goals.

first differences In a relation between two variables, the difference between successive values of the second variable for regular steps in the first variable.

$$y = 2x + 1$$

x	y	First Differences
-2	-3	
-1	-1	$-1 - (-3) = 2$
0	1	$1 - (-1) = 2$
1	3	$3 - 1 = 2$
2	5	$5 - 3 = 2$

first mortgage A loan of up to 75% of the purchase price.

fixed costs of a vehicle Expected costs that do not depend on how the vehicle is used.

fixed expense An expense that is the same dollar amount every budget period.

fixed interest rate An interest rate that stays the same for the length of the term.

fixed-rate mortgage When the interest rate stays the same for the term of the mortgage.

foreign exchange rate The cost of purchasing one unit of foreign currency.

function A relation in which each *x*-value (or first variable value) has only one corresponding *y*-value (or second variable value).

geometric sequence A sequence that has a common ratio between consecutive terms.

2, 6, 18, 54, … is a geometric sequence.

geometric series The sum of the terms of a geometric sequence.

gross debt service ratio (GDS ratio) The ratio of mortgage payment, property taxes, and heating costs to gross income.

gross income Income before deductions and taxes are paid, sometimes called gross earnings.

GST Goods and services tax (7% in 2001).

guaranteed investment certificate (GIC) A deposit investment purchased from a bank, trust company, or credit union, usually with a fixed interest rate that can be compounded or simple. A minimum investment is often required. There are no purchase fees but there may be penalties for early withdrawal. Guaranteed and insured by the Canada Deposit Insurance Corporation (CDIC).

half-life The period of time taken for an amount of radioactive material to be reduced to half its original quantity.

high-risk investment An investment with a high probability of decreasing in value but a high potential rate of return.

home-inspection fee The fee that a professional building inspector charges a potential home buyer to inspect a home and report on any problems before the buyer finalizes the purchase.

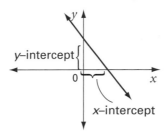

income Money received during a specific time period from investments or employment.

increasing function A function for which the first differences increase.

inflation When prices for consumer goods and services rise.

integral exponent An exponent that is an integer.

The integral exponent of 5^{-8} is −8.

intercept The distance from the origin of the Cartesian coordinate plane to the point at which a line or curve crosses a given axis.

interest The amount earned on an investment or savings alternative, or the cost of borrowing money.

interest income Money paid by a borrower to a lender. It is taxed at the same rate as employment income.

interest rate The rate, as a percent, at which an investment or savings alternative increases in value, or the cost of borrowing money, expressed as a percent.

investment An asset that has the potential to earn income (interest income or dividends) or increase in value.

land-transfer tax A fee charged by the province for the transfer of title, or ownership, of real estate property. It ranges from 0.5% to 1.5% of the purchase price.

lease A legal contract between the owner of a property and a person using that property for a monthly fee. All the conditions that apply to the agreement are written out in a lease document.

legal fees The fees charged by a buyer's lawyer to arrange the purchase of property, including the costs of a title search and drawing up the title deed.

liability Anything owed by an individual, family, or business. Unpaid loans are liabilities.

life insurance A contract that agrees to pay a fixed amount of money to a named beneficiary upon the death of the insured.

linear equation An equation that can be written in the form $mx + b = 0$, where m and b are real numbers.

linear function A relationship between two variables defined by an equation of the form $y = mx + b$, where m and b are real numbers.

linear growth Growth represented by a linear function and a straight-line graph. Arithmetic sequences and simple interest show linear growth.

linear relation A relationship between two variables that forms a straight line when graphed.

liquid For investments or assets, easily cashable and with no or minor penalties.

liquid assets Assets that are easily convertible to cash. Non-liquid assets are those that cannot be cashed or are cashable with significant penalties.

liquidity ratio The ratio of liquid assets to total assets.

low-risk investment An investment with a low probability of decreasing in value, or low risk, and a low potential rate of return.

market value The value of an asset if it is sold.

mathematical model A description of a real situation using a diagram, a graph, a table of values, an equation, a formula, a physical model, or a computer model.

maturity The process of a loan or investment or savings alternative coming due or reaching the end of its term.

moderate-risk investment An investment with a medium probability of decreasing in value, or medium risk, and a medium potential rate of return.

mortgage A special type of borrowing arrangement between a borrower and a lender. The borrower uses property as a guarantee of repayment of the debt.

mortgage broker A licensed individual who, for a fee, brings together a borrower in need of a mortgage and a lender willing to provide one.

mortgage broker's fee The fee charged by a mortgage broker to arrange a mortgage.

mortgage payments Regular payments made toward paying back the principal and interest on a mortgage.

mortgagee A person or business that lends money in a mortgage agreement.

mortgagor A person or business that borrows money in a mortgage agreement.

net income Income after all deductions and taxes are paid, sometimes called net earnings.

net worth The difference between total assets and total liabilities as shown in a net worth statement. It is what would result if all assets were sold and all liabilities paid off.

net worth statement An organized list of an individual's or family's assets (what is owned) and liabilities (what is owed).

non-linear relation A relationship between two variables that does not form a straight line when graphed.

open mortgage When any or all of the amount borrowed as a mortgage may be repaid at any time.

ordered pair A pair of numbers, such as (3, 8), used to locate a point on a coordinate graph.

ordinary annuity A series of equal payments made at equal intervals of time for a certain term, where the payments are made at the end of each payment interval.

origin The point of intersection of the x-axis and the y-axis on a coordinate graph. It is described by the ordered pair (0, 0).

percent A number that represents a fraction or ratio with a denominator of 100.

$\dfrac{34}{100}$ as a percent is 34%.

performance The rate of return on an investment.

portable mortgage A mortgage that can be transferred to another property.

portfolio The financial investments held by an investor.

power An abbreviation for repeated multiplication.

The power 6^3 means $6 \times 6 \times 6$.

power of attorney A document that authorizes one person to act on behalf of another for legal purposes.

prepayment privilege A legal clause allowing part of a mortgage to be repaid early.

present value The amount of money that must be invested today at a given interest rate, compounding frequency, and term, in order to result in a given final amount. Or, the discounted value of a debt.

present value of an annuity The amount that must be invested today at a given interest rate, compounding frequency, and number of payment intervals, in order to provide regular payments over a given term.

primary labour market Occupations that require education beyond high school.

principal The original amount borrowed or invested.

proportion An equation that states that two ratios are equal.

$\dfrac{2}{4} = \dfrac{x}{100}$ is a proportion.

PST Provincial sales tax (8% in Ontario in 2001).

quadrant One of the four regions formed by the intersection of the x-axis and the y-axis.

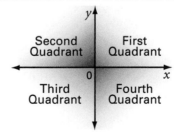

quadratic equation An equation that can be written in the form $0 = ax^2 + bx + c$, where a, b, and c are real numbers and $a \neq 0$.

quadratic function A relationship between two variables defined by an equation of the form $y = ax^2 + bx + c$, where a, b, and c are real numbers and $a \neq 0$. It forms a parabola when graphed.

quarterly Every 3 months or four times a year.

radical sign The symbol $\sqrt{}$.

range of a relation The set of all second coordinates of the ordered pairs of a relation.

rate A comparion of two quantities with different units.

8.4 L/100 km is a rate.

ratio A comparison of quantities with the same unit.

3 cans of water to 1 can of juice is 3:1.

rational exponent An exponent that is a rational number.

$5^{\frac{1}{2}}$ has a rational exponent of $\frac{1}{2}$.

recursion formula A formula that relates each term in a sequence to the term before it.

$t_1 = 1$, $t_n = t_{n-1} + 5$ is a recursion formula.

relation A relationship between variables that can be represented by a table of values, a graph, or an equation.

retirement fund Money set aside for retirement purposes. A registered retirement savings plan (RRSP) is a retirement fund registered with the federal government that allows income tax on earnings to be deferred until a later time. An RRSP has conditions attached.

return The potential for an investment to earn income or increase in value.

risk The probability that an investment will decrease in value.

risk tolerance An individual's comfort level with investment risk.

savings alternatives Investments that are guaranteed with a guaranteed interest rate, such as savings accounts and GICs. They tend to earn lower interest than higher-risk investment alternatives.

second mortgage The amount borrowed above 75% of the home purchase price. If the owner cannot make mortgage payments and the property is sold, the funds raised by the sale are used to pay off the first mortgage first, and then, any extra amounts go to the second mortgage holder. This is why interest on a second mortgage is often higher, because the lender is taking more risk.

secondary labour market Occupations that do not require a high school graduation diploma.

semi-annual(ly) Every half year, or twice a year.

semi-monthly Twice a month.

sequence An ordered list of terms.

series The sum of the terms of a sequence.

simple interest Interest calculated only on the original principal using the simple interest formula $I = Prt$.

slope A measure of the steepness of a line. The slope, m, of a line containing points $P(x_1, y_1)$ and $Q(x_2, y_2)$ is $m = \dfrac{\text{vertical change}}{\text{horizontal change}}$ or $\dfrac{\text{rise}}{\text{run}}$

$$= \frac{y_2 - y_1}{x_2 - x_1}, \quad x_2 \neq x_1$$

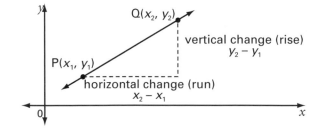

solve To find the value of a variable in an equation.

When $2^x = 16$ is solved, $x = 4$.

student loan A loan taken out to finance education. Special federal and provincial student loan programs exist, with conditions on repayment and interest.

table of values A table used to record and relate the coordinates of ordered pairs in a relation.

$y = 2^x$

x	y
−1	0.5
0	1
1	2
2	4

tax planning Developing strategies to minimize income taxes.

term The time between the issue date and the maturity date of a loan or investment.

term deposit See guaranteed investment certificate (GIC).

term of a mortgage The length of time that a mortgage agreement is in effect.

total debt service ratio (TDS ratio) The ratio of total monthly debts to gross income.

treasury bill A short-term government bond held for less than 1 year and guaranteed by the government. A minimum investment is required. It does not earn interest but trades at one price and matures at a higher price.

unit rational exponent A fractional exponent with a numerator of 1 that is equivalent to a root.

$81^{\frac{1}{4}}$ has a unit rational exponent of $\frac{1}{4}$.

$81^{\frac{1}{4}} = \sqrt[4]{81}$ because $3^4 = 81$.

variable costs of a vehicle Costs that the driver has some control over.

variable expense An expense that can vary in dollar amount each budget period.

variable-rate mortgage A mortgage for which the rate of interest charged varies as the bank rate changes.

volatile Tendency for an investment to change a lot in value. Often a measure of risk.

will A legal document specifying where a deceased person's estate will go.

x-axis The horizontal number line in the Cartesian coordinate system.

x-coordinate The first number in the ordered pair describing a point on a coordinate graph.

For the point P(2, 8), 2 is the x-coordinate.

x-intercept The distance from the origin of the point where a line or curve crosses the x-axis.

y-axis The vertical number line in the Cartesian coordinate system.

y-coordinate The second number in the ordered pair describing a point on a coordinate graph.

For the point P(2, 8), 8 is the y-coordinate.

y-intercept The distance from the origin of the point where a line or curve crosses the y-axis.

INDEX

CREDITS

Photo Credits

Cover, back cover, iii: © John Stills/Photonica; **back cover** E-stat logo: Courtesy of Statistics Canada, E-STAT database for educational institutions, updated periodically at *www.statcan.ca*; **vi–vii** Steve Mason/PhotoDisc; **viii–ix** Larry Dale Gordon/The Image Bank; **Tour of the Text: x** © Comstock Images/George Hunter; **xi top** Rubberball Productions yl_83, *Young Lifestyles* CD-ROM; **bottom** Robert Ginn/PhotoEdit; **xiii** © David Young-Wolff/PhotoEdit; **xiv top** Eyewire #e012756, **bottom** 2001-Ontario Tourism; **xv top** Courtesy of Texas Instruments, **top middle** Robert Breener/PhotoEdit, **bottom** Sexto/Sol/PhotoDisc; **xvii bottom** Courtesy of Statistics Canada, E-STAT database for educational institutions, updated periodically at *www.statcan.ca*; **xviii–1** All © Digital Vision from *Personal Finance* CD-ROM; **3** Stewart Cohen/Stone; **4** Ryan McVay/PhotoDisc; **10** Courtesy of Paul Lachine; **11** Andrew Ward/Life File/PhotoDisc; **16** © Digital Stock *Business and Agriculture* CD-ROM Vol. 102; **19** © Doug Menuez/PhotoDisc; **24** © Digital Vision from *Personal Finance* CD-ROM; **31** Stewart Cohen/Stone; **36–37** Corel Corporation #460086; **39** Rubberball Productions yl_83, *Young Lifestyles* CD-ROM; **46** © Digital Stock/Corbis CB023694; **49** Dick Hemingway; **51 top** Casio Canada, Ltd., **bottom** Courtesy of Texas Instruments; **55** © David Young-Wolff/PhotoEdit; **56** Neal Preston/CORBIS/Magma; **60** Jeff Greenberg/Visuals Unlimited; **61** Rubberball Productions yl_83, *Young Lifestyles* CD-ROM; **66–67** Billy E. Barnes/PhotoEdit; **69** PhotoDisc; **70** Robert Ginn/PhotoEdit; **77** Courtesy of Bobcat Company; **84** Nick Rowe/PhotoDisc Vol. 72; **91** Robert Breener/PhotoEdit; **99** Keith Brofsky/Photodisc Vol. 43; **104** PhotoDisc; **106** Rob Van Patton © Digital Vision; **111** PhotoDisc; **112** © Digital Stock/CORBIS CB007324; **113** PhotoDisc; **118–119** All © Digital Vision from *Personal Finance* CD-ROM; **121** Jon Riley/Stone; **122** Photolink/PhotoDisc; **130** David Young-Wolff/PhotoEdit; **138** SW Productions/PhotoDisc; **143** Eyewire chi-036-1; **145** David Buffington/PhotoDisc; **151** Jonathan Nourik/PhotoEdit; **154** Doug Menuez/PhotoDisc; **160** © Digital Vision from *Personal Finance* CD-ROM; **161** Jon Riley/Stone; **168–169** First Light/

J-P Nova; **171** Ryan McVay/PhotoDisc; **172** © Digital Vision/Eyewire 198087; **179** Simon Bruty/Allsport; **186** Steve Mason/PhotoDisc; **194** First Light/Pedro Coll; **202** First Light/Jeff Zaruba; **210** Courtesy Infocus. Reprinted with permission; **211** Ryan McVay/PhotoDisc; **216–217, 219** Comstock Images/E. Otto; **220** Anne-Marie Weber/FPG International; **231** © Digital Stock *Four Seasons* CD-ROM Vol. 101; **238** David Young-Wolff/PhotoEdit; **242** PhotoLink/PhotoDisc; **244** 2001-Ontario Tourism; **245 inset** Geostock/PhotoDisc, **main** Comstock Images/E. Otto; **250–251** Comstock Images/George Hunter; **253** Eyewire #e012756; **254** Skip Nall/PhotoDisc; **259** David Young-Wolff/PhotoEdit; **260** Donald Johnston/Stone; **262** Adam Crowley/PhotoDisc; **270** Ted Brellisford/Canadian Press Picture Archive; **271** Tony Freeman/PhotoEdit; **272** Corel Corporation #243024; **275** Herman® is reprinted with permission from LaughingStock Licensing Inc., Ottawa, Canada. All rights reserved; **277** Adam Crowley/PhotoDisc; **282** Myrleen Ferguson Cate/PhotoEdit; **283** Eyewire #e012756; **285** Herman® is reprinted with permission from LaughingStock Licensing Inc., Ottawa, Canada. All rights reserved; **288–289** Suzanne & Nick Geary/Stone; **291** Jeff Zaruba/Stone; **292** DENNIE CODY/FPG International/Getty Images; **298** © Graham Harrop. Reprinted with permission; **301** Herman® is reprinted with permission from LaughingStock Licensing Inc., Ottawa, Canada. All rights reserved; **303** © Digital Vision from *Personal Finance* CD-ROM; **309** James Blank/West Stock Inc./Image State; **311** Benjamin Rondel/First Light; **315** Sexto/Sol/PhotoDisc; **316** Mug Shots/First Light; **317** Jeff Zaruba/Stone; **324–325** © Michael Newman/PhotoEdit; **327** Larry Dale Gordon/The Image Bank; **328** Cartoon: Courtesy of *www.brilliantidiot.com*; **331** © David Young-Wolff/PhotoEdit; **333** © Tony Freeman/PhotoEdit; **338** Cartoon: Courtesy *www.brilliantidiot.com*; **341** © Tony Freeman/PhotoEdit; **354** Charles Pearson/West Stock Inc./Image State; **359** Herman® is reprinted with permission from LaughingStock Licensing Inc., Ottawa, Canada. All rights reserved; **362** Ryan McVay/PhotoDisc; **369** © Digital Vision from *Personal Finance* CD-ROM; **378** © Michael Newman/PhotoEdit; **384–385** left Jack Star/PhotoLink/PhotoDisc, **middle** Wayne Cuddington/Canadian Press Photo Archive, **right** Rob Van Patton © Digital Vision; **386** Rene Sheret/Stone; **389** © Digital Vision from *Personal Finance* CD-ROM; **390** E-stat logo: Courtesy of Statistics Canada, E-STAT database for educational institutions, updated periodically at *www.statcan.ca*; **391** John Laptad/West Stock Inc./Image State; **394** Mark Harmel/Stone; **396** First Light/Pedro Coll; **398** Eyewire #e012756

Text Credits

22 Graph: Reprinted with permission – The Toronto Star Syndicate; **23** Line Graphs (both) Reprinted with permission from the Canadian Institute of Financial Planning (CIFP) **159** Reprinted with permission – The Toronto Star Syndicate; **278** © Progressive Financial Strategies Incorporated. Reprinted with permission; **406–414** Courtesy of Texas Instruments; **415–421** Microsoft® Excel are either registered trademarks or trademarks of Microsoft Corporation in the United States and/or other countries; **422–425** Screen shot(s) from Quattro® Pro, Corel, and Quattro® are trademarks or registered trademarks of Corel Corporation or Corel Corporation Limited, reprinted by permission.

E-stat logo is used with permission. Courtesy of Statistics Canada, E-STAT database for educational institutions, updated periodically at *www.statcan.ca*.

Chapter Expectations: © Queen's Printer for Ontario, 2001.

Technical Art

Tom Dart, Alana Lai, Claire Milne, Greg Duhaney of First Folio Resource Group, Inc.